Dairy Goat Reproduction

Breeding, Kidding, Milking + Goat Milk Recipes

Rachel Payne

ISBN: 978-0-692-03954-0

All photos by Rachel Payne.
Illustrations by Carol Massa.

DEDICATION

To my parents, Fred and Lynn, for always suffering my oddities and encouraging my talents.

CONTENTS

ACKNOWLEDGMENTS

Many thanks to my editor, Brannan Sirratt, for going through my work with a fine-toothed comb. Without your hard work and expertise, this book would not be in existence!

Thanks also to my illustrator, Carol Massa, for completing my vision for this book by capturing the whimsical nature of goats in your illustrations.

Lastly, thanks to everyone along the way who has supported me in this endeavor (and others). Without your encouragement and belief in what I worked to accomplish, I might never have put pen to paper in the first place (or fingers to keyboard, as it were). You know who you are!

Know well the condition of your flocks, and pay attention to your herds [. . .] The lambs will be for your clothing, and the goats will bring the price of a field, and there will be enough goats' milk for your food, for the food of your household, and sustenance for your maidens. — *Proverbs 27:23-27*

Introduction

Nothing strikes fear and excitement into the hearts of goat owners quite like kidding season. Breeding, birthing, and rearing kids presents new challenges every year for both experienced and novice goatherds. Being a skilled goat midwife is both a science and an art. You must know what the books and the experts say, but you must also know your own goats and use your intuition. Like humans, all goats are individuals. Each pregnancy, labor, and delivery is unique. That doesn't always mean things are going wrong, but inevitably every goat midwife must face difficult situations that challenge our knowledge, experience, and decision-making skills. Goats are complicated creatures in many ways.

Kidding season is especially daunting the first few times one experiences it. New goat owners have a million questions: "Is my goat pregnant? When is she due? How do I know she's going into labor? How do I know if something is wrong? What do I *do* if something goes wrong?" Perhaps the most frequently asked question of all is simply, "Is this normal?" Many times, the answer is yes, it is normal. Goats have been giving birth for centuries without human help, but likewise birth complications have been a part of life since the beginning of time as well. The mystery of it all is what causes goat owners to lose sleep at night. As much as we want to be in control, we simply aren't. Control is an illusion when it comes to livestock. That lack of control combined with the mystery of birth can send a novice into a tailspin of worry and stress. We've all been there.

So where does that leave the novice goatherd? Or even the more experienced one who still wants to learn more, or still feels anxiety during kidding season? After all, you can only ask your friends, veterinarian, and mentors so many questions before feeling like a mosquito buzzing in their ear. Meanwhile, the internet can also be unreliable. With forums and online groups merely a click away, literally anyone can share "advice." There are too many contradictory opinions and misinformation quoted as fact, and it can be hard to distinguish the good information from the trash. On top of that, reproduction and birth are typically only given a chapter or two in most goat husbandry books.

Enter *Dairy Goat Reproduction.* My goal for this book is to create a resource for all things involving goat reproduction-from choosing your breeding pair, to using the milk your does will provide, and everything in between. It is my goal not to cover every possible scenario—an impossible feat—but to provide a broad enough and detailed enough guide to hit the major points and provide a useful reference for goat owners of all experience levels. While it is impossible for any single book to cover every possible topic and their offshoots, I have done my best to leave as few stones unturned as possible. My hope is that this book will offer useful knowledge, helpful encouragement, and a bit of reassurance for the reader.

In addition, this book also contains true stories about goat pregnancy, birth, and other experiences. These *Tales from the Kidding Stall* can be found peppered throughout the book and are personal anecdotes from myself regarding my personal experiences with unusual situations revolving around goat reproduction, pregnancy, kidding, and raising kids. It is my hope that these real-life tales will encourage you and allow you to gain wisdom through the experience of others. If nothing else, hopefully reading about the struggles I've experienced will make you feel less alone when you run into trouble of your own.

Now go grab your favorite beverage, sit back, relax, and let's talk about goats!

Glossary of Terms

- Buck - intact male goat
- Doe - female goat
- Wether - castrated male goat
- Kid - baby goat
- Kidding - giving birth
- Abortion - miscarriage of pregnancy, natural or induced
- Bleat - vocalization
- Blubber - vocalization and spitting normally done by bucks when a doe is in heat
- Bolus - pill
- Browse - broad-leafed woody plants, bushes, trees, or shrubs
- Butting/Head Butting - when a goat uses its head to hit another goat or human; sometimes playful, sometimes in aggression
- Caprine - a goat or pertaining to goats
- Chèvre - soft cheese made from goat milk
- Cud - the partially digested food that is regurgitated, chewed, and swallowed again by ruminants
- Dam - female parent
- Sire - male parent
- Disbud - remove horn buds from kids to prevent horn growth
- Buckling - male goat kid
- Doeling - female goat kid
- Drench - liquid medication given orally
- Dry Off - to allow a doe to stop producing milk
- Drylot - keeping goats in a pen with no pasture/browse; all feed is provided by owner
- Free Choice - provided for goats to consume at will at all times
- Freshen - when a doe kids and starts to produce milk
- First Freshener - a doe kidding for the first time
- Gestation - the duration of pregnancy from conception to birth
- Herd - a group of goats
- In Milk - producing milk/lactating
- Bred - pregnant; also past tense of breed
- Settle - conceive after mating
- Rut - the period from late summer to early winter when breeding season is at its peak
- Let Down - to release milk
- Dystocia - difficulty giving birth
- Open - not yet bred
- Parlor - place when dairy animals are milked

- Polled - naturally hornless
- Roughage - bulky feed high in fiber such as hay
- Ruminant - an animal with four stomachs that chews cud
- Ruminate - to chew cud
- Parturition - birth, kidding
- Scours - diarrhea
- Stanchion - the headstall or milking stand used to keep a doe secure while being milked
- Yearling - a goat between the ages of 6 months and 1 year
- Cull - to remove a goat from the breeding program by selling, retiring, or processing for meat
- Billy - an undesirable slang term for a buck, considered to be derogatory
- Nanny - an undesirable slang term for a doe, considered to be derogatory
- Udder - the mammary of a doe
- Bagging Up - when a doe's udder becomes full and distended with colostrum prior to parturition

Goat Quick Facts

Temperature	102.5-104
Pulse	70-80
Puberty	7 weeks - 8 months
Estrus Cycle	21 days average
Gestation	145-155 days
Lifespan	12 average does, 8 average bucks
Growth Rate	Breeding size by 2 or earlier, full size by 3-4 years
Weaning	Minimum of 2 months, 3+ ideal

Fun Caprine Trivia

- Goats have no front teeth on their upper jaw.
- Goat milk is naturally homogenized, meaning the fat does not separate from milk on its own.
- The fat molecules in goat milk are smaller than those in cow milk.
- Goats are most closely related to sheep, but their nutritional needs are more similar to cows, and their grazing habits are more similar to deer.
- Goat milk is the most widely consumed milk in the world.
- A goat's pupil is rectangular, not round.
- A cow is a bovine, a sheep is an ovine, and a goat is caprine.
- Julbocken, also known as the Yule Goat, is a traditional Swedish symbol of Christmas.
- Goat meat is called chevon or cabrito (young goat).
- Goats were one of the first animals to be domesticated and one of the first to be brought to America.
- Goat milk was a popular replacement for breast milk before formula was invented.
- Goats have four stomach compartments.
- All goats produce cashmere as their soft undercoat in the winter, but certain breeds produce more than others.
- Angora goats have long curly hair and are raised for their fiber production.
- LaMancha goats have very short ears that give the appearance of being earless, Nubians have long pendulous ears, and other dairy breeds have standard, erect ears.
- Goats cannot "eat anything" as the old wives tale claims; they have specific dietary needs and are sensitive to changes in diet.
- Goats can be trained to pull carts or carry packs.
- To call someone "goat headed" is to say they're being stubborn.
- Both male and female goats will grow beards.
- The sound a goat makes is called bleating, and it can sound remarkably close to a human yell.

Tales from the Kidding Stall: *I owned pet goats for the first time as a teenager. One day my parents found a neighbor wandering through our backyard unannounced. When they confronted him, he said he'd heard a woman screaming. The sound he'd actually heard was my Nubian doe, Star!*

General Goat Anatomy

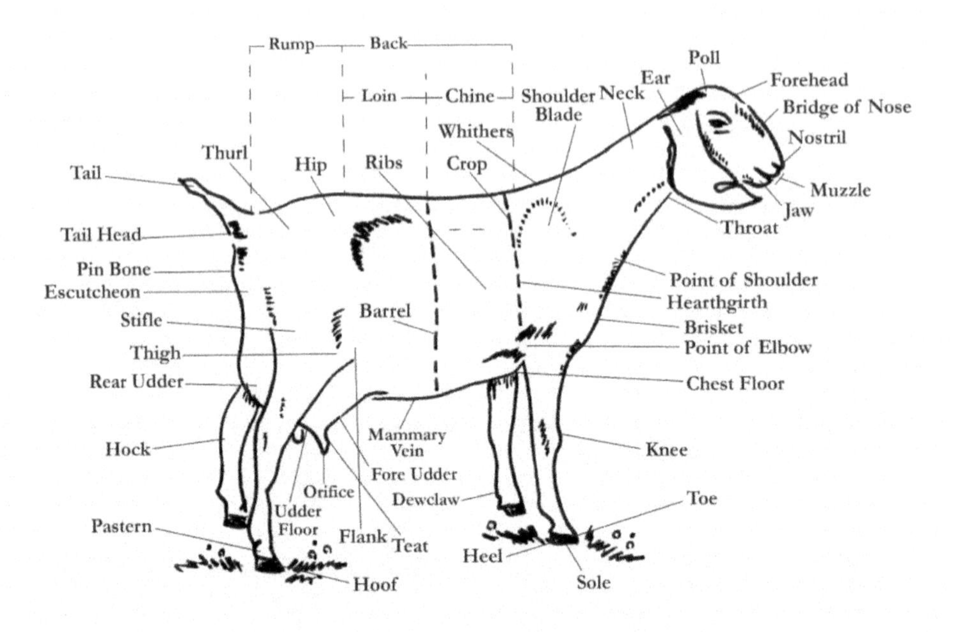

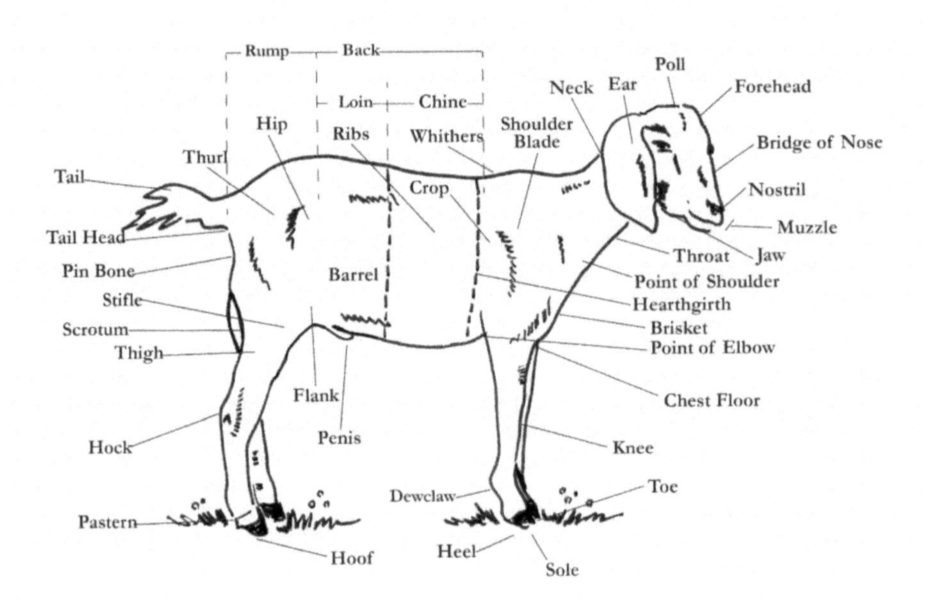

Chapter One: Planning

Planning can be one of the most exciting stages of goat breeding. This is the part where you get to play matchmaker! Making these decisions may seem inconsequential at the time, but several months down the road you will see the outcome of this planning stage. When kids start hitting the ground, it will be a direct result of the choices you made long before your buck and doe went k-i-s-s-i-n-g in a tree. By the same token, planning is also one of the most important parts of the process. The decisions made months before kidding takes place will have a long-term impact on your herd. Choose wisely!

Choosing Breeding Pairs

How do you choose which bucks and does to mate to each other? If you have a small herd and only own one buck, that decision has already been made for you. However, for the purposes of this section, let's assume that you don't own any goats yet at all. We'll start where all good plans and stories start: the beginning.

Purchasing Your First Goats

There are a number of things you should consider when shopping for your first goats. I have broken these things down into a five-step checklist:

1. Prepare

Before ever putting a deposit down on a goat, you should have the necessary supplies to care for them. Because this book is dedicated to goat reproduction rather than general goat husbandry, I will not go into detail about all the things you need to properly care for goats. (Please see the section in the back of this book titled *Recommended Reading* to see books I recommend for information on general goat husbandry and care.) However, secure fencing and appropriate housing should be your first priorities.

2. Determine Goals

If you don't know what you're looking for, you won't know it when you see it. You might also be swayed by advertising into purchasing something you shouldn't. Before you start shopping, sit down and outline your priorities. Do you want goats to produce milk for your home? Do you want show quality goats? Do you want goats for both milk and meat? What breed do you want? Do you want registered or non-registered? Small, medium, or large? Narrow these things down first and then go find what you *really* want. Don't settle.

3. Educate Yourself About Disease

There are several contagious diseases that you do *not* want in your goat herd. At minimum, your new goats should have recent blood test results that show them negative for Caprine Arthritis Encephalitis (CAE), Johne's (pronounced "yo-knees"), and Caseous Lymphadenitis (CL). If you plan to drink your milk raw, you may also want to do additional testing for Q Fever, Brucellosis, and Tuberculosis. I describe these in detail later on in this book in chapter eight. There is also a picture tutorial for drawing a blood sample in chapter four.

4. Find a Reputable Breeder

This step is a combination of steps two and three. First and foremost, a reputable breeder has a healthy, disease-free herd. They should perform routine disease testing of their own and be willing to allow you to perform any additional blood tests you desire prior to, or as a contingency of, sale (usually at your own expense). They should be willing to show you documented proof of their prior tests. Their herd should be free from abscesses or abscess scars, and their goats should be in good condition. The goats should not be underweight, have overgrown hooves, snotty noses, or cloudy eyes, and they should be in good spirits (not listless or off feed). They should not have loose stool or swollen knees. Every breeder occasionally has ill animals, and a sick goat is not an immediate indication of an unhealthy herd, but the breeder should be able to explain why any goat in their herd is ill and what they are doing to treat it. It should be obvious that the overall condition of the herd is good even if there is a sick individual within it.

Your breeder's goats should also be doing what you want your goats to do. If you want to milk your goats, your breeder should be able to tell you how much milk each doe produces as well as the good and the bad about the goat's udder, milk production, conformation, and kidding history. Choosing registered goats can be an extremely useful tool in determining whether goats from the herd you are considering will be a good fit for your personal goals. Registries keep track of pedigrees, show awards, and milk production records and awards for any goat you may be considering and/or their relatives. Good quality registered goats usually cost more that unregistered stock, but keep in mind that you often get what you pay for.

Also look for breeders who are raising their goats under similar management protocol to your goals as a goat owner. If you do not want to raise goats in intensive management with little to no pasture access, heavy medication usage, routine bottle feeding, and the like, then do not buy goats from people raising their goats in such a manner if you can avoid it. Breeders each expect different things from their goats and expect them to thrive under different management styles. While being totally organic with goats is not possible under most circumstances, due in large part to their sensitivity to internal parasites, if you wish to raise your goats with fewer inputs and high natural parasite and illness resistance then you should be seeking out breeders with similar goals.

Beware of sale barns, "traders" (people who frequently buy and resell cheap livestock), and auctions, as these are not good places to find healthy, productive animals of any species. There are times when people can get lucky with sale barn stock, but those are the exceptions rather than the rule. Sale barns and the like are often where culls are sent, and they are also excellent places to expose livestock to illness and disease. It is not a good idea to "rescue" goats if you intend to have a productive working herd. That is a fast way to bring in disease, sickness, and undesirable traits to your herd. Don't allow an emotional reaction to a sick animal put the future of your entire herd at risk. At the end of the day, it's not worth it to bring in disease to your land for the sake of a bleeding heart.

A Note on Showing and DHI: *Some breeders do not partake in milk production programs, but this doesn't mean their herd is of poor quality. I have also had a negative experience purchasing a very well-bred doe with all sorts of genetic history of excellence, only to find that she also had a genetic abnormality that caused excessive hair loss and a weak constitution. Keep in mind that dairy records can be manipulated in some cases as well, and generally records are only as reliable as the people keeping them. Does can also be pushed to peak production by certain practices, like overfeeding, that the average home milker will not engage in. The moral of the story is that not every award-winning herd will be what you expect and not every herd that doesn't participate will produce lower quality animals.*

5. Buy Your Goats

That's *goats*, plural. Goats are herd animals, so you must always have at least two. Many reputable breeders will have a waiting list or reservation list, especially for does. You will more often find doelings available than adult does, but adults do sometimes become available. Keep in mind that there is always a reason an adult animal is being sold. It could be something as simple as the breeder needing to downsize and making hard choices, but it could also be that the animal is being culled from the herd for some flaw. Sometimes something that is a deal breaker to one person may not be a big deal to another, but it's always a good idea to find out why an adult is being sold before purchasing it.

Be prepared to reserve a kid in advance, and be prepared to pay a deposit up front. Most breeders will not hold goats for a buyer without first having a deposit. Some breeders who have a high demand for kids will also require deposits to be made on unborn kids to reserve them. Don't be alarmed; this is common practice and is not a scam. When reserving an unborn kid, the deposit should be fully refundable or transferable if the desired kid is not born. Always check your breeder's sales policy and deposit policy prior to payment.

Registered vs Unregistered

When choosing your breeding animals, you have the option of buying registered or unregistered stock. I highly recommend choosing registered stock for a few reasons. First, goats must be registered to participate in any of the production or conformation programs like milk production tests, linear appraisals, and shows. While not required, these programs help breeders produce top quality animals and help buyers track the desirable traits and family history of their goats. Registries also keep track of lineage and make it easy to know how closely two goats are related with just a glance. Registered goats are also worth more monetarily as well, and registered stock will always pull higher prices than unregistered. Even if you think you don't want to participate in shows or milk DHI now, owning registered goats leaves that option open for you in the future should you change your mind. It also opens a larger market for excess kids and increases the profits from selling them.

I will also recommend sticking to a larger registry rather than a smaller, breed-specific registry. The largest registry for dairy goats in the United States is the American Dairy Goat Association (ADGA). The American Goat Society (AGS) is also prominent, though not quite as large. Miniature dairy breeds (crosses of Nigerian Dwarf with standard breeds) include The Miniature Goat Registry (TMGR) and the Miniature Dairy Goat Association (MDGA). The larger, multi-breed registries offer more opportunities and resources, carry more clout, and have a better turnaround time for paperwork. Keep in mind that goats registered with ADGA or AGS can also be cross registered with each other and other registries, while neither organization accepts animals for registry that are registered under different outside registries. While I won't name any specifics, my first two does were registered only with a small breed-specific registration. I didn't know at the time that I wouldn't be able to register them with ADGA or AGS. Unfortunately, I have had several negative experiences with their smaller registry, with registration paperwork taking months to arrive or arriving incorrect. In one instance it took over a year to finally get registration back on a doe. I have never had any major problem with the larger registries. The one instance in which a doe's paperwork came back incorrect from a larger registry, they quickly responded to my email and corrected the discrepancy.

Record Keeping

As you delve into the world of breeding dairy goats, you will want to establish a functional record keeping method. You will need to keep track of registrations, medical history, kidding history, breeding plans, kid reservations, and more. This can be done with pen and paper or digitally according to your preference. I personally use a combination of the two. I keep a binder filled with registration papers, disease testing results, bills of sale, and anything I need in a hard copy. Important dates through the year such as bred dates are jotted onto a personal yearly calendar. Lastly, I keep a herdbook and kidding history spreadsheet file. In this file I have a master sheet with all my currently owned goats, their birthdays, registration numbers, retained kids in my herd, kidding history, and general notes such as production awards or anything worthy of jotting down and remembering. I keep a separate sheet for the kidding history of each year. On that sheet I keep track of which does were bred to which bucks, the date of breeding, date of kidding, number of kids in the birth, kids retained or sold, kid reservations, and notes. Saving this information is helpful not just for records and organization but also to notice trends such as a doe who tends to kid slightly early or late, which does are having the highest litter sizes, names I've already used, any complications in the birth, and other such useful information.

The Doe

New goat owners typically purchase their does first, and that is what I recommend as well. Owning a buck presents its own set of challenges, and beginners often do not feel prepared to deal with the hormone-fueled behaviors (and smells) of bucks. In addition, your buck should be chosen based on the traits that need improving in your does, so it makes sense that you would need to know the traits of your does before choosing a buck.

In addition to all the general information above, there are several things to look for specific to does that you wish to breed. A breeding doe should be a healthy goat with good conformation and constitution. You want to breed for traits such as an ability to kid with ease, a tendency toward multiples (single kids often grow too large and cause kidding problems), good resistance to internal parasites, and conformation that is suited to her breed or type. Understanding correct conformation will require a bit of independent research, but it is an important trait. Conformation isn't just for the show ring but for the lifetime of the goat. Function follows form. All the qualities needed for good conformation—such as a wide level rump, strong level topline, depth and length of body, good width, and well attached udder—are directly related to a doe's production, ease of kidding, and longevity. No doe will be perfect. Each goat will have its own strengths and weaknesses, so you must decide which things are most important to you and which areas are weakest in your herd. Don't throw the baby out with the bathwater based on a flaw.

Remember when choosing your does or doelings that the traits they have will likely be passed on to their offspring, and the traits that their ancestors have were likely passed on to them. One thing that is important to consider is ease of kidding. If a doe has had difficult births that required intervention repeatedly, that doe should not be bred again regardless of how wonderful her production, conformation, or genetics may be. Ease of kidding can also be a genetic trait, so choosing a doeling whose mother has a history of kidding without problems is a good idea. It is true that sometimes things go awry during birth that have nothing to do with the doe's genetics or body structure, but that is not always the case. Whether or not a doe or her dam is a good mother should also be considered, as should her personality (particularly if you plan to milk her).

Tales from the Kidding Stall: *As an example of function following form and the effects of conformation on productivity, I would like to tell you the story of Rumor. Rumor was one of my first goats and the first goat to have a major problem with kidding. It was only my second year owning goats, and unfortunately Rumor did not make things easy for me. Thankfully I recognized that she was in labor and was present for the birth—or lack thereof, really. When it became clear to my inexperienced mind that she was having trouble, I brought Rumor into the veterinarian. (I was still too inexperienced to even attempt checking things out on my own at that point.) Rumor's pelvis was so narrow that my vet could barely fit her hand inside to check what was happening. Rumor ended up with a C-section, and we lost both of her kids. Rumor's conformation, while not terrible, was too narrow. She was a very long-bodied doe, the longest I've ever owned, but she lacked depth of body and width of rump. That narrowness was reflected in her internal structure as well, and it was because of that conformational flaw, combined with the fact that I overfed her during pregnancy, that her kids were unable to fit through her birth canal.*

The Buck

Always keep in mind that your buck is half your herd, and sometimes more than half. In one kidding season, you may have kids from several different dams, yet they may all have the same sire. Your choice in bucks will quickly have an impact on your entire herd. Every retained doe kid is genetically 50% of your herdsire, and all his faults and virtues will be reflected in his offspring as well. Buy the best bucks that you can find and afford—you won't regret it.

When looking at bucks, you want to choose one that is strong in the areas where your does are weak. No goat is perfect, but by careful selective breeding you can improve the faults of your dams in their offspring. If your doe has a lovely udder, but small teats, choose a buck to pair her with whose dam and granddams have generously sized, milkable teats. If your doe stands on straight feet and legs but has an overly steep rump, choose a buck with a nice level, gently sloping rump. This also works in the reverse; if your doe is strong in one area, her genes can be used improve a flaw in your buck. Pay close attention to the offspring of every pairing to see if it worked the way you wanted. As much as we would like it to be a simple, foolproof process, genetics are complicated and unpredictable. While we can look at traits and statistics, we can't usually predict the outcome perfectly. Just because a goat has a particular trait doesn't mean that trait will be passed onto its offspring.

When choosing your buck, pay close attention to his female relatives including the dam, granddams, sisters, and daughters if he has any. Breeding bucks should always come from proven dams, because it is from his dam and other female ancestors that the dairy traits will be passed on. They will be the ones to show you what kind of udders and milk production the buck might pass on to his daughters. As with choosing a doe, your buck should always have traits that you desire in your herd such as good conformation, parasite resistance, health, and personality. His dam and sire's dam should be the exact types of does that you want to produce in your own herd.

Even if you've done your research and carefully made your plans, you still might not see the results you want immediately. Sometimes it takes a little patience to see how well your pairings are working. After all, you won't know how much a buck improved on his daughter's udder over her dams until she freshens herself. Moreover, sometimes it will take a few generations of careful breeding to really start seeing improvement in the traits you need. They might be slightly improved in the offspring, then improved a bit more in the next generation, and so on. You might also get lucky and see some improvement immediately or get unlucky and have the offspring go backwards for one reason or another. Sometimes undesirable traits crop up due to recessive, unexpressed genes passed down from the parents.

When to Breed

Does should be an appropriate size before kidding. For Nigerians and miniature breeds, does should be at least 40 pounds before being bred to reduce the risk of kidding problems. Standard does should be at least 80 pounds before being bred. Generally, does will reach the appropriate size by two years of age or sooner; typically, the miniature breeds mature slightly slower than the standard breeds. However, certain other factors can cause a goat to mature slowly or be undersized. This can be caused by lack of appropriate nutrition, illness occurring during early growth, or infection from the protozoa coccidia at a young age. These may sometimes simply slow development, but in other cases the doe might never reach an appropriate size. Her immune system may be compromised as well. Such does should not be bred regardless of age. Reputable breeders will never intentionally breed Nigerian or miniature goats to be unusually small. This will negatively impact their production and ability to kid with ease. The ideal height for Nigerian does is 19" at the withers with up to 22.5" being allowed by most registries before the doe is considered over height. Does should not be less than 17" high. Standard breeds should of course be taller, but there are no standard height requirements set for standard dairy breeds.

Does should ideally freshen for the first time by their second year of age. Unbred does can become overweight, and excess weight can cause infertility or difficulty kidding. Does should be neither over or underweight before breeding, because pregnancy is not the time to put a doe on a diet or try to make her gain weight. Bucks, on the other hand, can reach sexual maturity as young as two months old. However, they should be at least six months old before they are expected to successfully breed a doe. Young bucks should also not be given too many does to service at any one time, because this can negatively affect their fertility and therefore your birth rates. Allow your young bucks to mature before giving them more than two to three does at any given time.

Even though does will come into heat regularly after their offspring reach weaning age, they should be bred to kid only once per calendar year. Standard dairy goats are most often seasonal breeders to begin with, but Nigerian Dwarf and sometimes Nubian does may cycle year-round. This allows their body time to rest in between pregnancies, and it also allows the human midwives to utilize their milk for a longer period. A typical breeding schedule may look like this: The doe is bred in October and gives birth in March. The goatherd begins milking the doe and starts separating the kids at night when they are two weeks old. Her kids are weaned in June, and she is bred back again in October. The goatherd dries her off in January to give her a break before she kids again in March.

Sometimes a doe may also "milk through" if her production is good enough. Milking through is the process of milking a doe through the next breeding cycle instead of breeding her back to kid again. This mean that she does not kid again the next spring, and she is milked continuously throughout the year before being bred again the following fall. This lets the goatherd skip a year of breeding and kidding for that doe. This is an ideal situation for those who only want milk for their households and do not want kids each year. However, not all does have the genetic capability to do this. You may find that your doe dries up naturally on her own before you plan to stop milking. It's impossible to force a doe's body to bend to your will if her genetics don't allow for an extended milking season. Also consider that does who milk through are prone to becoming overweight, which may cause issues when trying to breed them back.

Understanding Pedigrees

Understanding the terminology on a goat's pedigree can be extremely beneficial when choosing goats to purchase or breed. There are many symbols and acronyms present on goat pedigrees, and these are meaningless to the untrained eye. Though it can be confusing to a new goat owner, these indicators are a valuable tool for understanding the production and traits of a potential breeding goat. This data, when understood, allows you to track the performance history of a goat for several generations. While it can't predict the success or failure of an individual goat, it can point to a genetic predisposition for certain traits. Pedigrees also allow you to track whether or not a goat is linebred and to what percentage.

Each registry has its own system of symbols, but for the purpose of this chart I am explicating the symbols used by the American Dairy Goat Association (ADGA), which is the largest registry for dairy goats in the United States. To understand the symbols on other registries, I suggest research on the registry website or contacting them directly.

Does	Bucks
1*M: This doe has met or exceeded the requirements to earn a milk star based on her production. This award can represent either a one day or 305 day test. This doe may also have earned her star based on her offspring: either three daughters who have earned stars or three sons who have earned +B status.	***B:** This buck has inherited a star by his dam and sire's dam both earning their milk stars.
2*M: This doe has met or exceeded the requirements to earn a milk star in either the one day or 305 day test. In addition, her dam has also earned her star. The number in front of the star represents the number of generations of does in her direct lineage that have earned stars. For example, a 3*M doe is one whose dam and dam's dam have also earned their stars. This designation does not skip a generation and does not take into account the stars earned by a doe's paternal lineage.	**+B:** This buck has a minimum of three daughters out of different dams who have all earned their milk stars, or he has two sons who have each earned +B status.
Ch: This doe has won grand champion in three shows in which a minimum of 10 does were competing.	**++B**: This buck has three or more daughters out of different dams who have earned their milk stars and two sons who have earned +B status.

GCH: This doe has won grand champion in three shows in which a minimum of 10 does were competing, and she has also earned her milk star.	**Ch:** This buck has won grand champion in three shows in which a minimum of 10 bucks were competing.
	GCH: This buck has won grand champion in three shows in which a minimum of 10 bucks were competing, and he has also earned his +B.

Understanding Linear Appraisal

Linear Appraisal (LA) is a program provided by ADGA that allows goats to be scored based on their adherence to the breed standard. This is an excellent tool for evaluating the conformation quality of a goat without exposing them to the stress and potential spread of illness at shows. In many ways, LA can be considered more valuable than show titles, particularly when planning your breeding. LA scores demonstrate how well the goat is put together in specific areas of conformation, and it compares the goat against the breed standard itself rather than against a group of other goats of varying quality. These scores can also show you whether or not the kids your breeding program is producing are improving over their parents or falling behind.

LA uses a series of letters to designate the score a goat receives. It should be noted that the highest score a first freshener can earn is an 89, and the highest score any goat is allowed to receive is a 94. There are, after all, no perfect goats. When calculating a final score, General Appearance is 35% of the score, Dairy Strength is 20%, Body Capacity is 10%, and Mammary is 35%. On bucks or unfreshened doelings, General Appearance becomes 55%, Dairy Strength 30%, and Body Capacity 15%.

Letter	Score	Grade
E	Excellent	90+
V	Very Good	85-89
+	Good Plus	80-84
A	Acceptable	70-79

F	Fair	60-69
P	Poor	59-

There are several areas evaluated during an appraisal. The following traits are given a numerical score corresponding to the correctness of the trait. These scores can range from 5 to 45, with 35 being ideal. Too far in either direction is not desirable.

- Stature
- Strength
- Dairy Character
- Rump Angle
- Rump Width
- Rear Legs, Side View
- Fore Udder Attachment
- Rear Udder Height
- Rear Udder Arch
- Medial Suspensory Ligament
- Udder Depth
- Teat Placement, Rear View
- Teat Diameter
- Rear Udder, Side View

LA also evaluates the following structural traits, which are designated a letter score rather than a number:

- Head
- Shoulder Assembly
- Legs, Front
- Legs, Rear
- Feet
- Back
- Rump
- Udder Texture

When reading pedigrees and websites, you will most often see LA scores listed something like this: "1-10 VG 89 V+VE." Here's what that means when translated:

1-10	Goat was one year, 10 months old at appraisal

VG	Overall score was in the Very Good category
89	Final numerical score was 89
V	Very Good in General Appearance
+	Good Plus in Dairy Character
V	Very Good in Body Capacity
E	Excellent Mammary (Not included on bucks)

In general, you should look for scores in the V range or above for the overall score and structural scores when LA records are available. In the trait scores, you should look for scores of at least 25, with 35 being ideal. In some cases, a lower score in a certain area may be acceptable for a doe if she excels in other areas that you feel are more important. However, as always, we must be more particular regarding our bucks. Any goat receiving an overall poor score should not have a place in your breeding program. Even if you do not have access to the detailed reports, the overall scores, which are available on ADGA pedigrees and often advertised on websites, can still be a helpful tool when making decisions for your breeding program. Let's say a doe has a score of VG 85 EVE+. For that particular doe, you would look for a buck whose score read something like VG 90 EEV whose dam's score was along the lines of E 90 EVEE. Of course, the ideal would be E 94 EEEE, but those goats are few and far between. More often than not, you must simply make the best possible decisions regarding your breeding pairs by choosing the best goats you can and pairing goats so that wherever one parent needs improvement the other excels.

Understanding Linebreeding, Inbreeding, and Outcrossing

One last thing to consider when working your matchmaker magic is whether you want to linebreed, and if so, to what extent. A lot of old colloquial advice is thrown around about linebreeding and inbreeding. One you will hear a lot is, "If it works, it's linebreeding, and if it doesn't, it's inbreeding." That's not exactly true. Sometimes inbreeding works, sometimes linebreeding doesn't, and sometimes outcrossing doesn't work. In addition, the words do have specific definitions:

Inbreeding: Inbreeding is the very close breeding of relatives. Parent-offspring and sibling-sibling breeding is what most people are referring to when they mention inbreeding, but technically pairings such as aunt/uncle-niece/nephew, cousins, and grandparent-offspring are also inbreeding. The percentage of inbreeding increases depending on how closely related the animals are. For instance, if a female is bred back to a male that is her sire but also her cousin, that's an even higher percentage of inbreeding than a simple sire-daughter pairing of otherwise unrelated animals.

Linebreeding: Linebreeding is a form of inbreeding. However, linebreeding deals with pairs that are related more distantly than first-generation relatives. For example, it might involve breeding two animals that have a common grandparent. The object of linebreeding is to bring an animal in the pedigree forward again and increase its genetic influence over the resulting offspring. This is the goal of all forms of linebreeding and inbreeding, but we'll get to that shortly. Linebreeding is frequently utilized by many breeders.

Outcrossing: An outcross is when two animals who are completely unrelated within the past six generations are mated. Typically, outcrosses are done within the same breed, but outcrossing is also sometimes done by mating two animals of the same species but different breeds.

Linebreeding and inbreeding are very nearly the same thing. The major difference is the extent to which the mated pair are related. If we follow the definition, inbreeding refers to anything from parent-offspring to cousins. However, there is a great distance between those two. A parent and offspring have a 50% coefficient of inbreeding (COI), whereas first cousins only have a 12.5% COI. Half siblings and aunt-nephew/uncle-niece have a COI of 25%. Animals with no common ancestor for six generations are considered unrelated, and the breeding is considered an outcross.

The more closely related two goats are, the more likely it is that they contain like genes. This can be an asset in your breeding program when you wish to increase a certain trait in your herd and build greater consistency. If two goats share a common ancestor that carries a trait for well attached udders, when those goats are bred the chances of their offspring having well attached udders increases. Some of the nicest goats ever to exist have been produced via linebreeding. However, breeding related animals also carries a certain level of risk. This is because there are inevitably undesirable traits carried in a particular lineage, no matter how nice those goats are or have been. Mating two related goats increases the chances of a *negative* trait to be duplicated just as much as it increases the chances of a *positive* trait being passed on.

Goats who have an obvious defect should not be linebred; only the best quality goats with the fewest undesirable traits should be used in linebreeding programs. Additionally, if a linebreeding of a certain lineage has produced defects such as cleft palate, supernumerary teats, or cryptorchidism, future breeding along the same lineage should be done with extra caution, and the parents should not be bred to one another again. In general, the closer the relation, the riskier the pairing. Full siblings should never be bred to one another, and parent-offspring pairs should be rare and only done with exceptional animals. When choosing to linebreed, especially closely, you must be willing and able to take a critical eye to the resulting offspring and cull undesirable goats from your herd.

Complete outcrossing can be used for several reasons. Many new breeders begin with totally unrelated bucks and does to extend the time they have before needing to purchase another buck to introduce new genetics. Outcrossing can also dilute a line that has become too closely inbred for your tastes or comfort. Outcrossing can also result in heterosis or "hybrid vigor." Hybrid vigor is an increase in the size, growth rate, fertility, and general health in offspring from unrelated parents. Of course, whether linebreeding or outcrossing, we should always breed for optimal health as well; parasite resistance and natural immunity can be influenced by genetics in addition to management and environment. Outcrosses should be made with as much care as linebreeding. Outcrossing can be less predictable, so choosing pairs who complement each other is equally as important in outcrossing as it is in linebreeding.

Coefficient of Inbreeding

Understanding how to calculate the coefficient of inbreeding (COI) can be helpful while planning related pairings. The COI measures the genetic similarity of two animals. To measure this accurately, more must be considered than simply the relationship of the two goats being bred. The various factors that contribute to the COI include the relationship of the breeding pair, the distance in the pedigree of their common ancestor(s), how many common ancestors the pair shares, and how many times a common ancestor(s) appears in a five to six generation pedigree. Calculating the COI allows you to prevent accidentally mating two goats who are more closely related than you may realize on the surface.

If you are raising ADGA-registered goats, you have an advantage. You can go to their website, www.adgagenetics.com, and use their "Planning" feature to select a potential pair and automatically calculate the COI as well as generate the planned pedigree of the offspring. However, if you are working with non-ADGA goats, figuring out the COI will require a bit of math. Thankfully, the University of Missouri Extension Office provides the necessary equation on their website:

Rbc = sigma[(½)n+n'(1 + Fa)] ¸ Square Root of (1 + Fb)(1 + Fc)
Where:
bc = the coefficient of the relationship of animals b and c.
sigma = the Greek symbol meaning "add"
(½) = the fraction of an individual's genetic material that is transmitted to its progeny
n = the number of generations between animal b and the common ancestor
n' = the number of generations between animal C and the common ancestor
Fa, Fb, Fc = inbreeding coefficients of the common ancestor and of animals b and c, respectively

If none of the goats themselves are inbred, the equation is shortened to:
Rbc = sigma[(½)n + n']

This is admittedly a complex mathematical equation to parse, but if you are math-minded (or have a math-minded friend or relative), calculating the COI of potential breeding pairs can go a long way to helping you make a decision. Just remember that breeding goats, like being a goat midwife, is both a science and an art; the COI is only a number and cannot guarantee the outcome of any planned breeding.

If that equation left your head spinning, you're among good company. Math is my worst subject, so I feel your pain. The good news is that while figuring out the COI can be useful, it isn't always necessary. In many cases a basic understanding of the pros and cons of linebreeding and how genetics work will lay a solid enough foundation for you to begin pairing your goats.

Why Linebreed?

Breeding related animals is the quickest way to bring out the best traits in your lines and tighten up the consistency. As we discussed earlier, when two animals that share common genes are bred it increases the chances of the desirable genes, including recessive ones, being passed on in the offspring. The objective of linebreeding is to increase the influence of a particular ancestor(s) in the offspring. It also increases the reliability of your results. Linebred offspring are more likely to come out sharing the traits of their parents and other relatives, meaning that the goats will be more likely to share similar type and traits across the board through multiple animals. There are fewer wild card genes in the mix.

For example, if you really love the quality of milk production from a certain doe and that doe's mother as well, you may choose to breed doe #1 to her uncle (her mother's brother) in hopes that the offspring will have an increased chance of inheriting that production. It's not a guarantee that the offspring will milk well, but it increases the odds.

Why Outcross?

Outcrossing has its benefits in your herd as well. Typically, offspring from outcrosses show additional vigor and health. Not that linebred, or even inbred, animals are unhealthy, but we do always come back to the idea of heterosis and the offspring of outcrossed mating exhibiting better vitality than their parents. Essentially, broadening the genetic pool limits the chances of bad traits, particularly recessive ones, from getting passed on. However, it also lessens the chances of positive recessive traits being passed on in the same way. A recessive gene is one that requires both parents to pass it on in order for it to be present in the offspring. It needs two copies to be revealed, whereas a dominant gene only requires one parent to have the gene in order for the offspring to inherit it. (I'll explain a little more about dominant and recessive genes in a moment.) An outcrossing is more or less a wild card breeding, because you don't know how the two lines are going to interact with each other.

However, outcrossing can also be very useful. You can use outcrossing to increase vigor or to dilute an overly-linebred herd. Outcrosses are useful for diversifying your herd genetics and preventing livestock from getting too inbred over time. An outcross can also introduce a certain quality into a line that lacks it. For instance, you may love a certain line, but hate that it doesn't have straight enough legs. You might then use an unrelated animal from lines with wonderful, straight legs in hopes of adding that quality to the all the traits you admire about the other line.

Having more distantly related goats is also useful in a smaller herd that is just starting out for two reasons. One, in a smaller herd there are less options for breeding pairs. Assuming that your intent is to keep offspring to build your herd, starting out with an already heavily linebred herd might back you into a corner genetically before you're ready to bring in new outside genetics. Some people choose to sell their bucks every couple of years for new blood, but I personally never find it easy to sell adult goats I've owned for some time, including bucks. In addition, if you sell your bucks prematurely you may regret it in the future. It's impossible to truly know the positive impact a buck is having until several of his daughters have freshened. If a buck is sold before that has happened, you don't know what valuable traits you might have just gotten rid of.

Secondly, some new breeders simply aren't comfortable linebreeding. I wasn't comfortable with linebreeding when I first began my herd of goats, so I can understand where this hesitation comes from. The idea of possibly having your first few kids be duds due to a failed linebreeding attempt is daunting—you want to keep those babies, after all! Some breeders who are either experienced in breeding other types of animals, or who are simply more comfortable linebreeding and interpreting the results, may choose to start their herd with a few somewhat related animals from one breeder with the intent of carrying on linebreeding to lock in the type and traits they admire from that herd. Neither choice is the wrong one; it is entirely up to you to decide what you are comfortable doing in your own herd.

Dangers of Over-Inbreeding

We know that linebreeding increases the chance of genetic traits, both undesirable and desirable, to be duplicated in the offspring. If a negative trait is passed on it might be nothing more than an annoyance, but it might also be a very bad thing. You may breed two animals with no outward sign of a problem, but when bred to each other a hidden recessive gene may show up in the offspring. Whereas each parent only had one copy of the negative gene and therefore did not outwardly express it, the offspring inherited a copy from each parent. Suddenly you have a goat that goes bald each summer, or potentially an even worse problem. You had no way of knowing that the line carried that undesirable trait until you mated the two related animals.

This can be a positive in some ways, because it will ultimately reveal the weaknesses in your lines as quickly as it will reveal the strengths, but it can also result in more cull animals. The more closely related the two goats are, the more likely major faults will show up. You also risk losing some vigor in the offspring, which is due to the increasing of specific genes. If the common ancestor of your two animals had trouble resisting parasites, the offspring of the pair may be even more prone to poor parasite resistance—and poor parasite resistance is often a death sentence in goats. What's more is that you may not have even owned the common ancestor and not know about its weaknesses at all. Chances are if the ancestor they have in common was not your own animal, you've only ever heard all the great things about it and none of the negative ones.

Linebreeding too closely may also cause something known as inbreeding depression. The opposite of heterosis, inbreeding depression causes the offspring to lack vitality. They may have dramatic genetic problems, infertility issues, lack survivability, be stunted in growth and development, or simply be less hardy. Inbreeding depression can result in offspring that are slow to grow, prone to sickness, weak, or who simply fail to thrive for no obvious reason. Inbreeding depression is especially dangerous in the rarer breeds of livestock which lack an abundant gene pool to begin with due to low numbers. Always be careful to avoid overly inbreeding your goats and other livestock, and pay extra close attention to your linebreeding decisions if working with a rare breed. Their survival depends on careful, conscious breeding choices.

Ask yourself a few questions before linebreeding. How well do you know the animals in these lines, including both their strengths and weaknesses? How experienced are you with your breed and breeding in general? Are you confident that you can spot potential flaws in the offspring? Lastly, and most importantly, are you willing to cull?

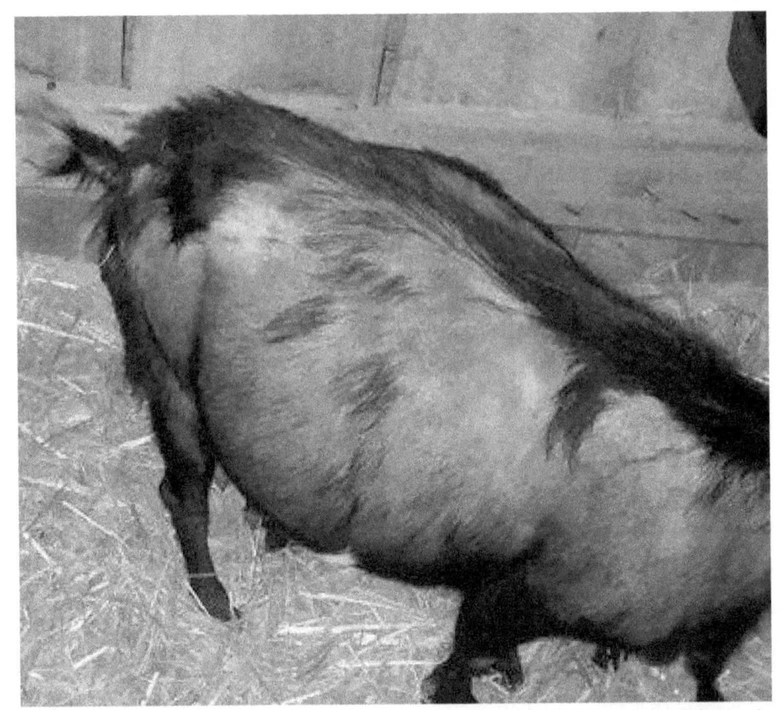

This is the only picture I took of Joy during her baldness. I was, quite frankly, embarrassed at having a bald goat. I'm thankful to have this picture now, though, to educate others.

Tales from the Kidding Stall: *As an example of the potential risks of negative recessive genes, let me tell you Joy's story. Joy first lost her hair during pregnancy, and nothing I tried encouraged growth. She was treated for copper deficiency, zinc deficiency, mites, and lice and given herbal supplements and treated with various ointments all to no avail. Eventually she lost almost all the hair from her body except what was on her legs, face, and tail. It was truly bizarre. Our veterinarian advised us that it was likely a systemic, autoimmune issue and might be treated with steroids; however, that wasn't an option due to her pregnancy. I spoke with a breeder who owned her full littermate sister and discovered that she, along with other relatives from that bloodline, also lost her hair, confirming the genetic component. Joy's hair grew back after that pregnancy, but she continued to lose it each year during the summer. Joy was also a hard keeper, and maintaining her in good condition required more feed and care than normal. She was more prone to sickness like pneumonia. Ultimately, she passed away a few years later after we had a breech in our feed room and several goats gorged on chicken feed. Joy was the only one to become ill, and she did not respond to treatment. I contribute that in part to a generally weak constitution due to genetic weakness. Although she was only minimally linebred herself, there was clearly a negative recessive gene in her lineage. I still have Joy's daughter, who so far has not gone bald, but I will never linebreed on those genetics.*

Culling

Culling is the process of eliminating undesirable animals from the gene pool of your breeding stock. This can occur in the form of culling to the freezer as meat, selling to a pet home, or—if the animal lacks severe faults but just doesn't make the cut for your program—selling it to another breeding program with full disclosure of its flaws. However you choose to cull, you must be willing to trim the fat from your breeding program. You will get more comfortable with culling as you gain more experience. It's hard the first couple of years to get rid of those cute little babies, but if you want to have a serious breeding program, and especially if you are linebreeding, you have to be willing and able to recognize the traits you don't want and cull them from your herd. Farming, even on a small scale, requires you to develop a thick skin and be willing to make hard decisions. You can't keep them all, and even if you could financially and logistically keep them all, you shouldn't. It's not beneficial to your farm and it's not beneficial to the genetic wellbeing of goats in general to keep breeding subpar animals.

Understanding Dominant and Recessive Genes

When two goats are bred to each other, each one passes down a set of genes to their offspring. The resulting kids are genetically 50% of their sire and 50% of their dam. That means that they're half like the buck and half like the doe, right? Wrong. Genetics are extremely complex, and even the highest achieving experts in the field still don't know everything there is to know about genes. Each parent animal has two copies of each specific gene, but they only pass down one copy to the offspring. That's how you can have two buckskin goats have a solid black kid. Each parent in that instance carried a gene for the black coat color, and each parent passed it down to the offspring. Because some genes are displayed while others are hidden, due to being dominant and recessive, we can't look at two goats and know for certain what their kids will look like. Knowing the traits of the parents and their offspring can help us make an educated guess—for example, you know that any goat that produces a black kid carries the black gene regardless of the expressed color of their own coat—but ultimately it's a surprise. Although narrowing it all down to dominant vs recessive genes is still an oversimplification, understanding the two can go a long way to helping you understand some basic genetics.

Dominant Genes

Dominant genes require only one parent or one copy of the gene to be observable in the offspring. They are also always physically expressed in the animal when present. To give some examples, the genes in goats for blue eyes, polled (naturally hornless), and moonspots are all dominant genes. If the gene is present in the animal, it is also expressed in the animal. If a goat does not have blue eyes, does have horns, or does not have moonspots, then they do not carry the gene for those traits.

If a truly dominant gene is not expressed on the animal, it cannot be passed on from that animal to its offspring except when bred to another animal that does have the dominant gene expressed. This is why two brown eyed goats will never produce a blue eyed kid, two horned goats will never produce a polled kid, and two non-moonspotted goats will never produce a kid with moonspots. Even then it already becomes more complicated, because a goat can have a tiny, invisible moonspot you can't see with the naked eye. That's how kids are born with moonspots from parents who visibly don't appear to have the gene. Likewise, some genes have variable abilities to write over other genes. For example, certain coat patterns such as buckskin are considered dominant. However, gold will overwrite buckskin and all other patterns that would otherwise be dominant over another color such as black. White spotting overwrites gold, and all other colors, meaning that a goat with extensive white overlay may visibly not appear to be the color or pattern it is genetically.

Some genes are also co-dominant with one another, meaning that both genes are expressed. When this happens, the physical appearance of the gene is altered. This is often seen with certain coat patterns such as buckskin, chamoise, swiss marked, and cou clair or cou blanc. Two of these patterns can be present at one time if a kid has inherited one from each parent, and the resulting pattern looks different on the kid. Generally, the areas of the patterns that would be black are overwritten by the areas of the other pattern that are light. For example, a kid carrying both cou clair and buckskin will have neither a black cape nor a black hindquarter due to the pattern mixing. Of course, these genes are easy to observe because they are present in the phenotype (physical appearance) of the goat. Genes which are carried in the genotype (genetic makeup) of the goat are not always obvious to the naked eye.

What dominant does *not* mean is "always passed on" or "more likely to be passed on." Dominant only means that if the gene is present in the genotype it is expressed in the phenotype, unless written over by another, more dominant or co-dominant gene. It does *not* increase the chances of the offspring inheriting that gene above the normal odds for them to inherit any gene from the parent. Remember a goat has inherited two copies of each gene, one from the sire and one from the dam. If a goat is polled, that means they inherited a polled gene from at least one parent. They might have inherited it from both, making them homozygous polled, or they might have inherited one polled gene and one horned gene. This is how two blue eyed goats can produce a brown eyed kid, for example. When two animals who both have a dominant gene are bred, it increases the chance that the offspring will be homozygous for the trait, meaning that 100% of that animal's offspring will have the trait because it carries two copies of the gene and therefore always passes it on.

Recessive Genes

Recessive genes require *both* parents and *two* copies of the gene to be passed onto the offspring in order for the offspring to physically express the gene. These are the types of genes that an animal can carry and pass on to its offspring when the animal itself does not visibly appear to carry the gene. A black coat color is an excellent example of this in goats. The black color in goats is recessive, which means that any black goat you own can only pass on the gene for a black coat because they carry two copies of that coat color—one on each allele. If a goat carries one gene for a gold coat from one parent and a gene for a black coat from the other, that goat will have a gold colored coat. Yet when bred to another goat of any color, they might produce a black kid if the other goat also carries a gene for the black coat color. If you want to know what possible color genes your goat is carrying, breed them to a (preferably solid) black goat. If they have a black kid, their second color gene is black. If they have a kid of any color other than the one you see on the parent, then you know that's their secondary, unexpressed color gene.

Recessive genes are often hidden in the animal, because dominant genes overwrite them when present. This is part of what makes linebreeding and inbreeding tricky. You can't always see what a goat is carrying around in their DNA. Breeding two related animals increases the chance that they each contain the same recessive gene and can potentially pass that gene onto their kids. If the two goats are carrying an undesirable, or even dangerous, recessive gene it puts their offspring at risk. Since we can't see all the genes our goats carry, we must take calculated risks. Of course, this is true for both linebreeding and outcrossing, because unrelated goats might carry the same recessive genes as well.

Punnett Square

Before we move on from the mysterious and fascinating world of genetics, let's have a little fun. A Punnett square is a quick and easy way to make some calculated guesses about the offspring of your two goats based on what you know of the parents' genetics. A Punnett square shows you the four options possible for each potential offspring by matching the two genes from the father horizontally across the square with the two copies from the mother vertically. In each space in the square you write in which genes are directly above and to the left of the space. Typically, dominant genes are capitalized. For example, let's see what the Punnett square says about gender:

Y= Male x = Female

Gender	Y	x
x	Yx	xx
x	Yx	xx

As you can see, the Punnett square shows us that there is a 50% chance for each kid born to be either a buckling or a doeling.

The Punnett square can be used to explore the options of any of the more basic, observable traits in the offspring, such as coat color or pattern, polled or horned, eye color, and the like. For example, here's what the square shows for the chances of blue eyed offspring when both parents are heterozygous blue eyed (carrying one brown eyed and one blue eyed gene):

B = blue b = brown

Eye Color	B	b
B	BB	Bb
b	Bb	bb

From this square we can see that each kid from two heterozygous blue eyed parents has a 50% chance of being heterozygous blue eyed (Bb), a 25% chance of being homozygous blue eyed (BB), and a 25% chance of being brown eyed (bb). Pretty cool, right? Let's do one more looking at some color genetics. In this case let's say the sire is a buckskin patterned goat carrying a black coat gene. Buckskin is dominant and black is recessive. The dam is a chamoisee also carrying a black gene, and chamoisee is the dominant gene.

B = buckskin C = chamoisee b = black

Coat Color	B	b
C	CB	Cb
b	Bb	bb

Each kid from this pairing has a 25% chance of being a chamoisee carrying recessive black, a 25% chance of being a buckskin carrying recessive black, a 25% chance of being homozygous black, and a 25% chance of carrying both the buckskin and the chamoisee gene. So what happens when a goat inherits a dominant gene from both parents on the same allele? Both genes are expressed! The CB kid from this example would show aspects of both the chamoisee and the buckskin gene, and the two color patterns would modify each other. See the picture on the next page to see how that works. The exception to this is a goat inheriting the gold gene; that goat will always appear gold because gold will overwrite any other pattern or color.

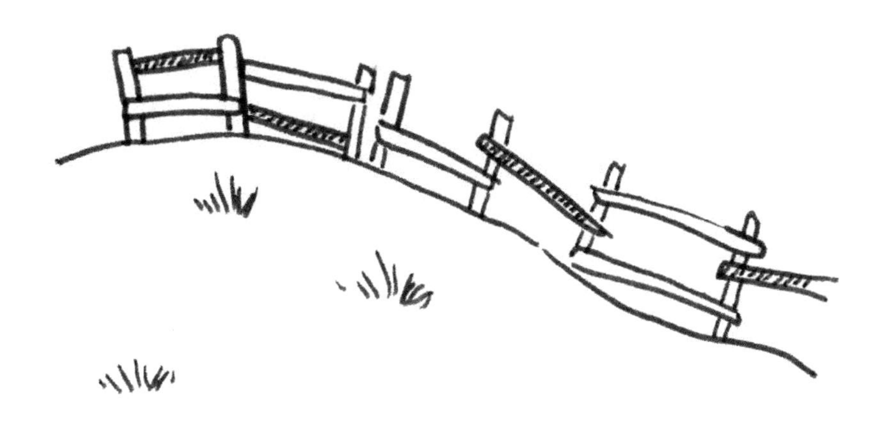

On the left in this picture is a classic buckskin pattern. Note the black cape and light facial and leg stripes. On the right is a classic chamoise. Note the solid black face, black legs, black underbelly, and black dorsal stripe.

Here is what those two patterns look like when a goat inherits both of them. Note the light facial and leg stripes and light underbelly from the buckskin and the black dorsal stripe and partial black belly color from the chamoise.

One last word on genetics and probability before I end this section. Having a 50% chance of a certain trait in the offspring does not mean an even half of the kids will inherit that trait. For example, each kid born has a 50% chance of being either male or female, yet it is common to have all male or all female litters. I have had triplet bucks born, twin does, triplets with two does and one buck, and on and on. Over the course of time, the rate of a given trait should come out to around 50%, but there's no guarantee. It all comes down to which gene is passed on from each parent. I have bred polled goats and had all horned offspring, two goats with dominant coat colors and all kids inherited only one, and so on. It is in many ways a game of chance—but that's part of what makes it fun!

As I'm sure you can tell, there is much more that can be said about genetics. It's such a broad, complex field of study. I am no geneticist, so this is where I will stop. I highly encourage doing a bit more research on the genetics of goats if this is an area that piques your interest!

Breeding Polled to Polled

In the dairy goat world, and especially in the Nigerian Dwarf community, you will see arguments being made about breeding polled goats to other polled goats. One side of the argument claims that the polled gene is linked to a recessive gene for hermaphroditism (intersex, infertile trait) and a recessive terminator gene that may kill female embryos before they develop. This is based on a few older studies that looked at the prevalence of intersex offspring when breeding polled to polled in dairy goats. In one study published in the Journal of Heredity, a total of 1,362 kids were born. The researchers found that the group in which a homozygous polled buck was bred to heterozygous polled does that 86 kids were male, 28 were female, and 26 were hermaphrodites. Those are not exactly good odds for dairy goat producers. The study indicated that offspring from polled x horned breeding were normal. In another study conducted in 1944, the researchers found similar ratios when breeding polled to polled. It is speculated that in those studies the hermaphrodites were initially female, which would account for the discrepancy between the ratio of male to female kids. When the researchers counted the hermaphrodites as females, the numbers evened out to 103 bucks and 100 does.

On the other hand, some breeders are determined to test this theory, especially considering the age of the studies and the desirability of not needing to disbud kids. The information provided by these individuals is colloquial, but some do state that they are not seeing the horrendous buck:doe:intersex ratios the earlier studies would suggest. It takes a large number of goats to replicate a true scientific study, and I don't personally know of any individuals producing upwards of a thousand kids in a single year (though some surely exist out there unbeknownst to me). Ultimately, we can only go by what the old study states until a new study is performed, which may or may not happen. Choosing to experiment with polled to polled breeding is a personal choice and a calculated risk. Since hermaphroditism does not actually harm the offspring, it simply makes them "wethers" so to speak, it is not unethical to attempt a polled x polled cross. Just be aware that there is a controversy over this issue, and there's a chance it may impact the gender of the resulting kids. If you are willing to risk having a hermaphrodite born in place of a doe kids, then experiment as you will.

Other Considerations

Other considerations for choosing your breeding animals go beyond conformation and production and into important traits such as mothering ability, parasite resistance, hardiness, and longevity. It's important for the wellbeing of your herd, and the wellbeing of the species at large, that health and hardiness traits be considered when breeding. Goats who have lower resistance to parasites, are prone to illness, or are not productive into a mature age are not the best choices for your herd. They increase your workload and expenses while decreasing your production.

At times we can get caught up in the world of milk production and show wins to the point that we neglect natural health and hardiness. This is when linebreeding can be taken too far and cause inbreeding depression, and when our selections of goats to perpetuate can be damaging in the long run if we toss all else aside but the competitive traits. It's also a way to perpetuate a herd of high maintenance animals that require an excess of care to thrive. While conformation and milk production are important, we can't value those traits to the exclusion of health. It's of the utmost importance that we consider how frequently our goats need special treatment, coddling, medications, or dewormers when we place them in the breeding pen. A goat who has frequent recurrences of parasite overload can pass those genes down to their offspring, and that is a dangerous trait to have considering the problem that parasites can cause goats and the rise of dewormer resistant parasites. Likewise, a doe with traits that make her a poor kidder in frequent need of help can duplicate those genes down to her daughters. A goat who is prone to getting sick, or hard to keep weight on when in milk, or generally of a lower hardiness is a goat who might be considered for culling, depending on how severe the problem is and whether or not its offspring inherit the same troubles.

Keep in mind I am not advocating for neglecting goats and expecting them to thrive on naught but scrub pasture. We expect our goats to perform for us, so they must be given appropriate care in return. Goats have complex mineral needs and require high quality feedstuffs, especially hay, to produce and thrive. Starving any goat or neglecting their mineral needs will result in sickly, parasitized, underproducing goats. It goes without saying that the more we expect from our goats, the more we must give them in return. The highest producing does will need more nutrients to keep up both their body condition and their milk production. It is normal for does to lose extra flesh while in milk, but they shouldn't become emaciated. Goats as a species are also highly prone to parasitization due to their nature, which is discussed in chapter eight, so we can't expect them to never need to be dewormed, either. However, goats that are having their mineral needs met, eating an appropriate diet, kept in a clean and comfortable environment, and still frequently struggling with parasites or illness on a basis that exceeds the norm for your herd are not exhibiting the type of natural resilience you want in your livestock.

The perfect goat in my opinion is one that is conformationally correct, productive, an easy keeper, kids with ease, and exhibits natural hardiness and resilience. Things such as parasite resistance and overall vitality do have a genetic component to them and should be considered in every breeding program. Consider the health and hardiness traits of equal important to production and conformation and you'll be on your way to producing wonderful animals.

Closed vs Open Herd

Once your herd numbers are established, you have the option of keeping an "open" or "closed" herd. While purchasing you also have the option of buying from a closed herd. A closed herd is one that no longer purchases goats from other breeders, or in some cases no longer purchases does from other breeds but does occasionally add a new buck for genetic diversity. An open herd is essentially what your herd will be as you're starting out: a herd that brings in new goats from another person's breeding. There are, as always, both pros and cons to keeping a herd closed.

The benefit of keeping a closed herd is that it minimizes the possibility of bringing in new diseases or parasites from another person's farm. Biosecurity is very important with livestock, and there are diseases that you do not want to introduce to your existing herd. In addition, different strains of parasites exist on different farms, even if the goats there are healthy and disease free. Your goats may not have the natural resistance to withstand the introduction of a new parasite foreign to their immune systems, or the new parasite might be resistant to dewormers that have previously worked for the parasites on your land. The cons of keeping a closed herd are a lack of genetic diversity and a lack of introduction of new, desirable traits that are lacking in your herd. In a closed herd, most of the goats are related to one another in some way as well. This isn't necessarily a bad thing since linebreeding can be highly effective, but it may be limiting.

Regardless of what you choose, always quarantine new additions to your herd for a minimum of thirty days—preferably three months or longer—prior to introducing them to your own stock to prevent the transfer of disease, illness, or parasites.

Miniature Dairy Goats

A popular new trend in dairy goats, and livestock in general, is to go miniature. Miniature livestock breeds can be the perfect fit for many homesteads, because they require less feed, need less space, and produce less than their larger counterparts. Someone only wanting a home milk supply might be overwhelmed by the production of some of the larger dairy breeds. Nigerian Dwarfs are the only true miniature dairy breed, and many people today choose them. However, some people want a bit more production while still not having a full size dairy goat; for those people, the "mini" breeds derived from crossing Nigerians and standard breeds are a popular choice.

Any of the standard dairy breeds can be crossed to a Nigerian to make a mini, and the offspring can be registered by either The Miniature Goat Registry or the Miniature Dairy Goat Association so long as the parents were registered with one of the purebred registries such as ADGA or AGS. The breeds recognized include Mini Saanen, Nubian, LaMancha (often called "MiniMancha"), Alpine, Oberhasli, Toggenburg, Sable, or Guernsey (developing). Offspring are registered according to generations. For example, a Nigerian x Standard is considered an F1, which means it is the first generation. That goat bred to another F1 (or higher) creates F2, then F3, and so on. Breeding at any time to a lower generation sets the offspring's generation according to the lower generation's status. For example, an F5 bred to a Nigerian creates F1, and an F1 bred to an F3 creates F2. After F3, a goat meeting the breed standard is eligible for reaching American status, and after F6 a goat meeting the breed standard is eligible for being considered purebred.

The ideal mini possesses the physical characteristics of the standard breed on which it's based, but in a midsized package. The full-grown size of the minis is in between the height of the Nigerians and the standards. There is a lot of variation in the early generations, and it takes some time to obtain an F6 animal meeting the breed standard. It's important to remember when planning a mini breeding that the buck should always be from the smaller breed and the doe from the larger. For example, a Nigerian buck would be bred to a standard doe, but not the other way around. Likewise, a mini buck to a standard doe or a Nigerian buck to a mini doe would also work. The other appropriate breeding would be to breed miniature to miniature, while keeping in mind the percentages and the body size. Depending on the size of the doe, a difference of roughly 25% is acceptable. For example, a 50% Nigerian, 50% standard mini doe of appropriate size should safely be able to breed to a 75% standard, 25% Nigerian mini buck under most circumstances, considering her body size.

Breeding standard bucks to Nigerian does is not a safe practice and can result in oversized, difficult to deliver kids. Some people carry the belief that the kids will grow to fit the doe's body, but this simply isn't the case. Overgrown kids can result from overfeeding, breeding the doe to a large buck, or sometimes pure chance. You may hear of circumstances where such a breeding worked out, but these are exceptions rather than the rule. As I once explained to someone, a person can smoke cigarettes and not develop lung cancer, but that doesn't mean smoking is a healthy practice. Likewise, a Nigerian doe can be bred to a standard buck and have a safe delivery, but that doesn't mean breeding her to a standard is a safe practice. It is unfair to the doe to put her at a greater risk for a needlessly difficult or life-threatening birth. And truly, there is no need to even do so when you can achieve the same goal in a safer way.

Does eating hay from their hay feeder. Note that this feeder design has small squares along with a couple of larger holes that allow the goats to stick their head through. Goats are notorious hay wasters, so smaller squares prevent waste. Avoid feeders with long slats that taper to a narrower bottom as goats may become stuck and strangle in such a feeder. This doe's neck has a bare patch from a blood draw for a pregnancy test.

Chapter 2: Nutrition

Nutrition must always be at the forefront of any breeding plan. Before a goat can be expected to reproduce successfully, it must be provided with the proper nutrition to support fertility, healthy pregnancy, easy kidding, and milk production. As stated earlier, goats—especially does—should be in good condition before being bred. This means that they should be neither under or overweight, they should not be burdened by parasites, and they should not be deficient in any minerals. Although it's not as simple as some people think due to the "goats can eat anything" myth, good nutrition is relatively easy to accomplish for your goats once you have a basic understanding of their nutritional needs.

For most dry does and bucks, good quality hay, fresh water, proper mineral supplementation, and browse (when available) will meet their nutritional needs without any added grains or additional feed supplements. Occasionally bucks who are in rut will need additional groceries due to the stress of being in rut, breeding, and constantly sparring with other bucks. Does who are lactating need to be given appropriate grain supplementation as well to support the production of milk. Every so often a goat may be a "hard keeper," meaning that they do not keep body condition well. This is an undesirable trait and should be avoided in your herd, because goats who do not keep condition well cost more than easy keepers and are more prone to other issues as well. Before you assume a goat is a hard keeper, however, be certain that they are not parasitized, that your hay is of high quality, that you're feeding them enough grain to support their milk production, and that their mineral needs are being met. Overall, grain should always be only a small portion of any goat's diet and should only be fed when necessary; good quality hay and forage is the backbone of goat nutrition. This is the type of food their rumen is designed to digest. Overfeeding grain leads to deadly urinary calculi in bucks and wethers and excess weight and resulting health problems (such as infertility or dystocia) for does. Later on in this section I provide more details about feeding your goats. However, I first want to devote a healthy portion of this section to providing the appropriate minerals to support both male and female fertility and vitality.

Minerals for Reproductive Health

All goats should have a good quality loose mineral available at all times. This mineral should be formulated specifically for goats, or for cows if a high-quality goat mineral is unavailable, in order to provide the appropriate levels of the right nutrients. Goats should not be fed a sheep or sheep/goat mineral as it will be drastically lacking in copper and will not meet the goat's daily needs. While excess copper may cause toxicity in sheep, it is a vital part of a healthy goat's diet. Goats should not be provided a mineral or salt block. Since goats have small, smooth tongues and no upper front teeth, they cannot consume enough mineral from a block to provide for their needs. A good quality goat mineral should contain around of 1500-1800 ppm copper and about 50 ppm selenium. More on those two minerals and their important later on.

Even with appropriate loose minerals available, many goats will still become deficient for certain minerals, namely copper and/or selenium. This is due to a combination of factors. First, much of the soil in the United States does not contain adequate levels of certain minerals. Hay, browse, and other feed derived from deficient soil will thereby not contain the necessary minerals for the livestock eating them. Many minerals can also bind with other minerals which then prevents the needed minerals from being absorbed by the goats, even when consumed in high enough levels. For example, copper will bind with sulfur and become unavailable; if you have sulfur in your water, you will likely encounter copper deficiency even if your land has high enough levels and proper minerals are provided. This is just one example of mineral binding. Deficiencies caused by a lack of a mineral in the diet are referred to as primary deficiencies, whereas deficiencies caused by antagonists in the diet preventing absorption are called secondary deficiencies. Either way, the bottom line is that the goats aren't absorbing the levels of minerals that they need to thrive.

Another reason that goats may not be able to obtain adequate amounts of a specific mineral from the appropriate loose mineral is because the blend will contain several necessary minerals, including salt, rather than a single mineral. Therefore, goats will only eat as much of a mixed mineral as will meet their basic needs without overdosing them on any particular mineral. In order for a goat suffering from copper deficiency to obtain enough copper from a mixed mineral, they would be forced to consume more of many other minerals than they needed. This is not something that goats will typically do nor is it advisable. Mineral blends containing high levels of salt are especially likely to cause under-consumption, because the goats will initially eat the mineral for the salt and then stop once that need is satiated. Livestock have an incredible natural ability to consume just what they need of various supplements without overdosing themselves, but when salt or other minerals are mixed in, they will stop consuming before all needs are met.

Loose minerals should always be offered free choice and never added directly to a goat's feed. These minerals are designed for goats to consume what they need on their own, not to be fed as a direct supplement. You may inadvertently overdose a goat on a particular mineral by force feeding them. This is also why minerals should always be provided on their own rather than mixed with additional salt, feed, or another supplement or treat. Mixing blended minerals with another supplement will skew how much the goats will consume; they may eat too much or not enough if provided minerals in this manner. In some cases, you may offer multiple mineral options alongside your loose minerals, such as baking soda, selenium powder, kelp, or herbs. In that case each supplement should be provided alone in its own tub. Individually offered supplements should also not be mixed with salt or any other extra ingredient that may skew consumption.

Let's look now at some of the most vital minerals for goats, as well as the minerals for which they are most likely to experience a deficiency.

This doe has a classic fishtail, which is characteristic of mineral imbalance. Note the bald tail tip causing the hair to look like a fish's tail fin. In my experience, fishtail will linger the longest after copper bolusing.

Copper

Copper is an extremely important mineral for the overall health and reproductive ability of goats. Copper plays a key role in maintaining a goat's parasite resistance, healthy immune function, and optimal fertility. Copper deficiency is one of the most widespread mineral deficiencies in goats. In many ways, we are only beginning to scratch the surface concerning just how important copper is to goat health and the prevalence of copper deficiency in goat herds. Sulfur, molybdenum, calcium, lead, and iron are all antagonists to copper. Much of North America is deficient in copper in the soil, but secondary copper deficiency is also a common problem. Even if the diet of the goat contains adequate levels of copper, antagonists in the environment (food or water supply) can cause a secondary deficiency. It would be hard to overstate the importance of maintaining proper copper levels in your herd, so ensuring appropriate copper supplementation is of the utmost importance.

Symptoms of copper deficiency are many and varied. One of the most common symptoms is a faded, rough coat. Black coats fade to a rusty red or brown, brown coats fade to tan, tan fades to cream, and cream fades to white. The coat will also become curly or coarse in texture instead of smooth and sleek, and the goat may not shed their winter coat appropriately in the spring. Baldness also occurs on the tip of the goat's tail, referred to as "fish-tail," and on the goat's face down the bridge of the nose or around the eyes. The goat may not show proper resistance to parasites and be prone to frequent parasite infestation, parasite-inflicted anemia, and death resulting from internal parasites. Copper deficiency can also cause orthopedic problems such as weak or deformed bones, which can result in bent legs, swayed backs, and broken bones.

Deficient goats also struggle with reproduction. Does may not come into heat as expected or may have silent heats that are difficult to detect. You may also see lowered fertility resulting in smaller litter sizes or an increased prevalence of single births. Copper deficient goats may not become pregnant at all or may experience early term abortions, which are usually not detected by the breeder, or may go into labor early and deliver premature kids. Copper supplementation is extremely important for reproduction for this reason, and all breeding goats should be appropriately supplemented for copper where needed. Although levels of copper deficiency vary among herds, most goat breeders do experience some level of deficiency in their herd.

Copper can be supplemented by administering copper oxide wire particles (COWP) via a bolus every three to six months at a rate of 4 grams for adult goats weighing 50 or more pounds and 2 grams for kids weighing at least 25 pounds but less than 50. Frequency is variable based on individual farms, so you will need to closely observe your herd to determine how often copper needs to be administered. In my own herd, I have found that a schedule of every four months (three times a year) is needed to maintain appropriate levels, but other herds require less frequent supplementing, while more severe deficiencies may need to supplement every three months. To administer, the copper bolus is placed in a bolus gun and forced down the goat's throat whole. Goats aren't terribly fond of the process and might chew up and spit out the bolus if it is not administered far enough back in the mouth, past the teeth. A bolus gun or applicator is vital to this process—don't try to force the pill back with your fingers. Goat teeth are very sharp. Some people choose to top dress a tasty treat with the copper instead, and this works as well. Personally, I choose to bolus because I like the certainty of knowing the copper all got in the right place, and some goats are picky eaters and will nibble around anything strange.

The copper oxide particles are slowly released and absorbed by the goats. This method of supplementing is generally very safe. In one study, copper boluses were administered to sheep, a species with a lower tolerance to copper than goats, in an effort to study the potential use of COWP in against internal parasites in sheep. Pregnant ewes were given two-gram or four-gram copper boluses in the study, and there were no deaths from toxicity. Copper sulfate is another form of copper that some people use to supplement, but I do not recommend it. Copper sulfate is more quickly absorbed and less safe than copper oxide wire particles, and much more likely to be overdosed and cause toxicity. Copper oxide wire particles are the ideal, safest method for supplementing copper. However, copper toxicity can occur if goats are chronically deficient in other minerals such as molybdenum.

Proper balance is important in all minerals. Toxicity is less common than deficiency, but it is important to know your herd and address mineral imbalance specifically for your herd rather than blindly following what another herd does.

Selenium

Selenium is another key mineral for reproductive health. Does deficient in selenium may have trouble getting pregnant and staying pregnant. They are also more prone to having problems with kidding, developing mastitis, and retaining placentas after giving birth. Selenium deficiency can cause a doe to have a lower milk production as well. Selenium also affects the fertility of bucks, and bucks who are deficient may have trouble settling does (in other words, the does may not become pregnant).

Kids born to dams with selenium deficiency may be born weak or stillborn, and they may have weak legs and joints or suffer from white muscle disease. Selenium deficient kids will often exhibit muscular weakness and bend at the pasterns. Such leg deformities are not permanent, but they may require splinting to correct. In some extreme cases deficiency may even cause sudden death by heart attack or paralysis. In addition, selenium is also necessary for the metabolizing of copper, vitamin E, and other vitamins and minerals. So, in other words, if your goats are deficient in selenium it might also cause them to become deficient in other vital nutrients as well or exacerbate existing deficiencies such as copper.

Injectable selenium called BoSe is available by prescription only from a veterinarian and can be administered to deficient goats or weak kids. However, the risk for toxicity is much higher when using injectable selenium rather than orally dosed selenium, and the margin of safety for selenium is not as high as it is for some other minerals. The margin of safety refers to the amount by which a mineral (or medicine or another supplement) can be overdosed without injuring or killing the recipient. Certain mineral supplements such as copper oxide have a high margin of safety before toxicity occurs, but selenium is not quite as forgiving. When using BoSe it is important to carefully and correctly measure dosages. Another option for supplementation is an oral selenium and vitamin E paste. The paste does not have a high concentration of selenium, though, and may not be an adequate supplement for deficient herds. With both the injection and the paste, supplementation is generally provided prior to breeding each year, again prior to kidding, and at birth to any kids exhibiting deficiency.

Another option is to supplement via free choice selenium vitamin E powder. I personally used the oral selenium paste in my herd prior to breeding and kidding for several years, but I continued to see problems such as retained placentas and difficulty in getting does to conceive. I have since switched to providing a loose, free-choice selenium powder supplement that allows my goats to ingest selenium when they need it. Consuming the selenium orally is less risky than injecting it, minerals are better absorbed into the body when consumed orally, and offering it free choice allows the goats to consume the exact amount they need. Recent research has confirmed that goats are able to regulate their own consumption of minerals when provided individual cafeteria style supplementation; a practice that many cattle producers have used for years. The key is that the carrying agent for the individual minerals must *not* be salt. Instead it should be something neutral, like wheat middlings, which is the carrying agent of the selenium supplement I provide. Salt should be included in your mixed loose mineral only, because salt will influence the consumption of the mineral. While it is not practical to provide each and every mineral separately in such a manner—which is the reason for well formulated loose minerals—it is a viable option for supplementing selenium.

Selenium deficiency is often primary, but may be secondary as well. Calcium is an antagonist of selenium. Selenium toxicity (too much selenium) may result in diarrhea, unusual shedding of hair, lameness, or death.

Tales from the Kidding Stall: *I owned a buck named Wybie for many years, and for a time I believed he was infertile. I tried, unsuccessfully, to breed him to several different does with no luck, yet the same does would then settle with another buck. At that time I was still using the low-level selenium/vit e gel to supplement, and I was also experiencing frequent retained placentas. I did a bit of research on infertility and learned about the possible impacts of selenium deficiency and the free-choice selenium powder method of supplementation. I switched to free choice selenium, and suddenly Wybie was able to settle does. In addition, my does stopped retaining their placentas after kidding.*

Calcium

Calcium is necessary for the production of milk in lactating does. If a doe is not provided with enough calcium during lactation, she can suffer from hypocalcemia or "milk fever." Calcium deficiency can also cause a slow labor with weak contractions. Hypocalcemia is more prevalent in dairy goats than in meat or fiber goats due to the high milk production of dairy animals. Lactating does should be supplemented with alfalfa hay or alfalfa pellets to increase the calcium levels in their diets. Alfalfa and other legumes (clover, kudzu) have naturally high calcium levels. The supplement CMPK (Calcium Magnesium Phosphorus Potassium) should always be kept on hand in case of emergencies; this is available in drench form over the counter or as an injectable prescribed by a veterinarian. For more details on hypocalcemia, please see chapter eight of this book.

Phosphorus

Phosphorus is important to note due to its relationship with calcium. Phosphorus and calcium must be available in the right ratio to avoid deficiency in either mineral as well as to avoid urinary calculi in male goats. Phosphorus deficiency causes slow growth and an unthrifty appearance. The milk production of does will also be impacted in a phosphorus deficient situation. In some cases, it can also cause depraved appetite, or the ingestion of non-food substances such as rocks or wood. The calcium:phosphorus ratio for goats should be maintained around 2:1 and no less than 1:1. Phosphorus is found in cereal grains—this is one reason why bucks should only be fed grain when necessary to maintain their body condition.

Zinc

Zinc is a less common deficiency for goats. However, when present, zinc deficiency can cause infertility in bucks along with symptoms affecting the hair coat. Zinc deficiency causes symptoms such as an excess of dandruff, shedding off-season, dry flakey patches of skin, skin lesions, and missing hair. Zinc deficiency can also cause excess salivation, which will result in foaming at the mouth. Other symptoms include stiffness of joints, smaller testicles, and lowered libido. There is some speculation that a predisposition to zinc deficiency may be partially genetic, but this has yet to be confirmed.

Zinc deficiency is often caused by an excess of calcium in the diet, which is an antagonist to zinc. Lowering calcium intake may eliminate the problem. Zinc is also available in a powdered oral supplement and injectable supplements, the latter of which must be obtained from a vet. Because the hair symptoms can also be caused by mites or lice, rule out other possible causes before assuming a goat is zinc deficient.

Cobalt

Cobalt is not as widely discussed as other minerals, and a deficiency in cobalt is not as common as other deficiencies but is not unheard of. Cobalt's primary function is as a component of vitamin B12, which is a necessary vitamin for goats. The rumen of the goat uses cobalt to produce B12, and a deficiency of cobalt will result in a deficiency of B12. Symptoms of deficiency may include loss of appetite, anemia, a decrease in milk production, bad tasting milk, increased susceptibility to parasites, irregular heat cycles, or weakness. Goats with insufficient cobalt in their diet may also experience weight loss and have difficulty absorbing nutrients from their food.

Cobalt can be purchased as a block, which is artificially bright blue in color, but I do not recommend this. Cobalt blocks are 97-99% salt. Supplying a block may decrease the goat's consumption of its mixed, loose minerals due to the high salt content. In fact, some loose minerals have higher levels of cobalt than the blue cobalt blocks. Cobalt sulfate is available, but it must be carefully dosed to avoid toxicity. Most sources indicate that a diet with sufficient levels of cobalt will prevent deficiency, but lead is an antagonist of cobalt and excess iron may potentially prevent its uptake as well. Good loose minerals contain cobalt, and for most herds this will be sufficient. Consider cobalt deficiency as a possibility if you are seeing anemic goats who have been supplemented appropriately with copper and are not carrying a heavy parasite infestation.

Iodine

Goats need iodine for proper thyroid function. Iodine deficiency can lead to enlarged thyroid (goiter), failure to reproduce, poor growth, and kids born weak or unusually small. Kids may also be born without hair or with large goiters, and they are often stillborn if the deficiency is severe. Most of the iodine in nature in found in the sea, so locations that are well inland or at a high elevation are more likely to have deficient levels of iodine available than coastal regions. Loose minerals do contain iodine, and in most cases the levels in loose minerals will be sufficient. However, there are certain plants in nature, called "goitrogenous" plants, that can inhibit the uptake of iodine and have anithyroid actions. This includes plants such as horseradish, turnips, rutabaga, black mustard, cabbage, brussels sprouts, broccoli, cauliflower, kale, kohlrabi, meadowfoam, watercress, stinkweed, radish, rapeseed, and others. Goats eating large amounts of plants containing goitrogens may develop iodine deficiency even with appropriate levels in the diet. Kelp is an excellent source of iodine, along with other important nutrients, and many goat breeders choose to offer kelp free-choice alongside minerals.

A Note on Injecting Mineral Supplements: *There are two main reasons I don't recommend injectable mineral supplements such as MultiMin (a copper, selenium, manganese, and zinc injection) or BoSe in favor of oral supplementation. The first reason is that the margin of safety is much lower. It's much easier to accidentally overdose a goat by injection. The second reason is decreased efficacy. Minerals are best absorbed and used by the goat's body when given orally. When injected, the goat's body metabolizes the minerals quickly and they flush out of the body rather than lingering and providing what the goat needs over time.*

Oats and BOSS.

Food for Fertility

Feeding goats doesn't have to be a complicated process, but it's necessary to understand their dietary needs and potential problems that can resort from poor diet. The old saying that "a goat will eat anything" is a lie. Goats are actually rather picky about their food, and there are, in fact, foods that are toxic to goats as well. Improper diet can cause many consequences and waste a lot of money, while a proper diet can go a long way toward helping your goats stay in proper condition, have good birth rates, avoid metabolic diseases, and have easy deliveries.

What is a Ruminant?

In this chapter I mention two things frequently: rumens and goats being ruminants. Goats are a member of a group of animals called ruminants. This group includes cows, goats, sheep, and some wildlife species like deer, elk, and even giraffes. Ruminants have complex digestive systems that consist of four digestive compartments: the abomasum, reticulum, omasum, and the rumen. They draw their name from the rumen, which is the largest of the four stomach compartments. The rumen is a large fermentation vat filled with enzymes and microorganisms that break down fiber into fatty acids; the rumen is the reason that goats and cows are fed primarily roughage (hay, pasture, browse), as this is what they are uniquely designed to digest. The nutrients absorbed through the rumen make up to 80% of the goat's nutritional needs. The rumen also converts feed into important nutrients like vitamins B and K and essential amino acids. The rumen creates warmth while digesting and keeps goats warm during the winter; hay consumption will increase during colder weather. The rumen creates natural gases that the goats release by belching. It also creates a cud (partially digested food) that the goat regurgitates, chews, and swallows once more. Weird? Kind of, but effective if you're a ruminant. When we feed goats, we are really feeding their rumen. It's important to always keep the rumen in mind when making decisions.

Browse and Hay

One thing to consider about goats when feeding them is that they are browsers and are not grazers. Goats historically lived in deserts and mountains; they are not native to the continental United States. They are not grassland grazers like cattle, sheep, and buffalo. Instead they prefer to "eat up" into trees, weeds, and shrubs while snubbing grass. The ideal pasture for goats is at least six inches high and consists of a wide variety of plants instead of a monoculture of grass. Eating grass below six inches of height introduces more parasite larvae and eggs back into the goat's system, and grass that is grazed too short also becomes stunted and will not grow back as quickly. On the other hand, grass that grows too high (generally around twelve inches) will go to seed and die off, meaning it will be less palatable to goats and other livestock.

Rotating pastures is one of the best ways to keep goats healthy and free from parasite overload. Ideally paddocks should not be grazed below four inches of height at a bare minimum, which stunts the growth of the plants, and should be rested a minimum of thirty days in between grazing. Grass should be allowed to grow to six inches or higher, but less than twelve inches high, at which point the growth slows and grass begins to complete its natural life cycle. Resting pastures allows the grass to achieve optimal growth and prevents the parasitic larvae dropped in fecal matter to find a new host before dying, thus breaking the life cycle. In a perfect rotational system, another species is run on the pasture after the goats as well to consume and become dead-end hosts for the parasites to which goats are susceptible. Certain other livestock, such as cattle, do share similar parasites with goats, but rotating or sharing pastures can still be beneficial because the parasites will interbreed with each other. Cattle have much fewer problems with dewormer-resistant parasites, and the strains of parasites differ between goats and cattle, so mixing the strains can weaken the parasites.

Unfortunately, many of us cannot achieve the perfect pasture rotation due to limited amounts of land. Luckily, we are not limited to pasture alone to supply the needs for our goats. Hay will be the backbone of your goat's diet. Good quality hay should be available to goats at all times. Hay is essential in providing the necessary roughage and fiber, as well as protein and calories, for goats and other ruminants. The digestive system of a goat requires the roughage from hay (or browse, when available) to run smoothly and keep the rumen healthy. Hay and roughage is fermented and broken down in the rumen to be used by the body. This keeps the rumen healthy with natural gut flora.

Good quality hay can be identified by a few markers. First, it should be relatively fine and tender. Different types of hay vary in appearance, but no hay should be overly stalky or weedy. Goats will pick around the stems and waste a lot of the hay. It should have a nice, consistent texture throughout. Hay with a lot of weeds or tree leaves or consisting of thick, hard stalks is not safe or palatable for your goats. The hay should also have a nice green color. The sun may bleach the outside of the bale if exposed, but the inside should retain a green pigment. Hay that is completely brown throughout is over-cured, nutritionally subpar, and essentially dead. Hay becomes brown and lacks nutrients when the hay producer allows it to sit in the sun for too long during the drying process. Hay should also not be exposed to rain or baled when too moist. A damp bale of hay is a breeding ground for potentially toxic mold. Moreover, wet bales create heat and can catch your barn on fire, destroying your feed and possibly killing your animals. Hay also degrades in quality over time, so buy fresh cut hay each year. Because hay will be the main part of your goats' diets, it's vital to find a good source. Look for hay advertised as horse quality and then inspect it before purchase. Never buy cheap "construction" or "cow" hay which is poor quality and should never be fed to goats (or cows, for that matter).

Good choices for types of hay for daily feeding include grass hays like bermuda or orchard grass, mixed grass, or hays that are a mixture of a legume and grass. Alfalfa and sericea lespedeza are two common legume hays. Sericea lespedeza has been found to help inhibit internal parasites in small ruminants. As a legume, lespedeza is higher in protein and calcium than grass. AU Grazer is a less stemmy variety of lespedeza, and it is important that both lespedeza and alfalfa be baled correctly to prevent the leaves from falling off. As legumes, the nutrients lie not in the stems (like grass hay) but in the leaves attached to the stems. Alfalfa also has higher protein and calcium than grass hay and is a good choice for lactating does. Alfalfa also contains molybdenum, which when overconsumed can impact copper absorption and exacerbate copper deficiency. Alfalfa hay is also a bit different from grass hay in that its stems are not very palatable; goats will primarily eat the soft leaves. Alfalfa is a bit more woody than lespedeza in my experience, though this can vary depending on the variety and the producer's practices.

Legume hays are much richer than grass hay, which makes them most appropriate for growing kids and does in milk. However, legumes can be beneficial fed to bucks as well, because the higher calcium content can help keep the calcium:phosphorus ratios appropriate to prevent urinary calculi. The tannins in lespedeza can also help inhibit gastrointestinal parasites. Because alfalfa and lespedeza are both rich, the best way to utilize them for bucks, wethers, and dry does is to provide a mixed diet of both grass hay and legume hay, saving pure alfalfa or lespedeza for the lactating does and growing kids. There is an economical advantage, because grass hay is usually cheaper per pound than legume hay, as well as the advantage of slightly lowering the richness of the diet. However, if lespedeza or alfalfa are the only good quality hays available to you, they can be fed alone—just watch for over conditioning.

Hay as well as all other feeds and supplements should be fed off the ground. Not only does this replicate the goat's natural eating habits of eating up, it also helps prevent the feed from being contaminated by feces and subsequently parasites. Goats will walk in, climb on, and poop in their feed, water, and mineral dishes; minimizing this as much as possible will help with parasite control. Hay should always be fed in a manger that cannot trap the goat's head. Hay bags or nets made of rope can entangle goats and strangle them or injure their legs, and hay mangers with an open top that tapers down to a narrow bottom can trap or strangle them as well. Goats love to stick their heads inside things, and unfortunately that puts them at risk for all sorts of trouble. Look for, or build, hay racks that either have holes too small for the goats' head to fit or have an even size opening top to bottom of the bars. Stick with wooden or metal hay racks and avoid rope hay bags.

Goats are also notorious for picking through hay and wasting any parts they don't particularly like. To avoid this, use hay mangers and racks that rely on smaller square holes rather than large openings. These can be made from metal panels with square holes, available through many suppliers, or hay feeders designed for goats can be purchased directly. Panels can also be connected to form a "wall" inside the barn, behind which hay can be stacked. This is one of my personal favorite ways to feed hay to my does, because it allows extra room for multiple does to eat at once, prevents hay from being soiled, and allows a large amount to be placed at once, thereby reducing the labor of feeding hay each day. Lastly, you can build a wooden frame to hold the panels and attach them to the barn wall as well.

Round Bales

Round bales are often more economical to purchase than square bales. Unfortunately, in many cases this is because the hay quality used to make them is poorer than that used to make square bales—these should be avoided. However, you can find good quality round bales if you know the right sources. Round bales are more difficult to handle for obvious reasons, and although you can manually roll them short distances, it requires a tractor to lift them or move them a long distance.

Round bales may be used for goats in two ways. First, you can store a round bale in a barn and use a pitchfork to flake off layers of hay to distribute to the goats. Second, you may also feed the round bale to the goats directly, with a few caveats. The bale must be secured so that it cannot roll. Goats love to jump and stand on things and can push the bale over onto another goat. Other species like cows or horses may also push or rub against it, resulting in an accident. They can be secured by placing them in a ring, wedging them between t-posts, or using a specially designed goat round bale feeder. The net must be removed prior to feeding it so that the goats do not get tangled in or accidently ingest it.

Goats will waste more hay when using round bales than square, especially if it is not put in a goat round bale feeder with smaller openings designed specifically for goats and sheep.

It's best to have a larger herd or to share the round bale with another species (cows or horses) if feeding directly rather than storing it. The design of the round bale protects it relatively well against rain, but it is best to protect it from the elements to prevent mold. This is especially true if feeding to a small herd that is not consuming it quickly.

Hay Pellets

Hay pellets of several types are available to purchase at feed stores. These are not an ideal replacement for hay, but can be used in a pinch if good quality hay is not available due to drought or other issues in the area. The benefit of hay pellets is that they can be trucked anywhere across the country which makes good quality forage-based food available everywhere even in areas experiencing poor growing conditions. Alfalfa pellets are a common substitute for alfalfa hay, as alfalfa hay can be expensive and difficult to find. Although I like to find alfalfa hay when I can, I typically use alfalfa pellets for does in milk on the milk stand. I put a good portion of alfalfa pellets in the bottom of the feed pail and top with the doe's grain ration. This gives does something to continue to much on if they finish their grain before I'm done milking, which happens often. It also provides the extra calcium and protein does needs while in milk. Keep in mind that you may need to limit alfalfa pellets if feeding alfalfa hay, due to the protein content.

Dry Lot Housing

When pasture is unavailable and goats are penned on bare ground (or, rarely, concrete), this is called a "dry lot." Under dry lot management goats eat no pasture or browse, and all feed is provided by the owner in the form of hay year-round and additional grain when appropriate. Some people choose to dry lot purposefully as a parasite control method when they lack the necessary land to rotate pastures, while others dry lot out of necessity because they own more goats than their pasture can support. On my farm, my bucks are almost always on dry lot due to space restrictions while the does are rotated through pasture. The advantage of dry lot is that, assuming all feed is fed above the ground, there is less fecal-oral transmission of parasites. The disadvantage is that feed costs increase, and the goats lose the benefit of fresh green foods in spring and summer. There is also the concern of erosion as well; however, goats do not create a loblolly of mud the way that cattle or pigs do when on dirt.

What to Avoid

One of the most important things to avoid when feeding your goats is any kind of drastic, sudden change or increase in feed. The rumen of the goat is a delicate organ, and disruptions can cause serious trouble for the goat. Gorging on too much feed or suddenly changing a goat's diet can cause them to bloat. Bloat occurs when the goat's rumen overfills with fermentation gases faster than the goat can release them by belching, causing it to press on the other organs or rupture. This comes in two forms: frothy bloat, which is when the gas is trapped in foam, or free-gas bloat, which occurs when gas is free within the rumen. Bloat must be treated immediately, and it can develop and kill goats quickly. In some cases, the goat may be found dead unexpectedly. Both forms cause the rumen to extend quickly, and the goat will be in pain and off feed. Treatment involves breaking up the gas by massage, administering a baking soda drench, administering a small drench of olive oil, anti-bloat medications, or in severe cases, puncturing the rumen behind the last rib with a veterinary cannula or large gauge needle. Ideally you should involve your veterinarian if you suspect bloat, but because of its fast-acting nature, you may need to work quickly if the bloat is severe.

Sudden feed changes can also cause enterotoxemia, which is caused by the rapid reproduction of the bacteria clostridium perfringens in the goat's digestive system. Like bloat, it can be fatal and can kill quite quickly. Enterotoxemia is deadly due to the toxins released by the clostridium bacteria as they rapidly reproduce in the goat's system. Like bloat, enterotoxemia may be treated if caught early, but treatment is often ineffective and, again, enterotoxemia strikes fast. Enterotoxemia is also painful and will cause the goat to exhibit signs of distress and go off feed. In both bloat and enterotoxemia, the rumen may stop functioning. In a normal rumen, you can hear, feel, and sometimes even see the motions and rumbles of digestion. The goat will also regurgitate and chew its cud. For both bloat and enterotoxemia, prevention is key, and all dietary changes should be made slowly.

There are also a number of foods that are not safe for your goats. Goats shouldn't be overfed grain in general, as this causes a multitude of problems. When feeding grain, avoid "sweet feed" type grains with large amounts of molasses and corn. These are basically candy for the goats and are not good for their rumens. Overfeeding grain can also cause acidosis, which is a buildup of lactic acid in the rumen that leads to slowing or stopping of digestion, dehydration, and death. Goats rumens are designed to process roughage, not grain, so while some grain is needed during certain times, too much is not good for them.

I also choose not to feed soy or genetically modified grains to any of my livestock as a personal preference. Goats should not be fed most human foods either, nor should they be fed things like dog food or chicken food. In addition, there are several plants which are toxic to goats and will kill them if ingested; an incomplete list is included below.

Toxic Plants

Keep in mind that this list is not comprehensive. You will also find some contradictory lists when doing research, and sometimes you might find a list of toxic plants that includes something you've seen your goats eat on your pasture. An example of this from my own life is oak leaves—I have seen oak on a few lists of toxic plants, but our pasture is full of oak trees and I've seen my goats eat the leaves with no ill effects. One reason for these sorts of discrepancies is varying levels of toxicity. Some plants, like wilted cherry leaves and Japanese Yew, are extremely toxic and a very small amount is deadly. Other plants require higher amounts to be consumed before they're toxic.

Some toxic plants are not palatable to your goats as well. Although not always the case, goats will often avoid eating toxic plants whenever other, tastier plants are available. However, when other browse is low—or if a plant is offered as a treat from a human—the goats may eat them and become ill.

- Wilted leaves of stone fruit trees (cherry, peach, etc.)
- Yew
- Azalea
- Foxglove

- Boxwood
- Avocado
- Cassava
- China Berry Trees
- Chokecherries
- Many houseplants
- False Tansy
- Fiddleneck
- Holly
- Japanese Pieris
- Tansy Ragwort
- Larkspur
- Lilac
- Lily of the Valley
- Monkhood
- Lupine
- Mountain Laurel
- Oleander
- Nightshades
- Rhododendron
- Rhubarb
- Horse Chestnut/Buckeye
- Dogbane
- Pigweed
- Milkweed
- Brassicas
- Jimson Weed
- Bleeding Heart
- Poppies
- Bracken Fern
- Buttercup
- Johnsongrass
- Ponderosa Pine (causes abortion—white pine is safe)

Feeding the Dry Doe

The dry (not pregnant or lactating) doe is simple. Their nutritional needs can most often be met with nothing more than water, minerals, good quality hay, and browse when available. Dry does are not experiencing stress on their bodies and will typically keep condition well without anything extra. Feeding grain to goats who do not need it can cause them to gain excess weight. Over conditioned does may have trouble conceiving, and carrying extra weight can also cause does to have difficulty giving birth (dystocia).

Avoid feeding grain to dry does unless they are not keeping condition. If a dry doe is losing weight, look first at other possible causes (such as parasites or mineral deficiencies) before assuming she is not getting enough calories. Then supplement as needed to regain condition.

A Note on Flushing: *Flushing is the name for the practice of introducing extra feed to a doe immediately prior to breeding. The idea behind this is a belief that increasing the food for the doe will prompt her to drop more eggs due to an abundance of resources. I have not personally found any scholarly sources backing this up, but it is thought by some that a doe's body will respond in fertility based on environmental factors.*

Flushing is not something I practice personally. In the early years of goat ownership I experimented with it, but I saw no difference in fertility from flushing. The biggest factor in fertility is not an increase of food prior to breeding but in a long-term management plan that provides appropriate levels of necessary minerals and continuous nutritional support. I know of many breeders, myself included, who routinely have twins, triplets, or even quads or more without practicing flushing. Genetics also play a role in fertility as well, which is why we see some breeds being more prone to high multiples. Nigerian Dwarfs are notorious for producing large litters frequently, while anything more than three kids is fairly rare in the European breeds such as Alpines and Toggenburgs.

If you do choose to experiment with flushing, remember that all changes to feed must be made gradually.

Feeding the Pregnant Doe

Feeding the pregnant doe is no more complicated than feeding her at any other time. Whether a doe is in milk or dry when bred, her feeding regimen should remain the same after being bred. Her intake of hay will increase naturally as pregnancy progresses, but grain should not be increased. There are no changes in her nutritional needs at all during the first two months of pregnancy, and after that she will begin to naturally increase her consumption or hay and browse. One of the biggest risks of overfeeding the pregnant doe is creating oversized kids that are difficult for her to give birth to naturally. Every extra calorie that the doe doesn't use for herself will go directly to growing her kids, which means that an overfed doe will in turn overfeed her kids and they may grow too large. There is an idea sometimes tossed around that the fetus of an animal will grow to suit the size of the mother's body—this is hogwash. Sometimes kids grow large as a fluke or due to genetics, and sometimes they grow too large due to being fed too much. Babies can and do grow too large for their mother's bodies to birth easily, or even at all. Take a look into the cattle industry and you will see the emphasis they put on low birthweight bulls. It's for good reason—big calves lead to complications. The same is true of goats. Big babies can cause big problems. On top of the risk of oversized kids, overfeeding grain to pregnant does can also cause ketosis (pregnancy toxemia). I talk more about this condition in chapter eight of this book.

A doe who is in milk when bred should keep her normal milking diet up until she is dried off about two months prior to kidding again. As she is dried off, her grain ration should also be gradually cut back until she is back on a dry doe diet. As a doe enters the last week of pregnancy, begin introducing small amounts of grain. This should start out as a handful of grain and gradually increase until she kids, at which time feed will increase to a lactating ration. The doe can also eat alfalfa hay during pregnancy or be given alfalfa pellets starting the last week of pregnancy with the grain at an approximately 3:1 ratio of alfalfa pellets:grain.

Keep in mind that there are always exceptions to every rule. Some does may not need grain at all during their pregnancy even in the last week, while others might need it to be introduced slightly sooner than the last week. Evaluate the doe's body condition and overall health when making this decision. Does shouldn't be bred when underweight, parasitized, or mineral deficient, but I have in one instance had a pregnant doe contract a parasite infestation *during* pregnancy. She required additional feed supplementation that would not normally have been provided. It's impossible to write one-size-fits-all instructions for maintaining your herd or feeding your pregnant does due to the endless possible variables. It is safe to say, however, that *most* does will not require grain until the end of pregnancy or after birth. Also remember that no amount of grain or concentrated feed can make up for mineral deficiencies or does who are losing condition due to an underlying issue like parasites.

Tales from the Kidding Stall: *Do you remember Rumor, the doe with the narrow pelvis? While her narrow pelvis was a major factor in her C-section, I didn't help matters by overfeeding her. At that time, I didn't know about grain increasing kidding size, and so I fed her grain, black oil sunflower seeds, and alfalfa pellets throughout her pregnancy. Her kids were large, especially for twins, and that only served to compound the issue. Had I not overfed her, the kids might have been small enough to squeeze through her pelvis despite its small opening.*

Feeding the Lactating Doe

When your doe comes into milk, her body experiences a major increase in dietary needs, particularly for calcium and calories. While some cows with the right genetics can produce milk while eating a 100% forage-based diet, dairy goats usually cannot. Grain is almost always needed for the lactating doe. Goats need grain to produce milk and maintain their body condition. Some lower producing does may get by with less grain, but in general you can also expect them to only give as much as they get, or on the other hand to whittle themselves away to skin and bone if not fed enough to make their milk.

The last week of her pregnancy your doe may have been receiving up to about a cup of grain. After she kids, that amount can be increased slowly (remember, all feed changes are done gradually) until she is ultimately getting her full milking ration. The average amount of grain needed for a doe in milk is one pound (1 lb) grain for every three pounds (3 lbs) of milk the doe produces. Each doe is an individual, so this amount will need to be adjusted based on the doe and her body condition. Easy keepers may need slightly less while high production, very milky does might need more.

Alfalfa is also an important part of the lactating doe's diet and alfalfa hay can be fed free choice while the doe is in milk. Alfalfa is an excellent source of the additional calcium and protein your doe needs to produce milk. However, alfalfa hay is not readily available in some areas. It does not grow well in all climates, and though some small bales of trucked-in alfalfa hay can sometimes be found at feed stores, it's generally not the best quality and is expensive. If getting alfalfa hay is not an option in your area, alfalfa pellets are easy to find as they are easily shipped to feed and farm stores. Look for a brand with a bright green pellet and little dust. When feeding alfalfa pellets, you may let your does eat it alongside their grain on the milking stand, or you can communally feed it as well. Chaffhaye is another option in lieu of alfalfa hay. Chaffhaye is a fermented alfalfa product that is highly nutritious and tasty to goats; however, the downfall of Chaffhaye is its higher price and moisture content. Because of the moisture, Chaffhaye will mold if not fed quickly, especially in the hot summer months. It comes in large bales, so this makes it less feasible for small herds.

Feeding the Buck

Feeding the buck is much like feeding the dry doe, with a few caveats. Bucks do not have to produce milk, and for the vast majority of the year they aren't doing any work at all. During the fall when rut rolls around things change, but spring and summer sees the bucks living the good life and doing little to earn their keep. Because they have few demands on their bodies during this time, bucks only need water, minerals, good quality hay, and browse to thrive. Furthermore, feeding bucks grain increases their chances of developing urinary calculi. Urinary calculi are stone deposits that become trapped in the goat's urethra and prevent him from urinating. This is extremely painful and will ultimately kill the buck if left untreated. Urinary calculi are formed from phosphate salts and are frequently caused by overfeeding grain.

Occasionally bucks will struggle to keep condition during rut. The hormone-driven breeding season can cause them to spend all their time flirting, breeding, and fighting with other bucks, thus their activity goes up and their eating goes down. If grain supplementation is necessary, be certain than the calcium:phosphorus ratio of their feed is at least 2:1 (and up to 4:1) and never below 1:1. Bucks do not typically need pure alfalfa due its richness, however it can be used to add additional protein to the buck's diet during rut, and it can add additional calcium to the diet when mixed with grass hay.

If your buck develops urinary calculi, ammonium chloride can be used in mild cases. In severe cases or total blockages, your goat will need to see a veterinarian immediately. The vet might cut off the pizzle, or tip of the penis, to allow the stone to pass, or perform other methods of treatment for the buck. Without treatment the buck's bladder will eventually burst and kill him quite painfully. Ammonium chloride may also be added supplementally to the buck's feed to aid in prevention of calculi but should not be fed to does.

A Note on Wethers and Stones: *Wethers are even more susceptible to urinary calculi than bucks. I have not mentioned wethers in depth in this book because they are not breeding animals, but wethers should be kept strictly grain-free unless an illness has caused them to become emaciated and need extra calories for a temporary period of time. Goats should not be castrated before one month of age and waiting longer is beneficial when possible. The goat's urethra stops growing when testosterone is cut off. Wethers are also quite prone to becoming overweight if fed grain.*

The two doelings in this picture—can you spot the second one's ear peeking out?—were seven months old, nearly as big as their dam, and still nursing. Most does will wean a bit earlier than this, but it's not unusual at all to see them nursing past three months of age.

Feeding Kids

The ideal diet for growing kids through three months of age and up to six months of age is their mother's milk. Dam raised kids will begin sampling solid foods like hay and their dam's feed early on as well, however bottle raised kids do not begin tasting solid food as soon. When not forcefully weaned, many does will allow their kids to nurse up to six months of age and sometimes even longer. I have routinely seen better growth rates in goat kids that are allowed to nurse until the dam weans them than goats who are weaned or bottle fed. Of course, it is not always possible for this to happen for a number of reasons, but ideally I prefer to let my retained doe kids nurse until their dam decides they should be weaned.

If the kids are not nursing their mother, it will be your responsibility to bottle raise them. Regardless of whether they are bottle raised or dam raised, kids should have hay available to sample from the beginning. Dam raised kids will start to eat their mother's, but bottle raised kids must be given their own. I also supplement growing kids with grain, especially bottle raised kids, until about six months of age to encourage growth, though it is often not necessary in dam raised kids unless they are being weaned. I start to offer grain to kids as they reach three months of age. I discuss the pros and cons of dam raising versus bottle raising, as well as detailed instructions, later on in chapter six.

Tales from the Kidding Stall: *One year I had a first freshening doe kid with the tiniest triplets I have seen to date. The birth went smoothly with no major complications, though I did have to assist one buck kid who was presenting hocks first, which means he was breech (backwards) and his back knees were coming out first instead of his feet. Because first time mothers often do not produce enough milk for more than two babies, the kids were being supplemented with bottles in addition to nursing. About a week after birth, one of the bucklings was down and unresponsive at feeding time. I couldn't figure out what the problem was—he had no obvious injuries, he hadn't been sick, and he didn't seem to be chilled. I started a basic protocol for stimulating a weak kid, but he wasn't responding.*

Then I noticed a piece of hay hanging out of his mouth and pulled on it. To my surprise, more and more hay kept coming. I finally stuck my fingers in his mouth to swipe it clean and found a big chunk of hay completely blocking his throat and suffocating him. I pulled it out, but unfortunately it was too late and he passed. That was the only time I have seen anything like that, and I hope to never see it again. It's a perfect example of freak, unavoidable accidents. It's completely natural—and healthy—for kids to start sampling hay early in life, but somehow in this case the kid managed to swallow a chunk that was too big for his throat. Perhaps he was not able to chew well for one reason or another. I will never know for certain exactly how this happened. I'm not telling you this to make you paranoid about kids eating hay, but to remind you that in farming these things unfortunately happen. We are not actually in control, as much as we'd like to think we are.

Types of Grain

When it's time to feed your goats grain, you will be presented by a few different options in the feed store. Not all feeds are created equal, so let's take a look at a few of them. Also, don't forget that your roughage (hay, browse) is the most important part of your feeding regimen and will supply a portion of the goat's protein as well as their grain. Depending on the protein levels of your hay, you may need to adjust the protein levels of your grain rations slightly. There is no one perfect feeding brand or protocol because so many variables exist between herds.

Traditional Goat Feed

Traditional goat feeds are common and easy to find. A few cons of this type of feed are that it often contains molasses, medication, corn, soy, and genetically modified ingredients. Depending on where you stand in the GMO argument and how you feel about corn and soy, this may not matter to you. I won't go into a deep examination of these ingredients; there is ample information available on the internet and elsewhere on these arguments, and this is a book on reproduction after all, not food. I personally choose not to feed genetically modified grains to my livestock. Soy and corn are both almost always GMO. Soy also contains phytoestrogens, and corn does not provide much in the way of nutrition for goats.

As for molasses, it's best to avoid in your feed. It's essentially candy for goats and is not good for their rumen. There is some indication that molasses may increase incidence of acidosis. Medicated feeds contain medication meant to prevent coccidiosis, however coccidiosis very rarely occurs in adult animals and feed-through preventative is not an ideal method of prevention for kids. I personally avoid prophylactic feed-through medications. Goat chows also often contain added ammonium chloride. This is included to help prevent urinary calculi in male goats; however, it is unhealthy for does to consume, especially when lactating, because it prevents the uptake of calcium.

When feeding formulated goat feed, look for rations without added molasses, medications, or ammonium chloride (unless only feeding to bucks). If you want to avoid GMOs, soy, or corn, look for organic or non-GMO feeds. Organic and non-GMO brands of livestock feed are available, and I am increasingly seeing options for these types of feeds become available in feed stores and by special order as demand rises. When it comes to the nutrition of these preformulated feeds, look for feeds that contain about 16% protein. You may also look specifically for a dairy parlor ration rather than a general goat chow. Some goat producers also feed dairy cow ration rather than dairy goat feed, as goat feed tends to be priced higher than cow feed even when the nutritional value and ingredients are similar (or even the same).

Oats and BOSS and Other Home Blends

Oats and black oil sunflower seeds (BOSS) is a popular combination for a basic grain supplement for goat breeders who want to avoid using conventional feed for any number of reasons. Oats are roughly 13% protein, while BOSS is high in dietary fat. I have personally used this mix with success. Oats and BOSS are generally mixed in either a 3:1 or 4:1 ratio depending on the preference of the breeder. Black oil sunflower seeds are quite rich, so their levels can be increased or decreased as needed depending on the body condition of the goats. BOSS is also an excellent top dressing for any type of feed to add extra fat or calories to the goat's diet. Sunflower seeds are 15% protein. Although mixing oats and BOSS will result in a total protein amount slightly lower than a formulated feed at 16% protein, remember that alfalfa hay and pellets contain about 16% protein themselves. BOSS does contain higher levels of omega 6 fatty acids rather than omega 3 fatty acids, so it should also be fed in moderation.

You can also increase the specificity of your homemade blend and make it as complex as you desire. Some of the common additions to home blends include chickpeas, field peas, barley, millet, and wheat berries. Some people add additional ingredients directly to the feed such as herbs or kelp. In addition, some people choose to sprout their whole grains before feeding them to their goats. Doing so is time consuming and you must watch out for possible mold development if the sprouts fail. Typically, feed is fed as whole grains rather than fodder, especially in large herds. However, if you have a small herd and the time and interest to learn a fodder system, it is an option.

A Note on Beet Pulp: *I am including beet pulp because it is often recommended as an addition to homemade feed mixes like oats and BOSS, as well as a supplement for underweight goats. Beet pulp is high in fiber and easily digested. However, beet pulp is a byproduct from the extraction of sugar from genetically modified sugar beets. If you wish to avoid GMOs, avoid feeding beet pulp. If you do not care about GMO status, beet pulp may be added to home blends.*

All Stock

All stock feed is an all-purpose feed mixed for use with multiple species. All stock is generally an affordable option, and it is often available in plain pelleted versions rather than sweet feed formulas. Another benefit of all stock is that is can be used for multiple species; however, keep in mind that as a feed intended for use across species it will not contain anything additional needed by one species but not another. For example, pig feeds are typically formulated with lysine, but all stock is not. All stock will not contain added copper. Protein levels will also be middle-of-the-road.

Supplements

In addition to the standard diet and mineral supplementation, there are additional supplements that can be provided for your goats to keep them in optimum condition and peak reproductive ability. While not as vital as minerals and basic nutrition, you can consider these as performance boosting supplements.

Red Raspberry Leaf

Red raspberry leaf is a personal favorite herbal supplement of mine for does who are in late pregnancy (typically the last month or so). Red raspberry leaf is an herb known to be a tonic to the female reproductive system and is thought to aid in the ease of delivery. It is also high in calcium, which does will need when lactating. It's a safe herb for pregnancy and is used by human women as well as livestock. Raspberry leaf is also rich in vitamins C, A, E, and B as well as magnesium and potassium. As a bonus, goats love it and will munch it right out of your hand like it's candy. It can be offered free choice, fed individually each day, or made into a large batch of tea and added to the goat's drinking water. I prefer to feed a bit each day to the pregnant does.

Herbal Supplements

In addition to red raspberry leaf, many goat owners supplement their herd with other herbs and spices to support their health and wellness. There are a variety of herbs safe for goats which can be used to increase mineral and vitamin uptake or support specific body systems. For example, activated charcoal (though not strictly an herb) can be used to support a goat that has eaten something toxic until veterinary help can be sought, echinacea supports the immune system, peppermint supports the respiratory system, ginger supports the digestive system, and so on. Certain herbs are also antiparasitic; however, I do not recommend relying on herbal dewormers as your sole parasite treatment, but rather as an additional support. I address this further in chapter eight.

Because this is a book on reproduction and not herbs, I won't go into any further detail on specific herbal supplements. Instead, I will advise you of few key things to remember when using herbs in your herd:

- Not all herbs are safe for goats. Always research carefully before reaching into your herbal cabinet and administering an herb to your goats.
- Some herbs are safe for goats but not safe during pregnancy. Once again, research thoroughly.
- Be aware that some herbs safe for goats are not safe for other livestock species like horses or llamas. Keep this in mind if supplementing in a mixed-

stock environment.

- Herbs are wonderful, but they are not always the answer. While it's nice to use natural aids and treatments, it is sometimes necessary to use modern medicine and supplements. Don't let your desire to stay natural kill your goats.

Icelandic Kelp

Kelp (a type of seaweed) is a common supplement that many goat breeders offer free choice. Kelp is available as dried, granulated, or flaked kelp. It is a wonderful natural source of iodine, containing 750 parts per million of iodine (ppm). In addition to iodine, it also contains selenium (0.5 ppm), cobalt (4 ppm), copper (4 ppm), zinc (12 ppm), potassium (2%), phosphorus (0.1%), and calcium (1.5%). While its levels are too low to replace properly formulate loose minerals and additional copper or selenium supplementation where needed, it makes an excellent addition to your herd's diet. Kelp has also been found to support healthy immune function and is prebiotic in nature, meaning that it encourages the development of healthy flora in the digestive system. In addition, kelp also contains fiber, folate, iron, magnesium, manganese, pantothenic acid, riboflavin, and vitamin C.

Many goat breeders offer kelp free choice to be eaten at-will. As with most new supplements, goats will consume a large amount of the kelp at first and then will taper off to a more reasonable rate. In my own herd I have both offered it free choice and offered it on a weekly basis. The benefit of offering it weekly is decreased financial costs, but in some cases the goats who are lower in the pecking order may not get their fair share. I have also mixed kelp with other herbal supplements and offered it in that way as well. Kelp can also be added to the feed ration daily when feeding grain.

When choosing kelp, it's best to purchase Icelandic kelp that is harvested from the cold waters of the North Atlantic and Artic oceans rather than Pacific kelp, which as the name implies is harvest in the Pacific Ocean off the coast of California. The kelp in the Pacific Ocean is more exposed to pollution than Icelandic kelp. Thorvin is a popular brand of Icelandic kelp, but there are others as well.

Baking Soda

Baking soda, or sodium bicarbonate, is found in most kitchens but is useful in the barnyard as well. As we've discussed, the digestive system—and particularly the rumen—of goats is sensitive. Baking soda is alkaline in nature, and goats will ingest it of their own free will when their rumens are too acidic. Baking soda can be offered free choice to goats next to (but not mixed into) their free choice loose minerals. If your goats aren't eating the baking soda, this is a good thing. That means their diets are well balanced and not causing them to have an acidic rumen. However, you never know when a goat might find something in the pasture or overeat something and cause their rumen to become upset. When that happens, they will take a few licks of the baking soda to balance things out.

Body Condition Scoring

The way a goat's body is structured can make it difficult for new goat owners to distinguish between a goat who is fat, a healthy weight, or underweight. Body condition scoring can help tremendously in determining whether your goats are a healthy weight for breeding and are keeping condition while lactating. In order to appropriately judge the weight of your goat, you must actually feel the goat. The visual appearance can be very misleading, especially during the winter when the goat is covered in their thick cashmere undercoat. Most people are also not generally acquainted with how dairy animals should look. They should not be underweight, but they should also not look like beef breeds which carry much more muscling than dairy goats.

The size of the stomach may be misleading as well. A goat's rumen cannot be taken into account when judging their weight and body score. The rumen is a fermentation vat, and as such it balloons up when filled with natural gases originating from the fermentation process, especially on the left side of the animal. Goats frequently look quite rotund in the stomach because of this, but they may or may not be in good condition otherwise. Some people will even think that a goat is pregnant—even if it's a male goat—because of their rumen.

Body scoring uses point scores from 1 through 5. A goat with a body score of 1 is extremely emaciated. A goat with a score of 5 is very over conditioned. The ideal score on the scale is a 3, which is moderately conditioned and not under or overweight. Dairy goats, especially when in milk, should be moderately lean without being underweight. An overweight goat will struggle with infertility issues and may also experience dystocia when it's time to give birth. It's equally important to allow the goats to be a healthy weight and not over conditioned as it is to not allow them to become underweight. Also keep in mind that milking does will generally lose a bit of their condition while at peak production. As long as she is not laden with parasites, is getting enough calories, is not dipping too low in body condition, and is generally healthy, it is normal for her to lose a bit of body fat while in milk. I recommend looking at showing pictures of goats who have won top of their class during lactation to get an idea of healthy body weight for milking does.

Body condition scoring takes into account three main body structures: the lumbar (spinal) region, including the spinous process (top ridge of the spine) and the transverse process (side ridges on either side of the spine); the sternum (breast bone), and the ribcage. A quick online search will also lead you to visual aids for better grasping body condition scores.

Body Score 1

The goat is weak and severely emaciated. The backbone is highly visible, the ribs can easily be seen under the skin, the flank is hollow, and the backbone creates a continuous ridge along the goat's back. At this point the animal is likely visibly weakened as well and is in grave danger of death if not immediately treated.

When felt, the ribs have no fat cover, and your fingers can go easily in between the ribs. The spinous process can be easily grasped between the finger and thumb, and there is little to no fat or muscle covering the lumbar vertebrae. The transverse process can be easily grasped by the hand, and there is a deep depression between the spinous process and the transverse process. The sternum of the goat has little to no fat cover and can be easily felt. The fat and skin over the sternum is easily grabbed and moved about side to side.

Body Score 2

The goat's backbone can still be seen, as well as the ribs, though there is now a slight covering of fat over the ribcage.

When felt, the intercostal spaces between the ribs are smooth but still easily penetrated by the fingers. The spinous process can still be felt and grasped between finger and thumb. There is now a muscle mass between skin and bone. There is still an obvious depression between the spinous and transverse processes. The transverse process can still be grasped in the hand, but the outline of the process is not as easily seen above the flank. The sternum now has more fat; however, it can still be grasped easily and moved side to side.

Body Score 3

The goat is at an ideal weight. Visibly the goat is healthy, the backbone is no longer prominently visible, and the ribs are only slightly visible under the skin. The outline of the transverse process is still slightly visible over the flank.

The ribcage may still be felt, and the spaces between ribs may be accessed with pressure, but there is now an even layer of fat over them. The spinal bones cannot be easily grasped now due to the layer of muscles and fat over them. There is a gentle slope from the spinous to the transverse process. The sternal fat is thick now and can be grasped but does not move side to side.

Body Score 4

Visibly the goat is sleek and smooth with an even layer of fat over the entire animal. The backbone is not seen and the ribs are not visible. The outline of the transverse process can no longer be seen.

The spinous process cannot be grasped. The transition from the spinous to transverse process is rounded. The outer edge of the transverse process is smooth and rounded and it cannot be grasped any longer. The fat pad on the sternum is thick and wide and difficult to grasp.

Body Score 5

The goat is grossly overweight. The backbone and ribs are buried under a thick layer of fat. The transverse process is not discernable, and flanks are full.

The spinous process creates a slight depression now due to fat build up on either side, and the transition from the spinous to transverse process is convex and bulging. It is impossible to grasp the transverse process or the fat pad on the sternum. The fat pad covers the entire sternum.

Here we have a buck rubbing his head (which contains scent glands) on a doe in heat while a wether attempts to fight him for the doe. Wethers don't always realize they aren't bucks anymore.

Chapter Three: The Goats and the Bees

Now that your goats are in optimal condition, you know how to feed them through rut, pregnancy, and lactation, and you've made your choices for buck and doe pairings, it's time to get down to business. In this section we will cover all the basics of reproductive anatomy of bucks and does, as well as the mating process.

The basics of conception are relatively uniform across the board for mammals. Goats are no exception. The short and simple explanation is that a male and a female goat mate while the female is fertile (in estrus and ovulating), and the sperm of the male goat implants into an egg(s) released by the doe. Then, if all goes well, the egg implants into the lining of the uterus and develops into a fetus. Approximately five months later a baby goat (or two or three) is born.

But of course there is a bit more to it than that. Both the buck and the doe exhibit unique behaviors, and there are many aspects to the anatomy of goats that are quite different from some other animals. In order to successfully breed your goats, you want to know a bit about how it all works, how to know when to breed your does, when she has successfully been bred, and what to expect from it all. Let's dive right in.

Reproductive Anatomy

First, let's take a look at the basic reproductive anatomy of goats. Although I won't go into textbook level detail, I will give a solid overview of the major players in the reproductive system of goats. After all, the reproductive system is only the sum of its parts. We'll start with the buck.

Buck Anatomy

Testicles

The primary male sex organs are the testicles, or testes. The testicles of a male goat should be appropriately large for his body size and even in shape, and the scrotum should contain two testicles. The scrotum should not be split but should be one oval-shaped sack with a visible line delineating the two testicles within. The failure of one or both testicles to descend into the scrotum is known as monorchidism (one descended testicle) or cryptorchidism (both testicles retained internally). Either is considered a major fault and such a buck should not be bred. Furthermore, due to the heat sensitivity of the sperm, a buck with neither testicle descended will be infertile.

The testicles are responsible for the production of both sperm and the hormone testosterone. They are contained within the scrotum, which is a protective covering of skin. Testicles are oval in shape and firm. Castration of the testicles stops the production of sperm and testosterone; however, when a mature buck is castrated he may remain fertile for up to thirty days. The epididymis is an external duct of the testicle that houses the sperm (spermatozoa) until it is ready to make its journey out of the buck. When the sperm is ready to be transferred into the goat's urethra, the sperm leave the epididymis to go into the vas deferens. The vas deferens are a pair of ducts that transport the sperm from the epididymis to the urethra to be released during mating.

A fun fact about testicles is that they are attached to the goat by a muscle called the cremaster, which allows the goat to raise or lower the testicles dependent on the weather. Sperm is temperature sensitive, so during hot weather the muscle relaxes and allows the testicles to dangle freely below the body of the goat, and during cold weather it contracts to keep the testicles close to the warmth of the goat's body.

Penis

The penis is the copulating organ of the buck and deposits sperm into the doe's reproductive tract. The penis remains sheathed until the buck is ready to mate, at which time it will become erect and extend outside of the sheath (also called a prepuce). The penis also extends to allow the male goat to pee on his face and front legs, which is done to attract female goats. Within the penis is contained the urethra, the tract by which sperm is transported to the reproductive tract of the doe. The urethra is also connected to the bladder and releases urine as well. During mating, the sperm travels from the epididymis through the vas deferens into the urethra, where it then exits the buck's penis.

Doe Anatomy

Ovaries

The ovaries of the doe are where egg (ova) production takes place. The ovaries are relatively small, oval organs located on either side of the goat's uterus. In addition to the eggs, the ovaries are also responsible for producing the female hormones estrogen and progesterone. Estrogen is primarily involved in estrus, whereas progesterone is responsible for changing the uterine environment during pregnancy. Does can develop cystic ovaries, especially when they are overweight, and this can lead to infertility and does who appear to always be in heat.

The ovaries are connected to the uterus via tubes called oviducts, which collect the developed eggs for fertilization. Once fertilized, the eggs are dropped into the uterus to implant in the uterine wall. Follicles in the ovaries contain the eggs and they develop in succession during ovulation. The follicles rupture as the eggs mature, and the ruptured follicles become corpus luteum. After ovulation, the corpus luteum secretes the progesterone needed to prepare the uterus for pregnancy. It also suppresses the secretion of gonadotropin hormones (follicle stimulating hormone and luteinizing hormone) to stop the development of more follicles and eggs. If the doe does not become pregnant after ovulation, the uterus releases the hormone prostaglandin, which will allow another ovulation cycle to occur.

Uterus

The uterus is the housing organ for developing fetuses. The uterus of goats is bicornuate, which means that the uterus is split into two separate uterine horns. Kids can develop in one or both sides of the uterus. A doe will develop a placenta for each horn if kids are present in both sides of the uterus. That means that if a doe has one or more kids that are both in the same side of the uterus, she will only pass one placenta. If she has one or more kids in both sides, she will pass two placentas. Goats do not develop a unique placenta for each kid.

The uterus is a small, muscular organ that stretches during pregnancy. Fertilized embryos implant in the uterus by the eighteenth day of pregnancy. Nutrients are passed through the uterine wall to the developing fetus during pregnancy through the placenta, which is attached to the uterus via placentomes. These placentomes consist of caruncles on the endometrial lining of the uterus and cotyledons on the placenta. Caruncles are oval thickenings on the uterus, which cotyledons connect to via the development of villi. These connections are the only places where the placenta attach to the uterus. Goats have approximately 75-125 placentomes.

The uterus and the vagina are connected to each other via the cervix, which is an opening formed by cartilaginous tissues. The cervix remains closed except during estrus, when it opens to receive sperm, and during delivery when it opens to allow the passage of the kids through the birth canal. The cervix also grows during pregnancy along with the uterus, and it produces a thick mucus that protects the uterus from infection.

Vagina and Vulva

The vulva is the external genitalia of the doe. Like the penis of the buck, the vulva is common to both the reproductive and the urinary system. The vagina is internal from the vulva and connects to the uterus via the cervix. The vagina is a large elastic tube and is the copulatory organ of the doe. The vagina is where the sperm from the buck is deposited during mating.

Udder

While not a part of reproduction, the udder is an important part of the female anatomy, especially for dairy goats. The udder is the mammary organ of the female goat. It consists of two chambers called halves or sides, a medial ligament that divides the two udder halves and supports the udder up the center, and two teats with orifices at the end that allow milk to be expressed. The udder is attached to the goat at the foreudder and the rear escutcheon. Udder and teats are the appropriate terms, not "sack," "bag," "tits," etc. An udder is not plural; there is one udder and two halves, not two udders. There is more information on evaluating a quality udder in chapter seven of this book.

This buck's face is covered in urine from peeing on himself during rut.

Buck Behavior and Rut

During the fall, bucks enter into what is known as rut. This is a period in which the buck is influenced by raging hormones and the desire to find does in heat and mate with them. Although certain male goats may mate year-round depending on breed, they are at their peak during fall and early winter. Even bucks of breeds that mate year-round still experience a rut in the fall and early winter.

Buck behavior changes drastically during the rut. They begin peeing on themselves and emitting an aroma of musk and pheromones. This lovely buck cologne attracts the female goats, and studies have shown that exposure to bucks in rut can also bring does into estrus. In addition to smelling, shall we say, *unique*, bucks will also spend a large portion of their time fighting with one another for dominance and running the fence line to flirt with the ladies. Bucks will yell, blubber, and stick out their tongue at does in an attempt to woo them. They will also lift their upper lip in the flehmen response to better smell the pheromones being emitted by does in heat.

Although most bucks are not aggressive to humans, rut is a time when they are more likely to display aggression. It can also be more dangerous than usual to enter the buck enclosure due to their increased fighting. I have found myself standing in between two bucks only to have one charge the other and butt me instead. Luckily the buck was small and I wasn't injured, but it could have been worse. Male animals blinded by testosterone can never be trusted completely to not display aggression.

A doe displays the flehmen response after smelling something interesting.

Doe Behavior and Estrus

Does come into heat (estrus) approximately every 21 days during mating season. Detecting heat in does is essential for a number of reasons. If you are transporting your doe to an outside buck or using artificial insemination, you need to be able to tell when they are in heat and ovulating to avoid wasting time and money. It's also important to know when your does are bred so that you know when to expect them to give birth. If you simply run a buck with your does at all times you will have no idea when to expect kids. This leads to does losing kids due to a difficult birth, extreme cold, or inexperience. The doe herself might die as well if she cannot give birth on her own and isn't assisted. There is more on kidding and potential complications later in chapter five of this book.

Does do not bleed during estrus. In some cases, they might have a slight white or pinkish discharge, but that does not always occur. You will primarily be relying on her behavioral changes to determine when she is receptive to breeding. Some signs of estrus in does includes tail flagging (wagging the tail back and forth), riding other does, walking the fence line to flirt with the bucks, and increased vocalization or even yelling. Keeping a wether, especially one which was castrated later in life, with the doe herd can help you determine heat. Wethers don't quite remember that they are missing a few parts and will blubber, paw, and mount does when they are in heat. Some wethers will even routinely fight bucks during rut when does are in heat. The most certain evidence that a doe is in heat is that she will willingly stand for a buck (or wether) to mount her.

Some does will have silent heats, which means they come and go through heat without obvious signs. This can be caused by mineral deficiency, but it can also be a personality trait of the doe. Heats can also be quiet in does who are not housed near bucks. If you are struggling to detect heat in your does and don't have bucks nearby, borrow a buck rag from another breeder. A buck rag is simply a piece of cloth rubbed generously over the face and head of a buck goat in rut and kept in a sealed jar or bag to hold in the odor. Smelling the buck rag will often cause does to either come into heat or express heat more obviously.

Lastly, if you absolutely cannot tell when a doe is coming into heat, I recommend leaving her with a buck for thirty days. This should catch her estrus cycle, and it also gives you a more narrow window for her due date. I often do this as well for ease and due to time constraints. When pen breeding, carefully observe the goats each day. In most cases you will be able to note when the doe was in season and bred based on their behavior.

Natural Mating

Natural mating refers to allowing a buck and doe to physically breed rather than using artificial insemination. Natural mating is the easiest and most common way to breed your goats. The entire process takes very little time. You can genuinely turn your back for a few seconds and miss the whole thing. In total, if you are able to detect the doe's heat, you should be able to introduce her to the buck and be done with the process in five minutes or less. In some cases, a doe may not like a particular buck in favor of another and fight with him, but generally if she is truly in heat she will stand for him without a problem. The buck may spend a little bit of time wooing the doe as well by pawing at her, blubbering at her, or rubbing his head on her face. Again, it generally doesn't take much time for him to get serious. Less experienced bucks and does will take longer to get down to business than more mature goats.

The actual mating takes so little time that many first-time goat owners doubt that anything actually happened at all. When the buck mounts the doe, there are two primary ways you can tell that they successfully mated. One is that the doe will usually hunch her back and squat similarly to as if she were peeing immediately after, but she will not actually pee. The second is that the buck typically throws his head back over his shoulders after mating. While one attempt might be sufficient, most breeders choose to allow the goats to mate about three times total before returning them back to their respective pens.

The advantages of natural mating are that the process is easy, usually successful, and doesn't require special equipment or an outside technician. The disadvantages of natural mating are that it requires access to a buck and offers fewer options for bucks. Typically, most goat breeders find it easiest to own a buck which they use to cover their does, and this means feeding and caring for the buck year-round even though he is only useful about once a year. The other option is to find a local breeder willing to stud out their bucks. Many breeders are not willing to offer stud service due to biosecurity concerns, and it is not a service I personally recommend offering. Using outside bucks presents new challenges in terms of transporting does and timing things just right so that they are in heat when presented to the buck. It's also important to ensure the buck is healthy and disease free as well.

Pairing Short Bucks with Tall Does

Another possible challenge of natural breeding is a height discrepancy. A popular breeding practice in the dairy goat world is to cross Nigerian Dwarf bucks over standard sized does to create miniature breeds. These mini breeds can be registered through The Miniature Goat Registry or the Miniature Dairy Goat Association so long as both parents are registered as well. One challenge that can arise through this practice is helping shorter bucks reach taller does during mating. In some cases, things will work out on their own, but in other instances the buck may struggle. There are ways around the height discrepancy, though, and with a little ingenuity you can make it work.

There are a few creative ways to get around a height problem. An obvious option is to use artificial insemination, but that is not viable to everyone. One work around is to find a natural slope in your pasture and place the doe downhill from the buck and hold her in place. In many cases that slight boost is just enough to help the buck reach. In a more severe height difference you might need to place the buck on a hay bale or other structure. In my experience, this is a little trickier because the buck will want to jump down to mate the more natural way, not realizing that he needs the additional height to make things work. In both cases you will need to hold the doe in place for the buck so that she stays in the correct spot.

It's also important to mention here that standard sized bucks should never be bred to miniature sized does. The kids resulting from that mating could grow too large for the doe to give birth to easily. When making miniature crosses, always cross the larger breed doe to the smaller buck and not the other way around.

Pen Breeding vs Hand Breeding

When breeders talk about "pen breeding" and "hand breeding," what they mean is either running a doe with a buck for a period of time or waiting until she's in heat and breeding her that day. There are advantages and disadvantages to both methods. When it comes to pen breeding, the convenience is the main benefit. If you struggle to know when your does are in heat, or if you have a flighty goat (buck or doe) who is difficult to catch, pen breeding might be a good choice for you. If the doe remains with the buck for a minimum of thirty days, she should cycle during that time and be bred. I have found in many cases I can still know the exact breeding date even when pen breeding, because it becomes fairly obvious that the doe is in heat when she's with a buck. Another advantage is the ability to breed a few does at once, though they might not all cycle at the exact same time. Having the buck run with a group of does takes a lot of the manual labor out of it all. However, the biggest downside to this method is the lack of a definitive breeding. Sometimes you will miss the does coming into heat despite watching them closely. Some heat cycles can be quite short as well, and some does are shy (or, on the other hand, very human-oriented) and will not be as receptive to the buck if a human is around.

Hand breeding sounds much more intrusive than it actually is. When hand breeding, the breeder watches the does and waits until they come into heat. When they cycle, the doe is caught and led to the buck of choice to be bred. The breeder allows them to mate about three times and then takes the doe back to her normal living quarters. Sometimes the breeder will repeat the process the next day as well if the doe is still in heat. The biggest advantage to this method is knowing an exact date for the breeding and therefore an exact time frame for the birth. The downside is that some does are not as obvious about their heat cycles as others, which can lead to breeders missing their estrus cycles.

Artificial Insemination

Artificial insemination (AI) is an option for goat owners who do not wish to own a buck or who want access to wider variety of bucks to use on their does. Artificial insemination, as the name implies, is the process of inseminating the doe manually or "artificially" without mating her to a buck. The main advantage of artificial insemination is that it allows for the introduction of desirable bloodlines without purchasing a buck. Any buck who has been collected and has semen available can be used on your does, even if they live halfway across the country. That opens up an entire new world of bloodlines, and usually at a lower cost than purchasing the animal itself and retrieving or shipping it.

On the other hand, there are disadvantages as well. The cost of AI can be quite expensive after buying the semen straws (the price of which will go up the better quality the buck), paying expensive shipping, and purchasing necessary supplies like a semen storage tank, liquid nitrogen, speculum, lubricant, and the like. Depending on whether or not you have been trained in AI, you might also be paying a veterinarian or AI technician to come and inseminate your goats for you. Timing is essential in AI as well; if you miss the doe's heat you throw all the money and time you spent down the drain. Artificial insemination is a pay-per-dose option as well, so if your doe doesn't settle on the first attempt you will be forced to pay yet again next time, unless you are collecting and using your own bucks.

Heat detection is vital for AI. For that reason, many breeders choose to get prescription hormones from their veterinarian to sync their does' estrus cycles. Using injectable hormones allows the breeder to know down to the hour when their doe will come into heat and be ready for breeding. At that time the semen straws are carefully thawed and administered to the doe manually. If using a veterinarian or AI technician, it's very important to carefully schedule the breeding date and only work with people you know to be reliable.

Tales from the Kidding Stall: *Although I have not yet used AI on my goats in favor of using my bucks, I have failed attempts under my belt from other livestock—namely a pig named Mabel and a cow named Elsie. In the case of Mabel, the semen arrived too late and she was no longer in heat, despite paying the expensive costs of expedited shipping. The AI attempt for Elsie was a nightmare. I worked with my vet to carefully sync her estrus using hormone injections and a CIDR (controlled internal drug release vaginal suppository). I worked with our AI technician to schedule everything down to the hour. Want to guess what happened when that hour rolled around? The AI tech never showed. Having not been trained in AI and not having any of the required tools, I was up the creek without a paddle. All in all, I've lost hundreds of dollars on artificial insemination. The wonderful thing about simply having your own male animal—be it buck, boar, or bull—is that if the first attempt fails you can try again without the loss of money, time, and sanity.*

Seasonal vs Year-round Breeding

The majority of dairy goat breeds are seasonal breeders. This means the does only have heat cycles in the late summer to early winter, and likewise the bucks are only sexually active in the normal breeding season as well. While there are always some anomalies, seasonal breeders typically cannot be expected to mate or give birth off-season naturally. The European breeds are all seasonal breeders. This includes Alpine, Oberhasli, Toggenburg, Saanen, Sable, and British Guernsey. LaManchas, which are an American breed, are seasonal as well. These breeds originated in cooler climates where the winter weather would make it difficult to kid any time of year other than spring and summer.

On the other hand, some breeds originated in warmer parts of the world where the climate is more conducive to year-round breeding, and therefore those breeds adapted to cycle year round. These breeds include the Nigerian Dwarf, Pygmy, Boer, and sometimes the Nubian. The Nubian breed is a mixed bag because they have both African and European influence in their heritage, which means sometimes they will breed out of season and sometimes they will not. Location and length of daylight may have an impact on how readily Nubians will breed off-season. Of the dairy breeds, the Nigerian Dwarf is the most reliable year-round breeder. In my own herd I have had does kid in fall, winter, spring, and even summer. An interesting thing to note about the year-round breeders is that they still go through rut in the fall, and in my experience the does cycle more strongly and regularly in the fall than any other time of year. Miniature breeds (Nigerian Dwarf x Standard Dairy) are often able to breed year-round as well.

There are advantages to year-round breeding. Being able to breed at any time of the year also means being able to choose when your goats kid. It's quite popular among Nigerian Dwarf breeder to have a secondary kidding season in the fall rather than freshening all does in the spring. This makes it possible to milk during all months of the year with ease as well, whereas breeding all does at one time means they are all in peak production at the same time and possibly dried off at the same time as well. On the other hand, breeding year-round also means it's much more likely to have accidental breeding of sons to dams or sisters. Nigerian Dwarf bucklings are notorious for reaching sexual maturity at a very young age, and because their dams and sisters will continue to cycle in spring and summer, the bucklings must be separated at two months of age unless wethered. In some cases, they might last longer if they have no female siblings and aren't acting overly "bucky," but all in all they are very precocious.

Another fun tidbit about the African breeds is that they are more likely to have high multiples like triplets or above than the European breeds. Nigerians in particular have been known to have quadruplets, quintuplets, and at least one known litter of septuplets born to Sinai Thunder Farm in Kentucky. Nubians also occasionally produce quads or more, but litters larger than three are less common than in Nigerians. Any breed of goat may have four or more offspring, but it is much rarer in the European breeds. It's nearly considered commonplace in Nigerians.

Male Effect

The male effect refers to the ability of a buck in rut to bring does into heat through exposure. This can be useful for people wanting several does to kid around the same time, or for people who do not own their own buck and need to use an outside buck for stud service. In addition, a buck in rut may be able to bring seasonal breeders into heat off-season and allow for breeding during times they normally wouldn't.

There are certain prescription medications that can be used to induce estrus off-season in does as well, but they may not be needed if one has access to a nice stinky buck. Interestingly, a study was conducted that indicates the bucks' sexual inactivity is the primary cause of anestrous in the off season rather than a lack of cycling in the does. Researchers found that they could induce the bucks to being sexually active by exposing them to artificially long daylight hours. Then when those bucks were introduced to anestrous does off season, their presence caused the does to come into season and mate. Whether or not this can be replicated on an at-home basis is unknown, but the possibility exists.

Chapter Four: Pregnancy

At long last, your does are bred. You have five months (145-155 days) of impatiently waiting ahead of you before the kids hit the ground. So…now what? In this chapter, we'll take a peek at the general timeline of pregnancy, how to know if your goat is actually pregnant, and preparing for birth.

Is My Goat Pregnant?

I think this absolutely must be the single most frequently asked question regarding goats. It is usually accompanied by a picture, sometimes from the side and sometimes from the rear of the goat, and an estimated time when the doe might have been bred. I have also seen people wait for six months or more on a "pregnant" goat to kid only to realize that she'd never been pregnant at all. That amounts to a lot of wasted time and energy for the anticipating owner. On the other hand, I've also known people who were completely taken by surprise when a goat who was "not pregnant" gave birth unexpectedly. Most new goat owners experience these kinds of surprises and let downs in the beginning. Hopefully this book will prevent you from going through the same thing!

It's impossible to accurately judge a goat's pregnancy status based on her physical appearance alone, especially early on in her gestation. Thankfully, that doesn't mean it's impossible to know for certain that a doe is or isn't bred. Let's take a look at some of the ways to determine pregnancy in your doe.

Physical Appearance and Behavior

Physical appearance cannot be relied on as a foolproof method of knowing when a goat is pregnant for a number of reasons. Things can cause a doe's body to be deceptive, like a distended rumen; a low-hanging stomach due to the stretching of muscles from previous kiddings; a single kid or twins hiding; a doe having a very long, deep, or wide body; a precocious udder; and more. Does can look very pregnant when they aren't or appear to not be pregnant when they are.

Although looks can be deceiving, there are changes that will take place in a doe's body throughout her pregnancy. You can pick up on these and make a decent guess if you know what to expect. The best way to notice these changes is to be familiar with your doe's body before you breed her. Knowing how she looks on a normal everyday basis will make it easier to detect changes. Below are some the visible signs you might see in your doe leading up to kidding.

- **Stomach Growth:** When watching for a growing belly, keep in mind that the rumen is on the doe's left side whereas kids will be on the doe's right side. (Right and left are always from the perspective of the goat as if you were looking at her from behind, not your right and left while looking at her from the front.) Depending on the number and size of the kids and the shape of the doe's body, her stomach may not grow drastically. On the other hand, the rumen can push into the right side and cause it to distend as well in a doe who is not pregnant. Does who have given birth to several times might also lose their girlish figure and have a stomach that is permanently distended due to the wearing down of the muscles. Bodies that are long, wide, or deep hide pregnancy better as well because there is more room for the kids to hide inside.
- **Kid Movements:** In about the last month of pregnancy you might be lucky enough to see or feel the kids moving around and kicking inside the doe. This is a really cool experience, and one physical change that is pretty hard to dispute. That said, a goat's stomach does move due to digestion and the rumen function as well, and sometimes owners mistake this movement for kids. If feeling for kids, feel along the right side and underbelly of the doe on the right and back toward the udder. While visible movement is sometimes less distinct, feeling the kids is often obvious because they will feel hard and bony. You won't be able to see or feel kids in every doe during late

pregnancy, so lack of movement is not necessarily indicative that the doe isn't pregnant.

- **Udder Development:** Most does will begin to develop an udder in the last month of pregnancy and sometimes a bit sooner. However, some does don't develop an udder until the last minute or sometimes not at all, especially first fresheners. Does can also develop precocious udders, which happens when the doe begins to produce milk without being pregnant (it happens on rare occasions in bucks, too!). Does may also have false pregnancies as well, which I address later in chapter eight.
- **Vaginal Changes:** In late pregnancy (the last month or so) the doe's vulva will loosen and become puffy in preparation to stretch for kidding. You might see intermittent whitish mucus discharge as well, though this will vary from doe to doe. Small amount of white discharge are not indicative of pending labor, and you may see them as early as a month out from actual delivery.
- **Ligaments:** The doe has a pair of ligaments that run alongside her tail head. These ligaments begin to loosen in the last month or so of pregnancy but can still be felt. Then in the 24 hours of pregnancy before kidding the ligaments will disappear completely and no longer be felt. This means birth is imminent. There are more details about ligaments and other signs of impending birth later on in chapter five.

Tales from the Kidding Stall: *Sandy was my first first-freshener and only my second doe to give birth. She surprised me with triplets out in the pasture, because I thought she wasn't pregnant at all. She didn't look pregnant. I believe her kids would have died if not for our guardian dog licking them clean, because Sandy had no clue what she was doing at all—this happens sometimes with the first timers. Sandy did not initially want to accept her kids, and her milk did not come in before she delivered. She had only a tiny bit of colostrum, and she had to be restrained for the kids to drink it. At that time I didn't know about minerals and retained placentas, and her afterbirth hung out of her without falling. The vet prescribed oxytocin to coax her milk in and encourage her uterus to expel the afterbirth. Forcing her to allow the kids to nurse assisted as well, because nursing stimulates the natural production of oxytocin and helps encourage milk production, maternal instincts, and the bond between the doe and her kids. Sandy accepted her kids in the end, though one did have to be bottle fed due to Sandy not producing enough milk for all three, which is common for first fresheners.*

Blood Testing

Blood testing is one of the most economical and accurate methods to use. It's also quite easy, and once someone teaches you to do it you will be set to do all of your own blood testing. A veterinarian or experienced goat breeder nearby should be able to come demonstrate the process for you. Blood is drawn from the jugular vein in the goat's neck using a needle and syringe. There is a picture tutorial for drawing blood in chapter eight of this book.

The blood is then sent to a laboratory like BioTracking Labs or Washington Animal Disease Diagnostic Laboratory. An added bonus to this method of testing is that the blood sample can be used for yearly disease testing (CAE, Johne's, CL, and/or any others of your choice). Blood tests detect pregnancy-specific proteins which occur in association with fetal and placental development. Does must be at least 30 days bred for the test to be accurate. If you're curious about accuracy, BioTracking reports its BioPRYN test's accuracy at over 99% accurate for open (not pregnant) results and approximately 95% accuracy for pregnant results. Some percentage of false positives are also attributed to early term abortion rather than test accuracy.

This doe may look pregnant based on physical appearance, but she was not bred at the time this photo was taken. She just had an active rumen.

Ultrasound or Radiography

Ultrasounds and x-rays are less convenient and more expensive than blood tests due to the need for trained professional technicians or expensive home ultrasound machines the cost of which is not justified for most small producers. Typically done in a vet's office, these two methods are both extremely accurate and carry the bonus benefit of allowing you to have an idea of how many kids will be born. Although the u-shape of the uterus makes it a bit difficult to distinguish the exact number of kids hiding inside, an ultrasound or x-ray can usually reveal if there are multiples. There is also a bit of a cool factor to seeing those tiny little goatlings swimming around in their mother's uterus.

In order for an ultrasound to be accurate the doe must be at least 25 days bred, and the heartbeat will be visible starting at 27 days. X-Rays are considered 100% accurate after a doe is at least 70 days bred, and they are more accurate in determining birth number than ultrasound after the doe is at least 75 days bred. One of the downsides of using an x-ray is that it requires a longer wait, meaning that you've wasted approximately 40 days in which the doe could be bred back to the buck in the case of an open doe.

Milk Tests

Like blood samples, milk sample testing looks for the pregnancy proteins and is similar in accuracy as well. One big advantage to milk testing is that it utilizes an activity many goat breeders are already doing daily—milking. For those who are milking their does each day throughout the year, collecting a vial for pregnancy testing takes a negligible amount of extra time or effort. On the other hand, the test obviously can't be used for does who are not in milk. That means first fresheners or any doe that has been dried off won't be able to be tested using this method.

Milk sample tests can be performed at 29 days post breeding or later. For those who are already on milk test, many DHI (dairy herd improvement) recordation laboratories offer the test to be added to monthly milk sampling. Even if you aren't on DHI, you can send samples to labs like Dairy One to be tested.

Urine Tests

Urine tests called P-Test are the new kid on the block. (For the record, the pregnancy testing strips designed for humans will *not* work on goats.) The biggest advantage to urine testing is that it can be completed at home and the results are immediate. The tests are affordable, and the collection is fairly simple—you merely have to wait around for your does to pee and collect it in a container. No more waiting for results sent through the mail or making an appointment at the veterinarians, right? Well…

The accuracy of urine samples is not as high as the other methods. The test was initially designed for cattle, though the developers state that they can be used on other species. I have spoken with people who have used the P-Tests and accuracy has varied. The producers of P-Test state that it is 95% accurate for cattle, but no information is provided for the accuracy on goats. While I don't think that P-Tests should be thrown away as useless, I do think this relatively new option is not yet quite as reliable as the other options at the time of this writing. I am hopeful that more work will be done in the future to determine a rate of accuracy specific to goats and improve the reliability. Does must be 50 days bred before testing with the urine sample.

Timeline of Pregnancy

The waiting game officially begins once pregnancy is confirmed for your goats. Does are pregnant for an average of 145-155 days or about 5 months. The earliest I have personally had a doe kid was on day 143; much earlier than that and kids are not viable. Nigerian Dwarf goats tend to have a slightly shorter gestation than the standard sized goat. Nigerians tend toward 145 days while standards kid more toward the 150 day mark. During these long months of waiting, your does are growing and nourishing their developing kids. It's hard to wait, but in the end it's worth it. Let's take a look at the timeline of your doe's gestation.

Conception to 30 Days

Prior to breeding, your doe should have received her general tune up. This includes checking for and treating parasites if needed, providing mineral supplements if needed, trimming hooves, and evaluating body condition. These are all things that should be done on a regular basis and should certainly be updated prior to breeding. Assuming your doe is in peak condition, she can then be introduced to the buck when she comes into heat. Mark the date on your calendar and make note of the possible due date. You can calculate this yourself, but there are also various websites online offering handy automated gestation calculators. I generally use the one available on the American Goat Society website. As the 21 day post-mating date approaches, keep an eye on your doe for signs of heat. If she comes back into heat, then you can assume she has not successfully settled and breed her once more. If she doesn't, you may just be in luck.

After the 30 day mark is reached you can pull a blood or milk sample to send off for pregnancy testing. At this time I also recommend doing your yearly disease testing for your herd. This should be CAE (caprine arthritis encephalitis), CL (caseous lymphadenitis), and Johne's as well as any others for which you wish to test. There will be no visibly obvious signs of pregnancy other than a lack of going back into heat and care will not change. Avoid deworming during this period unless necessary; if deworming is required, be sure to use a pregnancy safe dewormer.

30 Days to 3 Months

This is the midrange of the doe's pregnancy. By now you know for sure she is pregnant if you performed blood or milk tests; if you waited to pregnancy test by x-ray, ultrasound, or urine test, you will perform those during this time period at the appropriate date. The doe will begin to naturally consume more hay and browse around month three, but she does not need grain to be introduced or increased under normal conditions. Avoid overfeeding lest the kids grow too large.

The doe's body will start to change a bit during this period. You might notice her girth increasing, especially on the right side, though she also might not change much at all depending on her body. As always, she should have access to good quality free choice minerals, fresh water, and good quality grass hay. If she was in milk when bred to the buck, the doe should be dried off around three months to allow her body to rest for two months and develop the much-needed colostrum for her kids. It is now generally safe to deworm her if necessary, provided you only use a pregnancy-safe dewormer.

3 Months to Kidding

It's crunch time! This is the final stretch for your doe. Her body is growing and expanding, her ligaments will start to loosen, and her udder will begin to develop. Depending on how you choose to supplement selenium and copper, and how frequently your herd needs supplementation, it might be time to provide another copper bolus or selenium supplement if you don't provide selenium powder free choice. If you choose to vaccinate your goats with CD&T (clostridium types C and D and tetanus), administer the vaccination one month before the doe's due date. Her hooves should also be trimmed at this time.

In the last month of pregnancy your does might begin to have a bit of mucus discharge which should be whitish in color. This is normal and does not mean the doe is imminent or has "lost her mucus plug." Mucus is present at the cervix throughout the pregnancy and some drainage is normal. (If you see a long, abundant stream of clear or amber mucus, the doe is going into labor. Signs of labor are discussed in chapter five.) The ligaments around her tail head will begin to soften, and most does will begin to develop an udder. If feeding red raspberry leaf as an herbal supplement, begin offering it around one month prior to delivery. (There is no harm in offering red raspberry leaf earlier if desired.)

The last month of pregnancy is the time to begin assembling your kidding kit and have it in a convenient carrying case ready to be taken to the barn. There is a list of items to include in your birthing kit in chapter five. Begin to provide alfalfa hay along with the grass hay in the last month of pregnancy or begin feeding alfalfa pellets in the last two or three weeks if hay is not available. In the last week of the doe's pregnancy, begin introducing very small amounts of grain to adjust the doe to the new feed she will be getting after she gives birth. See chapter two for more detailed feeding information.

The last week of pregnancy the doe should be moved to a smaller kidding stall to give birth in a clean, protected, and private environment. Moving the doe to a private stall prevents her from giving birth out in the elements or an unsafe or filthy location, which would increase the risk of the kids dying and the mother getting a uterine infection or mastitis, as well as increasing the chance of the kids being killed by predators. It also makes it much easier for you, the goat midwife, to keep a close eye on her and be present when she kids. Check the doe's ligaments daily so you will recognize when they are gone. It is also beneficial to shave the hindquarters, rear legs, udder, and tail of the doe in that week of pregnancy. This makes cleanup immensely easier after the birth, and having a clean udder makes it easier for kids to nurse and keeps milk clean. It also allows you to clearly see the changes in the doe's body as she goes into labor. I like to use a barn security camera with both night and day vision to watch my does for signs of labor. Having a barn camera makes midnight checks much easier!

Looking at this picture, which goats would you guess are pregnant? The doe on the far left is not pregnant in this photo. The three does on the right side are all about three months pregnant in this picture. Is that what you expected?

Vaccination Philosophy

I follow a similar philosophy to raising my animals as I do for myself. I do not personally take vaccinations, medications, or other preventative medical care that I do not need. I believe that the best medicine is prevention through management (or for humans, lifestyle), and not through prophylactic medications. There are risks involved in vaccinations, they are not foolproof, and I believe they weaken rather than support the immune system. Other medication like feed-through antibiotics, medicated feeds, and prophylactic deworming present their own risks as well, such as antibiotic resistant bacteria and dewormer resistant parasites. The bottom line for me is, if I'm not giving myself a flu shot each year, why am I giving a vaccine to my goats each year?

Obviously different people have different philosophies and beliefs surrounding vaccination, so I have included the vaccine in the timeline of pregnancy for those who choose to administer it. The CD&T vaccine is designed to prevent enterotoxemia caused by clostridium perfringens types C and D as well as tetanus. Enterotoxemia is a metabolic illness most often caused by overfeeding carbohydrates. The clostridium bacteria found in the goat's digestive system rapidly multiples and causes diarrhea, abdominal pain, weakness, and death in a short period of time, often in spite of treatment. This is an illness that can usually be prevented through proper management, though of course there are instances of goats contracting it despite good management for one reason or another. However, there are also instances of vaccinated goats contracting it as well. Vaccination is not an excuse for poor management. Avoiding feeding too many carbohydrates and sudden changes in feed, and feeding smaller, more frequent meals rather than fewer, larger ones (including milk to nursing kids) is the correct protocol for prevention. I prefer to prevent enterotoxemia through appropriate feeding than through a vaccine. I do recommend keeping the CD antitoxin (not the toxoid) on hand for emergencies. The toxoid is the preventative vaccine, whereas the antitoxin is given as part of treatment protocol.

As for tetanus, it is caused by the bacteria clostridium tetani. Also known as lockjaw, it causes muscles to spasm and contract, eventually leading to an inability to chew (hence lockjaw) and eventually death. It, too, is difficult to treat once contracted. Tetanus lives in the soil, and it enters into the body through anaerobic wounds, especially deep puncture wounds. Tetanus has an association with stepping on a rusty nail for that reason, but of course that's not the only method of contracting it. Preventative management for tetanus includes avoiding leaving sharp edges on fences and structures and monitoring goats for wounds so that the tetanus toxoid vaccine can be administered if needed. In kids, castration via surgical castration or banding can increase the risk of exposure to the bacteria, which is one reason why I now use the bloodless burdizzo castration method for goat kids now. I choose to only administer a tetanus vaccine when needed, such as in conjunction with surgery or after injury, much I like I would for my own self.

At the end of the day, choosing to vaccinate or not vaccinate your herd is just that—a choice. There are calculated risks to either decision. I personally believe all medicines should be given only when needed for a number of reasons, and I feel that vaccinating my herd each year is not aligned with my personal philosophy. However, you must decide for yourself what is right for your own herd. Your method of castration, environment, management style, and personal beliefs all come into play for the decision.

Developmental Stages of the Fetus

- **Conception:** This is the ovum period. The egg is penetrated by the sperm. The egg immediately changes to prevent any other sperm from entering. As the egg travels down the oviduct, it splits from one cell into two in the first 24 hours. The cells continue to divide until they reach the blastula stage about 6-7 days after fertilization. About two weeks after fertilization, the egg, now an oblong blastocyst, finally attaches to the uterine wall and prevents prostaglandin production.
- **Embryonic Period:** Once the blastocyst attaches to the uterine wall it enters the embryonic stage. It is nourished at first by the fluids in the uterus.
- **Day 20:** The heart begins to beat.
- **Days 21-35:** Lung buds start to develop.
- **Days 28-35:** Limb buds appear.
- **Day 30:** The embryo is about ½" long and begins to be nourished by the doe's circulatory system through the placental connections called placentomes which consist of cotyledons (placental side) and caruncles (uterine side).
- **Days 35-42:** Mouth, digits, and dew claws can be differentiated.
- **Day 42:** The embryo is 1 ½" long. The major tissues, organs, and systems are defined.
- **Days 42-49:** Mammary buds in females and empty scrotum in males develop. The jugular vein can be seen.
- **Days 49-56:** Eyelids close and ear canals open.
- **Day 60:** Enter the Fetal Stage. The fetus is about 4" long. It has eyes, eyelids, and nostrils.
- **Days 77-84:** The horn pits appear.
- **3 Months:** The fetus is about 10" long and is starting to develop fine hairs.
- **Days 91-98:** Skin begins to thicken so that veins are no longer visible.
- **Days 98-105:** Temporary tooth buds emerge.
- **Days 112-119:** Dense hair covers the body and limbs.
- **Days 119-145:** Final development of the lungs takes place.
- **Days 145-155:** Birth takes place.

Chapter Five: Kidding

While mucking stalls and trimming hooves doesn't always thrill me, I never grow tired of being present at the births of my livestock. It may sound cliché, but witnessing the miracle of life is one of my favorite aspects of farming. Being there when brand new baby goats take their first breaths, and then minutes later their first steps, is an incredible experience. There are few things in this world more precious than newborn goat kids.

It's also important to be present at the birth. Most births go smoothly and require little to no intervention, but sometimes things do go wrong. Goat labors also tend to go very quickly once the kids start coming, and it's not uncommon for kids to die simply because they came out too quickly for the mother to clean them all. Being present when your goat gives birth greatly increases the chance of all the kids surviving and can save mom's life in a difficult labor, too.

If I could give one piece of advice for someone attending their first birth it would be to stay calm. I know well the sense of urgency that comes with watching a doe give birth. It's immensely exciting, but it can also be stressful. Many times we have a tendency to assume the worst, or to panic in a bad situation, but panicking will get you nowhere. Don't jump the gun. Instead, take a few deep breaths and force yourself to think rationally and calmly before proceeding. Most of the time, the doe won't need assistance. Most of the time when she does need assistance, things will still work out. Life and death situations do happen, but they are not the norm, and panicking never helped anyone anyway.

Preparing for Birth

Begin to prepare for the impending birth in the last month of pregnancy. This is the time when you should get the doe, the kidding stall, and yourself ready for kidding. We covered how to care for the pregnant doe in the previous chapter. For this chapter we will focus on getting yourself and your barn ready to go to welcome those new babies and what to do during the delivery.

The Kidding Stall

A clean, safe location for your doe to give birth in is an absolute must. Naturally a barn will never be a sterile environment, nor should we try to make it such, but keeping the birthing environment clean helps prevent issues such as coccidiosis, mastitis, and infection to a minimum (all of which are discussed in more detail later in chapter eight). Ideally the floor of the kidding stall should be a rubber or concrete surface, which can be thoroughly cleaned and disinfected by mucking any residual bedding out and spraying it down with disinfecting solution. Doing so will kill harmful bacteria that may have collected from prior births or simply from housing goats. Unfortunately, bleach does not kill coccidia; a 10% ammonia solution or hot steam cleaning are the only methods that are recommended against coccidia other than time. The oocysts of coccidia can survive a year or more if not exposed to direct sunlight, which is problematic for the barn environment. Coccidia is discussed in depth later, but it is one reason that I prefer to use my kidding stalls only for kidding and allow them to lie dormant for the rest of the year.

One additional problem with dirt-floor kidding stalls is that goats will paw the ground during labor. This exposes the dirt, which of course harbors bacteria and parasites. While exposure to dirt is unavoidable with livestock—they live outdoors, after all—it's not the ideal birthing environment. Luckily, rubber stall mats are easily found in most farm supply stores or can be ordered. These mats are designed primarily for horse stalls but work wonderfully to cover a dirt floor in a barn more quickly and easily than pouring concrete.

Once clean and dry, the kidding stall should be covered with fresh bedding such as straw. Unfortunately bedding brings in its own potential risks, as both wood shavings and straw carry bacteria and, in some cases, pests such as mites. I have on more than one occasion introduced mites inadvertently to livestock with straw. However, clean straw remains my personal preference for bedding despite its flaws, because it is absorbent, warm, easy to muck, and doesn't break down as quickly as wood shavings. Ultimately no bedding or environment is perfect, so it all comes down to personal preference and maintaining as clean a kidding space as possible without driving yourself mad trying to make everything sterile. If you choose to use wood shavings or don't have access to straw, be sure it is a non-toxic, non-irritant variety such as pine. Other options include pelleted bedding designed for horses, which tends to be more expensive and less easy to work with in my experience, or sand. Sand is a good option because it is inert and does not carry as much microbial growth as organic materials, but it is less absorbent, difficult to clean, and difficult to dispose of when soiled, which makes it less viable for most breeders.

Other considerations for the kidding stall include its safety and security. The kidding stalls should be inside a secure barn which blocks wind and rain but allows for ventilation. As kids are often born in late winter or early spring, it's vital that the kidding stalls protect them from direct wind or precipitation. While no wind should blow directly on the animals in the kidding stall, it should still maintain proper airflow and ventilation to prevent respiratory issues. Another concern with kidding stalls is safety from predators. Goat kids are an exceptionally easy target for wild predators as well as stray roaming dogs, and the sounds and smells of birth are attractive to predators. Kidding stalls should be well protected so that no predators can easily access them. I discuss protecting livestock from predators more in chapter eight.

A Note on Barn Cameras: *One addition to the kidding stall that I have found extremely useful is a surveillance camera that can be viewed from your home. The early stages of labor can last for several hours, and I will be honest and admit that it's quite miserable to trek through the cold every two hours to check on a doe in early labor. It's also no fun to sit in the cold waiting for the action to happen. A nice barn camera makes watching a doe in labor so much easier and prevents missed births. I have checked does before only to go out literally an hour later and find kids on the ground. Being able to watch them remotely prevents this from happening in most cases and ensures that I know when kids are on the way. It's also quite nice to be able to keep an eye on the does from the warmth and comfort of my own home until it's go-time.*

Coraline during her labor. Note how the udder is in contact with the ground during labor.

Tales from the Kidding Stall: *Coraline was one of the hardest losses I have experienced. She was a first-freshening doe and a bit older than my usual first fresheners at four years of age. Her birth went textbook-smooth with no complications, and her triplets were healthy and happy. Then she suddenly became sick about 24 hours later. She was shivering and exhibiting some signs that initially made me think she was hypocalcemic, but she did not respond to treatment for that. She also retained her placenta; this was before I started offering free-choice selenium. She seemed "off," and I decided to take her to the vet. At the vet's office she seemed normal aside from being listless and not interested in food. Her udder was pliable and soft, her temperature was normal, her rumen was functioning, and she had no retained fetus. She passed foul-smelling liquid at the vet's office, and we decided to treat her for a uterine infection and continue with a second dose of calcium supplement just in case. The treatment did not work.*

Long story short, on the third day out from kidding, we discovered that she had gangrene mastitis that had become septic. Her udder was now cold and discolored, and her "milk" was not milk, but a clear watery liquid. Our vet recommended she go to specialists at the veterinary university clinic in Starkville, Mississippi. Despite intensive care, Coraline passed away just six days after giving birth. Although the vet explained that the bacteria that cause gangrenous, septic mastitis are everywhere—the ground, bedding, our hands—it was Coraline's death that spurred me to place stall mats over the dirt flood in the kidding stalls to help prevent exposure to the bacteria during labor, which is when most animals contract that type of mastitis. I also now dip the doe's teats in an iodine solution immediately following birth.

A curious kid inspects the contents of my kidding kit.

Kidding Kit

Once you have the kidding quarters ready to go, it's time to assemble a kidding kit. The kidding kit is essentially a midwife bag that contains a few essentials and emergency supplies. It doesn't need to include the entire medicine cabinet, but it should contain a few basic supplies to help you get through the birth in case the doe needs assistance. I like to keep my supplies in a tote designed to sit inside a five gallon bucket because of the durable fabric and organization, but any tote or bag will do. Each kidding kit can be a bit unique to the farmer who assembles it. We all have varying preferences to the tools we like to have on hand for the birth, but here are a few suggested items to keep on hand:

- Obstetric (OB) lubricant (petroleum jelly or coconut oil can be substituted in a pinch)

- OB gloves (these are longer than normal glove in case you need to go into the doe's birth canal past the wrist)
- Standard non-latex gloves
- Iodine, betadine, or other OB disinfectant (used to clean gloved hands when assisting the doe)
- Naval cord dip of choice (iodine is a common choice, as is Vetricyn Navel Spray, Triodine, or Novalsan [chlorhexidine])
- Teat dip (I use an iodine solution)
- Non-reflow dip cup (for dipping teats and umbilical cords)
- Forceps (to clamp umbilical cords if needed)
- Medical scissors (to cut umbilical cords if needed)
- Bulb syringe/nasal aspirator (to clear airways of newborns)
- Towels
- Battery-powered headlamp (in case the birth takes place in the dark)
- Tube feeding syringe (for getting colostrum to weak kids unable to nurse)
- Bottles and nipples (to feed kids colostrum who can nurse but can't eat from their dam)
- Leg snare (to hold legs in place or pull kids when assisting birth)
- Kid puller (to help pull a kid that is badly stuck or hold the head in place for a kid poorly positioned)
- Kid resuscitator (inflates lungs of kids whose hearts are beating but are not breathing)
- Calcium drench/CMPK (in case of hypocalcemia in does)
- Drench gun (to administer medication to doe if needed)
- Thermometer
- Scale (to weigh kids)
- Selenium gel or BoSe (to administer to weak kids)
- Blackstrap Molasses (to provide energy to doe or stimulate weak kids)
- Cell Phone with Emergency Numbers (to call emergency backup if things go beyond what you can handle on your own)

Being Present at Birth

I have mentioned here and there throughout this book that it's important to know the due date and be present at birth, and now I'd like to go into a bit more detail about *why* it's so important. While it's true that the majority of births go smoothly, things can also go awry. When that happens, you being there can mean life or death for the kids or even the doe. That is compounded even more in freezing weather when soaking wet kids can become hypothermic or get frostbite long before they dry.

Kids can be lost even in a textbook delivery in warm weather. The actual delivery process can go very quickly once the kids emerge, and multiples kids can be born so quickly that the doe doesn't have time to clean them all in time. When this happens the kids either suffocate or freeze due to the amniotic fluid. Does can also be so absorbed in their first kid that they do not notice another one has been born, especially if the second kid is small. Usually, though not always, the larger kid is the first to be born, which means subsequent smaller kids can "slip out" undetected, for lack of a better word. Still other times your first-time doe may not have a clue what is happening to her body or what to do when the babies come out. As goat midwife, being present means you save these kids' lives by drying them off, clearing their airways, and ensuring they consume life-saving colostrum.

Other times there is a problem with the birth that puts both the dam and the kids in jeopardy. Malpresented kids or kids that are too large can have trouble passing through the birth canal. In cases like these, you must be present to assist or both the mother and the kids may not survive. In some cases, this means assisting with delivery, and sometimes it means seeking professional help from a veterinarian if the problem is too complex for you to handle on your own. Although relatively rare, C-sections are sometimes required to save mom and babies. Either way, your presence is needed to ensure your goats' survival. It's much better to attend 100 births without needing to assist than to miss the one birth when your doe needed you.

Tales from the Kidding Stall: *While it may seem impossible, sometimes small kids come out so easily that the doe doesn't even notice them. I lost a kid this way from a doe named Sandy. Myself and my mother were both present at the birth and watched as the first kid came out. Sandy stood up and began cleaning him, and we watched and waited for the next one. I felt that she wasn't done, yet she wasn't seeming to have any more strong contractions. Sandy was wholly devoted to cleaning her first little kid. The entire time she was standing with her rear to the wall, facing us. After a few moments I noticed a strange lump behind her and my heart sank. I rushed over and found a lifeless kid still in the amniotic sac. Unfortunately it was too late; the second kid never had a chance. The story of this kidding is a perfect example of how quickly and smoothly the second (or third, etc.) kid can slip out, particularly when it's smaller than the one before it. Not only did Sandy not notice she'd had a kid, but the two humans attending her kidding didn't notice it, either. That's how easily the second kid was birthed. I imagine to Sandy it likely felt like nothing more than the afterbirth.*

Signs of Labor

In order to be present at the doe's birth, it's necessary to actually know when she's going into labor. Does typically kid between 145-155 days, though some go a little shorter or a little longer. While ten days doesn't seem like a long time to watch, it's excruciatingly long when you're actively waiting for kids to hit the ground! That window grows even larger if you're pen breeding rather than hand breeding and don't have an exact date. It can sometimes seem like your doe is never going to show any signs of labor, or alternatively like she's going into labor every single day when she isn't. It's enough to pull your hair out, even after you've been at it for a while.

Changes in Behavior

There are several behavioral changes your doe might exhibit as she enters into labor. Keep in mind that every doe is different; some will start to act quite noticeably different while others will not. Knowing your goat's "normal" and what type of behavior is weird for her will help you determine if she is entering into labor. Some of the behavioral changes you might notice include:

- Separating herself from the herd
- Talking to her stomach/kids before they're born
- Using "mama voice" to her stomach or to you (or even the barn cat)
- Becoming more affectionate toward you
- Becoming more skittish around you
- Pawing at the ground
- Standing up and laying back down frequently

- Stretching (positioning kids) and yawning frequently
- licking
- Wide-eyed expression
- More frequent vocalization
- Seeming uncomfortable
- Generally behaving oddly

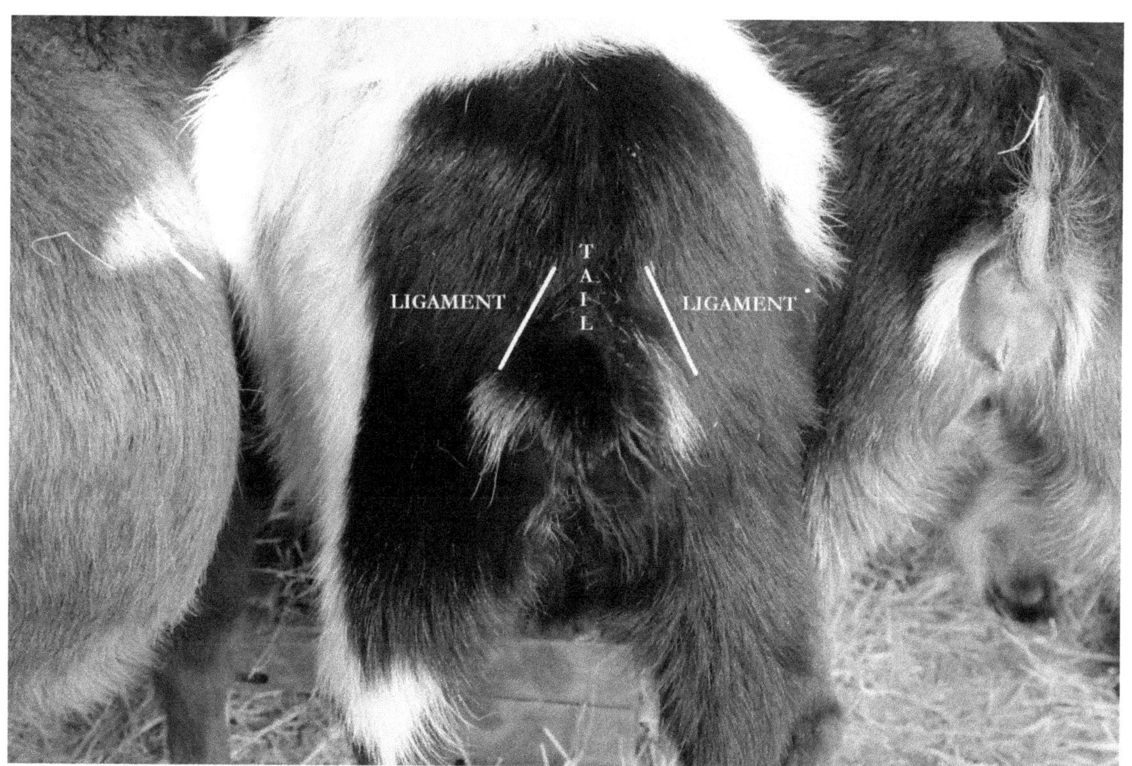

Ligaments are located on either side of the tailhead.

Physical Changes

Physical changes are more definitive signs of impending birth. While a doe's behavior might lie, her body certainly can't. That said, there is always a margin of error when it comes to these things. Each doe's body doesn't respond the exact same way to impending labor. There is a spectrum of bodily changes and the time frames in which they take place. Still, there are certain things that, if you see them, mean kids are on the way.

One of the best ways to detect approaching labor is to keep track of the doe's tail ligaments. A string-like ligament runs down either side of the tail from the base of the tail to the pin bones. When the doe is not close to delivery these ligaments are hard and easily felt, almost like two guitar strings running down the tail. As pregnancy progresses and the doe nears her due date the ligaments gradually soften and loosen. When the doe is within 24 hours of delivery her ligaments will completely disappear. Of course, they are still there, but they can no longer be felt. The area surrounding the tail head is mushy and soft, and you can almost completely encircle the spine with your fingers. The area next to the tail also sinks as the tail head raises. When the ligaments are gone, the tail head is raised, and the sides sunken, kidding will occur in the next 24 hours. Keep in mind that sometimes the ligaments are very soft but not completely gone, and this can trick you into thinking labor is imminent when it might be a few more days. If you see the doe's tail arching with the hips raised, tail head sunken, and tail arcing up and out in half-moon shape, the doe is most likely entering labor.

The udder is also a visible physical sign that labor is getting closer. Most does will begin to develop their udder about a month or so from kidding, though in some cases they might wait until the last minute or not come into milk at all until after the birth. Typically, first fresheners are more likely to not develop an udder early. In the case of does who do develop an udder, you will see it steadily growing as they near delivery. In the last few days before they give birth they will begin to "bag up" in earnest, which is when their colostrum comes in full-force. If the doe's udder is stretched to capacity so that the skin is smooth and shiny and the teats obviously full, that is a good indication that she will give birth soon. Sometimes the doe's udder will also leak a bit as the udder gets too full. Don't be tempted to milk the doe before she gives birth. The teats are closed by wax plugs (unless leaking, in which case the plugs are gone) which protect the udder from bacteria that can cause mastitis. Opening the orifices before kids are nursing puts her at risk for infection. When kids begin nursing, they "strip" the teat of milk which helps the orifice close more quickly after nursing than if you simply express a bit of milk. Wait until the kids get their first helping of colostrum, and then milk a bit of the colostrum to freeze for future emergencies if the doe still has a full udder.

If you see a long, amber colored stream of gooey mucus coming from the doe's vulva or a fluid-filled bubble (amniotic sac), then the doe is in active labor. Not all does present with the stream of mucus first. In some cases, the first thing you will see may be the amniotic sac. This looks like a dark bubble filled with liquid. It may or may not burst; kids are sometimes born with the amniotic sac completely intact. In other cases, you might not see the bubble, either, because it may burst while still inside the doe. If you see hooves or a nose, that obviously means baby is about to make its appearance. Contractions are also a dead giveaway that the doe is in active labor. Some does are more stoic than others, but signs of contractions include vocalizing (especially as things get serious), visible contracting of the stomach, laying down and stretching the hind legs out behind her or arching the neck back, heavier breathing, the area around the vulva sinking in as the tail arches, and visibly pushing. The area around the vulva also becomes soft and squishy as the doe nears birth.

A Note on the "Pooch Test": *I hate to step on any toes, but I think the "pooch test" is one of the most ridiculous pregnancy predictors I have seen. It seems to pop up every year in late fall and winter. People* *on social media post pictures of their doe's vulva—and only her vulva—asking others to tell them whether she's pregnant or not based on the way her vulva looks. This is bunk. It's impossible to tell whether a doe is pregnant based on her vulva, especially early in the pregnancy. While in late pregnancy it will soften and swell a bit in preparation for stretching during birth, it doesn't change early in the pregnancy.*

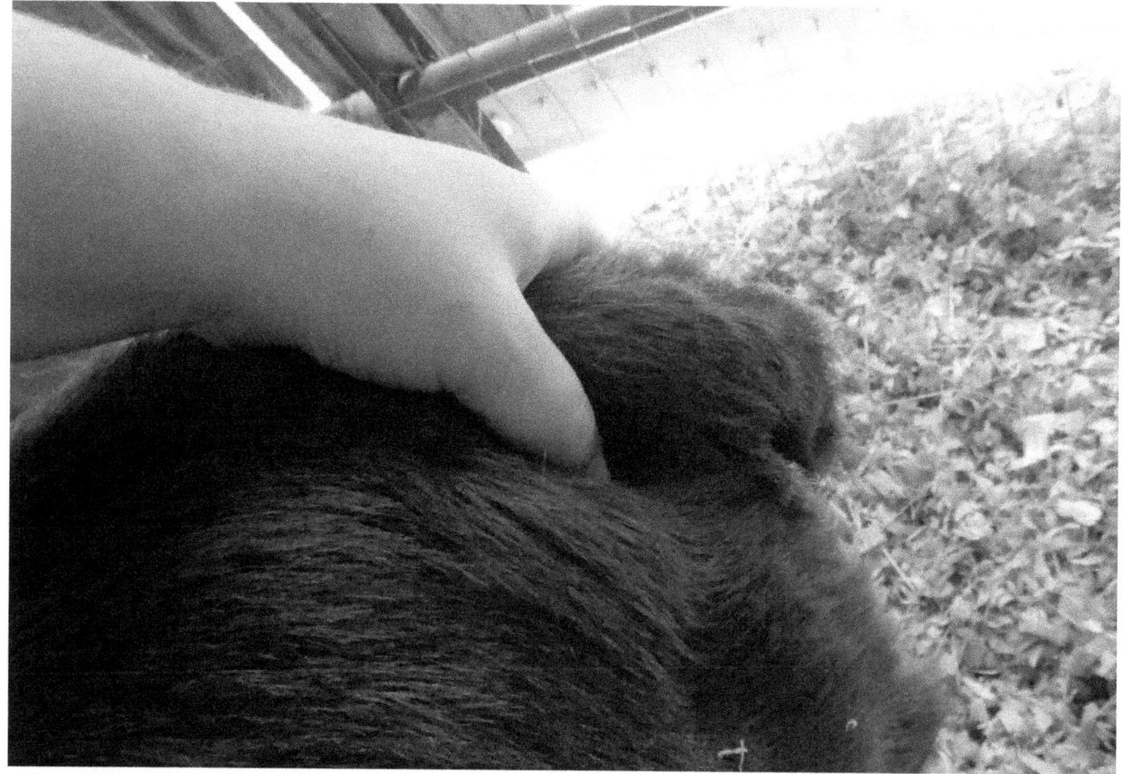

The doe in this picture kidded less than 24 hours later. As you can see, her ligaments were completely gone. The area around the tail head was soft and I could nearly wrap my hand completely around the tail head.

Normal Labor and Delivery

The early stages of labor, or "pre-labor" as it's sometimes called, can take several hours. I have sometimes waited all day long on a doe who was obviously in the early onset of labor only to have her finally get down to business well into the night. During this stage she will look uncomfortable, will likely be stretching to position kids, yawning, and otherwise showing signs of discomfort and impending birth. Patience is needed through all stages of the birthing process, because it does take some time to get things rolling. As the doe transitions into the active labor stage, you will begin to see her having contractions, which will grow more frequent over time. She might choose to stand, to lay down, or to do a bit of both. During contractions she might grunt or make noise, especially as they grow more intense. In my experience, most does don't loudly vocalize until the kids are on the way out, but this can vary from doe to doe. Some are more vocal than others, and some don't make much noise at all even during the actual birth.

If you see a bubble emerge, that means that the kid is in the birth canal and will be born very soon. In some cases, the bubble breaks before it emerges, however, so you will not always see it. It is fairly evident when a doe is pushing in earnest, though, and you know when that happens that things are getting serious and you need to stay by her side. The normal presentation of a goat kid is to emerge with the two front feet and the nose first. It is also normal for a kid to come back feet first, with the soles of the feet pointing upward. Does do not have trouble delivering kids in either of these positions, as long as the kid is not oversized (or the doe undersized). During a normal birth, the doe will constantly be making progress. This means each time she pushes in earnest the kid moves a bit further down the birth canal. Don't worry if you see a kid's nose but it isn't out yet. As long as the kid is still attached to the doe via the umbilical cord, it is getting the oxygen it needs; it's only once the cord is broken that it needs to start breathing on his own. It's also normal for a kid's tongue to be sticking out a bit as it's emerging.

Once the kid is out, the amniotic sac must be broken. This often happens naturally during the birthing process, but if it doesn't you can break it as the midwife. You can also break it as the kid emerges if desired. The doe will immediately begin to clean and lick the kid. The umbilical cord normally tears during birth, or the doe will bite and tear it herself. This is actually ideal, because tearing naturally prevents bleeding. If that doesn't happen, you can clamp the cord with forceps or dental floss and cut it below the clamp so that it doesn't bleed. Multiple kids come in quick succession, usually within thirty minutes or less. Does do sometimes have singles. You can tell if a doe is done by two things: she will pass the afterbirth, and she will stop pushing. If in doubt, you can also do a "bump" test, which involves gently lifting the doe's stomach directly in front of the udder to feel for kids. An empty stomach will feel loose and empty, whereas a stomach with a kid will feel firm or feel like there's a hard mass inside, or that something heavy has fallen into your hands as you lowered the doe's stomach. It's not a foolproof test, but it can give you a good idea. If the doe is in distress, still pushing, or appears to be in pain but no afterbirth or kids are emerging, it's time to check her.

Kids begin to stand within minutes of birth and *must* have colostrum within two hours after birth. Kids are amazingly adept at finding the udder on their own, but sometimes they need a bit of help to point them in the right direction. The doe will pass one or two placentas after giving birth, regardless of how many kids she has. You should **never** pull the afterbirth, because you can tear the doe's uterus if you do so. Remember that the placenta is attached to the uterus via the placentomes. These connections need to release before the afterbirth is expelled, and pulling prematurely on afterbirth can tear them. Each uterine horn will develop a placenta if kids are present in it. If the kid or kids are all in one side of the uterus, there will be only one placenta. If they are in both sides, there will be two. It all comes out as a gloopy, bloody mess, so unless you examine it you might not even know if there is one or two. It's completely normal for does to eat the afterbirth, but you can remove it if you are concerned (or grossed out) by the behavior. The doe will continue to bleed for about two weeks after giving birth—this is normal. However, if the discharge develops a foul odor it might be a sign of infection.

Routine Assistance

There are a few steps I take routinely in every birth even if things are going smoothly. Generally I prefer to intervene only as needed, but I also believe in giving the kids and the doe the best possible chance of success. Most of the assistance I give in a routine birth is to prevent infection and make sure the kids are clean, dry, and fed colostrum.

These are the routine steps I follow as a goat midwife:

- Break amniotic sacs and clear airways with a towel and bulb syringe/nasal aspirator.
- Help doe clean and dry kids, especially in cold weather.
- Dip umbilical cords and also clamp/cut them if they don't tear naturally.
- Help direct kids to nurse if needed. Sometimes they don't need any help, but sometimes they need just a point in the right direction or to have the teat held for them until they find it. In very stubborn or "lost" kids, I will place the teat directly in their mouth and express a small amount of colostrum.
- Dip the doe's teats in a no-reflow teat cup to prevent mastitis after labor.
- Wipe down the doe's udder and backside to clean her up a bit after birth.
- Muck out any residual mess in the stall and replace with clean bedding.

Kidding in the Cold

One challenge that can arise even in normal deliveries is kidding in extremely cold weather. Because goats naturally go through their estrus cycle in the fall, they also tend to kid from late winter through early summer. Breeds that can kid year-round, such as Nigerian Dwarfs, might also kid during any month of the year. Livestock are much more cold hardy than some people give them credit for. They grow their own substantial fur coats and adapt to the outside temperature. Under most circumstances healthy adult goats only need plenty of good hay to warm up their rumens, thawed water, and a well-ventilated shelter that blocks the wind and precipitation to do well in the winter. That said, newborn kids are not quite so well capable of withstanding extreme cold. Being born soaking wet puts them at risk for frostbite, becoming chilled, and dying from hypothermia if not found and warmed in time. Depending on how cold the weather is, they might not be able to regulate their own body temperature even after they're dry.

How cold is too cold? In my experience, completely dried kids are typically safe from hypothermia and frostbite as long as the temperature is above 32 F and they are in a dry place sheltered from the wind. Some kids will continue to be fine at lower temperatures than that as long as they are dry, but very small kids may not. Miniature breed kids, because they are so much smaller, are more prone to issues with the cold. Signs that kids are too cold include a hunched stance (this can also indicate sickness or lack of nourishment), shivering, weakness, and a cold interior of the mouth and subsequent lack of a sucking reflex. (I talk more about chilled kids and how to warm them in chapter eight.) It is vital that kids be thoroughly dried when born in temperatures of 40 F or below. If not, the dampness can cause hypothermia or frostbite on their ears and tails. Dry towels are the first line of defense against dampness, followed by a hairdryer to completely dry them when the weather is below freezing. Small kids who cannot maintain their body temperature may need to be supplemented with a heat lamp or jacket.

However, **not every kid needs a heat lamp or a jacket**. Keep in mind that both of those items are dangerous. Heat lamps cause barn and coop fires every single year. If the wires are chewed, they short or malfunction, a bulb breaks, or they fall on hay or straw, they can easily set the barn on fire. I once had a heat lamp malfunction, overheat, and kill several chicks; it was sheer luck that it didn't catch the brooder on fire as well. I always caution people against heat lamps, as they should only be used when absolutely necessary. When using a heat lamp, buy the proper kind that is designed for use with livestock. It should have a protective wire coil around the cord to prevent chewing, a secure carabiner attachment rather than a flimsy metal clamp, and a durable cage covering the bulb. Keep it off the straw and wrap the cord securely out of reach of the animals. I also use a cut wire panel to close off a corner of the barn for kids to go under the heat lamp when needed and to block the adults from coming near it and breaking it. Only use a heat lamp as long as needed, because prolonged use beyond what the kids need might suppress their ability to adapt to the cold later on.

Likewise, jackets can be a danger as well. The coats can get caught on fencing or other structures or on the limbs of other goats. This can cause the kid to become strangled if they get tangled up and cannot break free. I know of at least one breeder who lost a kid to an accident with a coat. Coats should also only be used as long as needed, as they actually press down on the fur of the kid and limit their natural insulation. The fur of livestock naturally puffs up in a process called piloerection to increases insultation. When a coat or jacket it placed over the fur it cannot erect. Kid jackets can be purchased, but you can also make your own by modifying the sleeve of a sweatshirt with holes for the front legs. Some sweaters intended for small dogs will fit baby goats as well. Coats are undeniably cute, and I've been known to slip one on a kid for a photo op, but always use caution and avoid unnecessary and long-term use. Sometimes they are lifesaving necessities, but they can be unnecessary risks when used inappropriately. I find it is human nature to baby our animals a bit more than needed, and in the long run that is only detrimental to the animals. It's important not to anthropomorphize our goats and forget that they are designed to live outdoors.

Tales from the Kidding Stall: *In my climate in southwestern Tennessee, I only rarely need to supplement kids with a heat lamp when I have does kid in the coldest months. I have also only had one experience with a chilled kid, and it was the runt of triplets—he was quite small and born in February, one of our coldest months. A quick dip in a warm bathtub followed by a session with a hairdryer fixed him right up. I avoid kidding in January and February now to minimize issues with cold. What I find funny about kids that do need heat lamps, though, is how quickly they learn that the heat lamp is warm. They will spend all their time basking in its red glow, only coming out from their protected heat lamp corner to nurse or play a bit. One of the funniest things I've seen is a group of kids all huddled under the heat lamp…while it was turned off because the weather had warmed. I have also used space heaters for kids brought onto the (enclosed, but not heated) back porch and watched them do the same thing when the heater was turned off due to warmer weather.*

Difficult Deliveries

While most deliveries will go smoothly, there are those unfortunate cases where things don't go as planned. The first rule to follow when this happens is this: **Don't Panic.** Remain calm and assess the situation. Figure out what's going wrong and what your next course of action should be. Sometimes the only help needed may be something as simple as gently pulling on a large kid as the doe pushes, while other times the best option may be to take the doe into a veterinarian's office.

How to Identify a Problem

Knowing when to step in can be as difficult as knowing what to do. It's easy to be jump the gun and think there's a problem when there isn't, but waiting too long can also result in the death of the kids or the doe. Ultimately you must trust your gut in these situations and do what you think is best, but there are a few ways to determine that something is going wrong and the doe needs help with delivery.

The key sign to watch for is progress, or rather lack thereof. If the doe is in active labor—meaning she is pushing in earnest—or if you've seen an amniotic bubble or part of a kid emerge but she isn't making any progress, it's time to check her. A doe shouldn't go more than 30 minutes of actively pushing without making any progress, and it shouldn't take more than an hour for a kid to be delivered once you've seen it emerging. That said, progress doesn't have to be dramatic to be progress. Our tendency as midwives is to want things to happen in a hurry, but they don't always do that. Sometimes progress means that over the course of a few good pushes the hooves emerge up to the ankles; that may seem like forever as you're waiting, but it's really not. Progress is progress. If a doe is taking a long time to deliver a kid, you can assist by gently pulling the kid in an out-and-down direction when the doe pushes. You should not pull when the doe isn't pushing. If the doe is actively pushing for thirty minutes or more and nothing is happening, it's time to perform a check.

It's also time to check if the doe has started labor but then stalled. If the doe was in early labor for an unusually long time and never progresses into labor, or if the doe was initially pushing but then stops pushing, labor could be stalling due to a malpresented kid or other problem. Labor should always be progressing—early labor into active labor, active labor to delivery, deliver to afterbirth. If the labor stops before reaching active labor or before delivery, something is wrong. A doe will become too tired to keep pushing if a kid is stuck. To an untrained eye it might seem that she's taking a break, but in reality, she's just not able to keep pushing because the kid isn't moving. Alternatively, if a kid is not positioned in a way that puts pressure on the cervix, the doe may not dilate and, without pressure on the cervix, may not push. This can also happen in cases of kids being stillborn, because a dead kid will not always present itself correctly for the doe. While early labor can last for several hours, it should not stop and should progress into labor. Active pushing should not stop until the doe has delivered the kid. A short break between kids with no pushing is normal but should not last very long before another kid or the afterbirth presents.

Other signs that something is wrong include an obvious malpresentation like a flat side of the body or an ear emerging first, a foul odor which may indicate uterine infection or kids that died in utero, or a doe pushing earnestly and then suddenly ceasing to push at all for over thirty minutes. There are times when you will need to trust your instincts. Sometimes we know in our gut that something is wrong even when we can't place an exact sign or symptom to the feeling. The first doe I owned to have complications presented with a bubble and then pushed for an hour with no more progress. At the time I didn't know what I was looking for. I didn't know how long to wait, or even what the amniotic bubble was, but I knew in my gut that something wasn't right. Trusting that instinct saved my doe's life, because her pelvis was too narrow for the kid to pass through.

A Note on Overzealous Intervention and "Letting Nature Take Its Course"

I have seen some people recommend to check the doe internally at every single birth. I wholeheartedly disagree with this approach, and it increases the risks of an internal infection or uterine tear for the doe for absolutely no reason. I once saw a person post online that had done an internal check on a doe because she was certain, based on the doe's stomach size, that she had given birth and the kid was missing. The doe had no outward signs of having given birth, and she hadn't been in labor at all when the owner checked her. The doe kidded on her own several days later. I have never seen a more obvious incidence of an owner panicking, jumping the gun, and doing a completely unnecessary check that could have caused complications in a doe who wasn't even in labor yet. It's also a good reminder that you can't rely on the size of a doe's stomach for pregnancy.

I am a firm believer that we should only do any kind of internal check or intervention when the doe needs it. One study found that only an average of 5% of births require any assistance. That means only five out of every 100 births on your farm should need your assistance. If you're experiencing problems more often than that, it's likely due to mineral deficiency (most likely calcium, selenium, or copper) or possibly poor genetics or improper management, specifically of diet. The other explanation would be that you are intervening too early and thereby warping the statistics by helping does that don't really need it.

Every time you go into a doe internally, even if you follow careful cleanliness protocols, you are putting her at risk for uterine infection or a uterine tear, both of which can be deadly. Every time you do an internal check beyond a finger's length of depth you are also advised to give the doe a prophylactic dose of antibiotic. If you know anything at all about antibiotic resistant bacteria, you understand that each exposure to an antibiotic increases the ability of a bacteria to adapt to become resistant to that antibiotic. In the United States, tens of thousands of people die each year and millions become sick due to antibiotic resistant bacteria. Routine use of antibiotics on your farm increases the likelihood of those antibiotics not working in the future when you desperately need them. Drug resistance is real, and it's something to be taken seriously.

Rest assured that taking a deep breath and giving your doe the opportunity to work things out on her own is generally safe. Even if a kid is stuck or malpresented, waiting for thirty minutes of no progress to pass is not going to be an automatic death sentence for your doe or the kids. I don't know of any instance where a doe has died in the middle of active labor within thirty minutes—or even an hour or two—of their owner assessing the situation or driving her to the vet.

One last reason to not intervene on every birth is that it destroys your ability to know what does in your herd are actually struggling to give birth on their own. It may seem like a doe's kid was positioned poorly or she wasn't going to be able to give birth naturally simply because you jumped in and checked before the kid achieved the appropriate position or the doe had the chance to finish labor. Kids aren't automatically in the perfect position for birth; they move into position as the doe's labor progresses. If you check early, they might simply not be done with their journey. Some positions that aren't considered "normal" can also be delivered regardless depending on the doe and the size of the kid.

It's important to have an accurate idea of which does are truly having trouble kidding. Birthing problems can be random or environmental, but they can also be genetic. I highly value a doe's ability to kid with ease on her own and care for her young with little intervention; I don't want to inadvertently breed a herd of does who routinely need help to give birth. When you internally assist on every birth unnecessarily, you have no way of knowing which births actually required help. Does with frequent trouble kidding should be culled from your breeding program, both for her own wellbeing and for the wellbeing of future generations of does. My personal rule of thumb is that any doe who needs serious assistance to give birth three times is out of my program, and any doe requiring a C-section is automatically retired.

On the other side of the coin we have the "let nature take its course" ideology. While being overzealous about checking does who are in labor is at least coming from a place of sincere care and concern, the argument that no intervention should occur in labor because "nature" should be left to its own devices is lazy and absurd. Ultimately it seems to be a gross misunderstanding of livestock husbandry at best and a justification for intentional neglect at worst. Any doe who is in need of assistance should be assisted, whether that means pulling a kid yourself, taking her to the vet, or ultimately making the decision to humanely euthanize her. Allowing a doe to suffer and die without attempting to assist the birth is needlessly cruel.

The argument to let nature take its course goes awry in a few different ways. First, nature is often cruel and brutal. In the wild, most animals die from disease, starvation, or predation rather than old age. They also sometimes die from complications of delivery or by being eaten by predators while in that vulnerable state of giving birth. Second, **your barnyard is not "nature."** I understand the desire to follow natural principals for livestock and to only keep desirable genetics in your herd, but choosing to own livestock means taking responsibility for their care. Why some people think that their responsibility somehow stops at birthing I don't quite understand. Your goats are only pregnant because you chose for them to be. They are not roaming the mountain ranges, foraging for their own food and water, and mating freely at will. They are confined in fences, rely on humans to feed and water them, and wait by the fence to the buck pen wagging their tails until you finally set them up on a date with a suitable mate. Your responsibility doesn't end there; it continues through birthing.

If a doe is having trouble kidding and you don't desire those kinds of traits in your herd, by all means cull her from your breeding program. However, culling her does not mean allowing her to suffer with an impossible delivery and ultimately die a painful death because of your own unwillingness to make difficult decisions and take responsibility. We cannot place animals in an unnatural environment and then deem that "nature" should take its course.

More than anything, I think common sense should come into play on this issue to strike a happy medium. Common sense says that not every doe needs an internal check at every birth, that a doe who does need help should be provided it, and that does with repeat issues shouldn't continue to be bred. If your doe seems to be struggling, take a step back, assess the situation, and determine a course of action. Don't prophylactically endanger your doe's health by going in when it's unnecessary, and don't do nothing when it's obvious there's a problem. Remember that your does should be your first loyalty always.

Brownie and her kids from the delivery in the Tale below, Cookie (front) and Oreo (hiding in the back). Oreo was the large kid with one leg back.

Tales from the Kidding Stall: *To give you an example of how sometimes does don't need help even when we think they do, I'll tell you about one of Brownie's kiddings. Brownie and her daughter, Sandy, were my first goats. For the first few years of owning her, I routinely missed Brownie's births. I was inexperienced, and she was sneaky. I was delighted the first time I actually knew she was in labor ahead of the birth. I waited with her all day and refused to leave her side, other than for potty breaks, for hours. This birth was only about the second or third I'd been present for, and I was hyped. Then the first kid finally came out, and true to Brownie's history, it was a big baby. Brownie's kids were always large, yet she never had any trouble giving birth to them. The sight of the kid's large head immediately worried me, though, and then I noticed that one of the legs was back. According to things I'd read, the kid was supposed to be born with both legs and a nose forward. I was certain this spelled doom.*

I leapt into action by disinfecting my hand and trying to hook the kid's leg to pull it forward. One thing you should know about the birthing process is that things get very slippery. I couldn't get a grip on the leg. What I wasn't noticing in my fervor to help was that Brownie was making progress with each push. The kid kept inching forward regardless of what I was or was not accomplishing in my attempts to assist. Before I knew it, the entire kid was out before I even came close to getting the leg forward. I was worried for nothing.

Many times, a doe will be able to give birth to a slightly abnormally presented kid, depending on the size of the kid and the size of the doe. A small doe might have struggled with a kid as large as Brownie's, and it's true that having one or both legs back can make the shoulders harder to pass for the doe as well. In many cases, though, the doe will do just fine. Don't automatically assume that a doe is in trouble based on kid position alone, unless you see a drastic malpresentation like ribs coming first or two kids trying to come at once. Abnormal birth positions are illustrated later in this chapter.

Assisting a Birth

Sometimes it's necessary to internally check or assist a doe. When that happens, you should follow a general safety protocol to help prevent infection or further complications. The first step in assisting is to clean and lubricate your hands. Although some breeders prefer to go in with bare hands, I always recommend wearing gloves. Gloves are cleaner than your hands and protect you from certain illnesses that can be passed through the amniotic fluids. Always wear gloves if you suspect the doe has any kind of illness or if the labor is preterm, and *never* assist in any birth if you are pregnant. Regardless, your hands should be clean, scrubbed with iodine solution or another obstetric-safe disinfectant, and lubricated to make the process more comfortable for the doe. Your fingernails should also be kept short to prevent scratching or tearing (not to mention that no one wants birth goo under their fingernails). I once briefly spoke to someone who had gone inside their doe without cleaning their hands and were concerned about infection. I asked why they had gone in with dirty hands, and they said they didn't have time to go inside to clean them. I'll point out once more that you typically have more time than you might think you do. If the kids are coming out quickly on their own, then you don't need to go inside the doe to assist her; if you do need to go inside then the few minutes it will take you to clean up a bit will not harm her or the kids. Always keep iodine or a similar product in your kidding kit so you'll be able to clean up in no time rather than needing to go back to your house.

In addition to keeping things clean, you should also take things slow. When repositioning or pulling kids, it's important to first know what you're feeling and not be rough on the doe. Don't rush in and start pulling without first being sure the kid is a deliverable position. Slowly feel the structure of the kid to determine where its body parts are and how it's positioned in the birth canal. Try closing your eyes and relying solely on touch if you're having trouble making things out. Feel for familiar points on the kid such as hooves, hocks, nose, ears, or tail. It can be a bit tricky at first to determine what you're touching, so stay patient and take your time. Also keep in mind that kids sometimes get tangled or try to both come out at the same time, so you might be feeling more than one kid as well. Once you've figured out what you're feeling you will need to reposition the kid if it's not in a deliverable position. In some cases, this is fairly simple and involves pulling a leg forward, but other times it can be more difficult. Sometimes a kid may even need to be pushed back into the doe to reposition—thankfully this doesn't happen often. Another problem you may run into is a kid whose body part won't stay in the correct position after you've moved it. If the leg or head keeps slipping back, use your leg snares, kid puller, or even baling twine if you're in a pinch to hold the kid in position until it's born.

Remember that you should always pull the kid only when the doe is pushing. When she takes a break between contractions, let her rest and don't pull the kid. Then when she starts pushing again, start pulling again. Kids should be pulled out and in a slight downward trajectory that follows the natural birthing path. Pull firmly, but don't try to yank or rip the kid out. Pulling with too much force might cause trauma to the doe. The only instance in which you may have to pull when the doe isn't pushing is if the doe has stopped pushing due to exhaustion or is having weak contractions. It can be a tight squeeze getting inside the doe as well, especially in smaller breeds like Nigerian Dwarfs. Make your hand as small as you can by curling it onto itself as if you were sticking your hand in the mouth of a jar that is just a bit too small. Use plenty of lubricant to ease things up as well. Slowly work your way back until you reach the kid. The contractions of the doe will also try to expel your hand, so be prepared for some squeezing.

Some does may have too small a body structure to enter—another reason to always keep structure in mind when breeding your goats. Wide, correct rumps are important for kidding season. If that happens, you can try recruiting someone with smaller hands, but if the doe is narrow it may be a lost cause completely. Sometimes the kid may simply be too big to pass through the birth canal as well, or so malpositioned that you can't reroute it correctly. Other times you might simply not feel confidant or experienced enough to assist yourself; this is completely okay and nothing to be embarrassed about. If you run into an issue you cannot correct yourself, it's time to seek help. Keep your cell phone and emergency numbers on you so that you can call in an experienced friend or your veterinarian to help you in more complex situations. Some kiddings simply can't be done and require a cesarean.

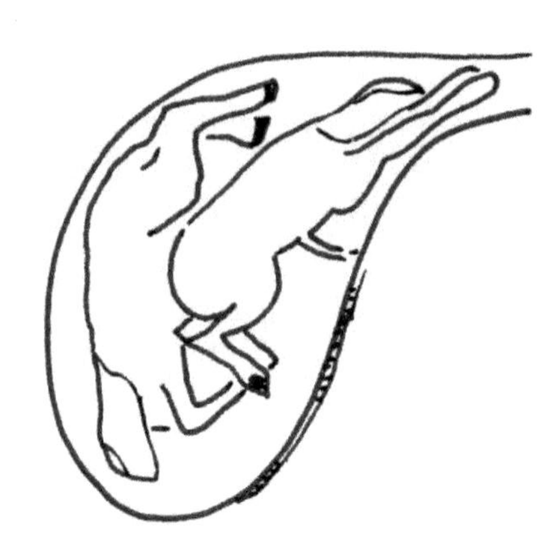

This is a normal presentation for twins. They are lining up to come one at a time.

Malpresentations

Most kids will make their way into the birth canal in a normal position, but of course there are those deliveries that do not go as planned. Below are illustrations of some possible malpresentations you might run into as well as an explanation of how you might go about correcting the position to assist the doe.

Normal "Diving" Position: Nose and one or two hooves coming first. No assistance needed unless kid is oversized or doe's pelvis is too narrow. This is the most common position.

Normal Hind Feet First Position: The kid is coming breech with hind hooves first and soles of hooves pointing upward (meaning the kid is not upside down nor coming front feet first). No assistance necessary unless the kid is too large, doe's pelvis too narrow, or the kid gets stuck with the head still inside the doe while the body is out. This is the second most common position, often seen in the second (or later) kid in multiple births.

True Breech: The kid is coming butt-first with the hind legs tucked under the body. This will feel like a solid mass with no discernable extremities other than the tail.

To assist, reach in and pull one leg forward so it is coming out first, then do the same for the other. Use leg snares to hold legs forward if needed. You may need to push the butt back into the doe to make room for the legs to be moved. Some does may be able to deliver this position without assistance.

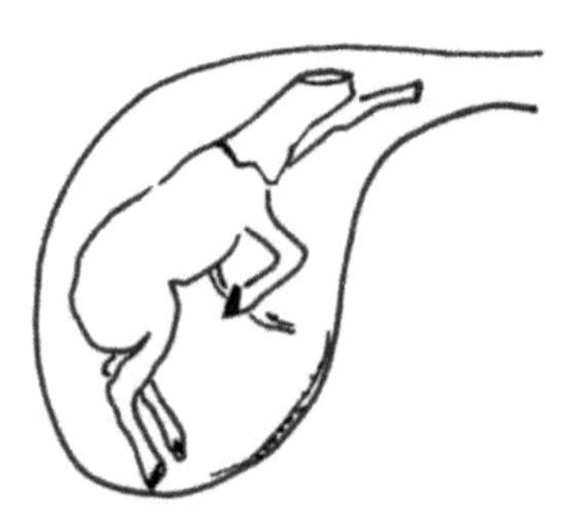

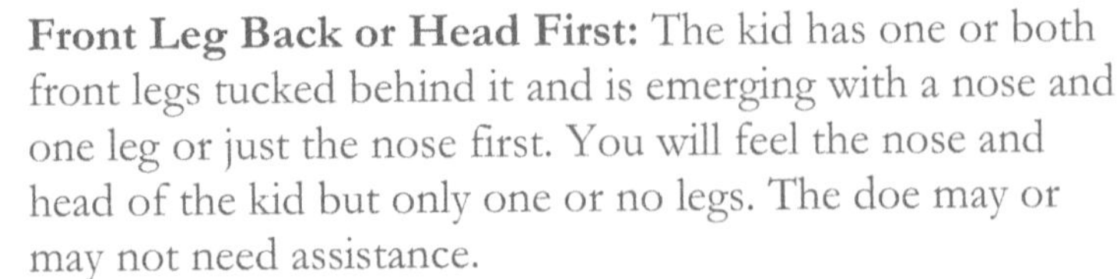

Front Leg Back or Head First: The kid has one or both front legs tucked behind it and is emerging with a nose and one leg or just the nose first. You will feel the nose and head of the kid but only one or no legs. The doe may or may not need assistance.

To assist, reach in and pull one leg forward so it is presenting with the nose, and follow suit with the other leg if both are back. Use leg snares to hold the legs in place if needed. You may need to push the kid back into the doe to create space.

Head Back: The kid is being born with its head laying back over its shoulders and the feet coming first. You will feel two front feet, the soles pointing downward, but with no head on top of them. The kid cannot be born this way.

To assist, reach in and pull the head forward so the kid is in the proper diving position. Use a leg snare or kid puller to hold the head forward if needed. You will need to push the kid back into the doe to allow space to move the head.

Tangled Kids: Two or more kids are trying to come out at the same time. They may or may not both be in a normal position. You will feel extra parts, such as three or four legs or two noses or tails at once. The kids cannot be born this way.

To assist, reach in and determine which body parts belong to which kid. Push the kid that is second in line back so that the first kid can emerge.

Hocks First: The kid is coming out with the back "elbows" presenting first, with or without the butt present as well. This feels like two sharp points in the shape of a triangle. The kid cannot be born this way.

To assist, reach in and pull one leg forward so it is coming out first, then do the same for the other. Use leg snares to hold legs forward if needed.

Upside Down: The kid is coming out upside down. In most cases hooves with soles pointing up indicate back feet, and hooves with soles pointing down indicate front feet; in an upside down birth, the opposite is true. This will feel like the soles of feet pointing up on front feet with the head below the hooves or the heels of the hind feet pointing down with the tail underneath them. The kid cannot be born this way.

To assist, reach in and slowly rotate the kid until it is in the proper upright position. You will need to push the kid back into the doe to make space for the rotation.

Stuck/Oversized Kid: The kid is too large, or the doe's pelvis too narrow, to pass through the birth canal. The kid cannot be born this way.

If it is a tight, but passable, squeeze, you can assist by firmly pulling the kid as the doe pushes and gently using your fingers and lubricant to stretch the doe. If it is impassable, the doe will require veterinary intervention and likely a cesarean.

Weird Presentations: The kid is coming out with any other incorrect body part presenting first, such as an ear or its side. These odd positions are not common. The kid cannot be born this way.

To assist, assess which body part is coming out first and reposition the kid into a normal presentation. It may be required to push the kid slightly back to reposition it.

Nightmare Malpresentation: If at any time you are overwhelmed by the situation, or the presentation of the kids is a jumbled mess, it's time to seek veterinary help. You should also seek veterinary help if the doe is not contracting well while delivering (in active delivery; weak contractions are normal during early labor), there are kids who have been dead prior to delivery (hair/skin will slip off easily, the kids may disintegrate, there may be a foul odor), or the doe appears to be hemorrhaging (indicating possibly uterine tear or placental abruption), or the doe is prolapsing. Anything that makes you think, "this is *not* good" or feel overwhelmed is grounds to seek help.

Lack of Dilation/"Ring Womb": If the kid is not putting pressure on the cervix due to a severe malpresentation, or if the doe does not release the proper hormones or is calcium deficient, the cervix may not dilate. This is very rare but does occur. If you go into the doe to check kid position due to a stalling labor and are met with a firm, closed, or partially closed cervix, the doe may be failing to dilate. Consult a veterinarian who may prescribe medication, suggest a C-section, or suggest trying to manually dilate the cervix. It's important to be *completely certain* that the doe is truly in active labor before assuming her cervix is not dilating, and manual dilation must be done gently, slowly, and with plenty of lubricant to prevent tearing or damage.

Tales from the Kidding Stall: *Sometimes a doe giving birth to multiples may have one or more kids presenting in the normal way with one or more being malpresented. Opal's birth of triplets is a good example of this. She was a first freshener and on the smaller size. She didn't have any major trouble and her triplets were small, which is always a benefit of multiple kid births. Her first two kids came out smoothly, one positioned nose and front feet first and one positioned in a normal back feet first stance. The third, however, decided to spice things up a bit. He was coming breech as well, but instead of coming with his back hooves out he was presenting hocks-first. He was also the largest kid of the litter, which was a little unusual as the first kid is often the largest, though not extremely strange or unheard of. I noticed something was wrong because Opal wasn't making progress as quickly as she had been, and although I couldn't tell what I was looking at, I knew it didn't look quite right. There was no white color of hooves and it didn't look like a nose. I cleaned up and went in to see what was wrong. As I felt the structure of the kid I finally realized the pointy knobs I was feeling were hocks. I hooked a finger behind the crook of one of the hocks and gently pulled it forward until I had a hoof coming out first, and then Opal gave a push and the kid easily slipped the rest of the way out.*

The kid on the far left was one of triplets, the two in the center were also part of a triplet litter, and the one on the far right was a single birth.

High Multiples

Some breeds, Nigerian Dwarfs in particular, are known for having high multiple litters. Typically having several single-kid deliveries points to either a mineral deficiency (if it's herd-wide) or genetic predisposition (if only happening with one doe). Some people claim that single kids are more common for first fresheners, but I have not observed a remarkable difference in birth rates between first fresheners and older does. First fresheners in my herd frequently have twins or triplets, and some of my does gave birth to four kids on their first freshening. Generally speaking, having multiple kids is a good thing. Single kids are much more likely to grow too large than kids with siblings. Having three or more kids is also not usually a problem for delivery, but of course there are always exceptions.

Two of the biggest concerns for high multiples are lack of milk and kids coming too fast for the mom to clean. Being present at the birth helps ensure no kids die because the doe couldn't clean them all quickly enough. In terms of milk production, most first time does do not produce enough milk to adequately feed more than two kids. I usually supplement kids with bottles if more than two are born to a first time doe unless she is doing very well in her production. When it comes to litters of four or more, many does will not be able to nourish that many kids—even experienced does. Part of the reason for this is milk supply, as most does do not produce high enough quantities to feed that many mouths. (There are exceptions, of course.) The other problem is bullying. Inevitably some kids will be larger or feistier than others. A doe only has two teats, and the runts of the litter are easily bullied off their dam so that they don't get their share of the milk. This leads to malnourishment, weakness, stunted growth, or death.

In some cases, a large litter might also complicate birth further if the kids are malpresented. If the kids get tangled when there are several of them it makes it more difficult to discern which kids are in what order and how they are positioned. In a badly tangled high-multiple delivery, veterinary assistance may be required.

A Normal Delivery in Pictures

Some does present long strings of mucus at the start of labor, but his doe had only a small amount.

Does will often sniff the birth fluid and show the flehmen response.

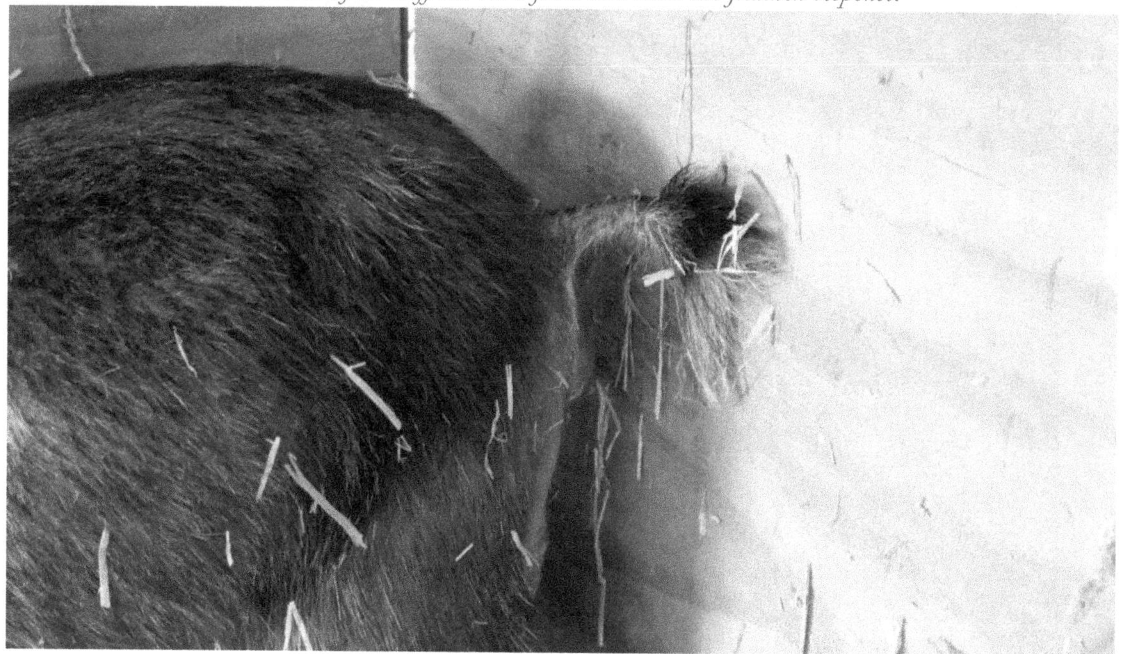

This doe is having a contraction. Note the arch in the tail head and how steep her rump has become.

Does will often stand up and down during labor. You can also see in her body language that she is uncomfortable.

Things are getting serious. The doe is obviously starting the push. Soon after she presents an amniotic sac.

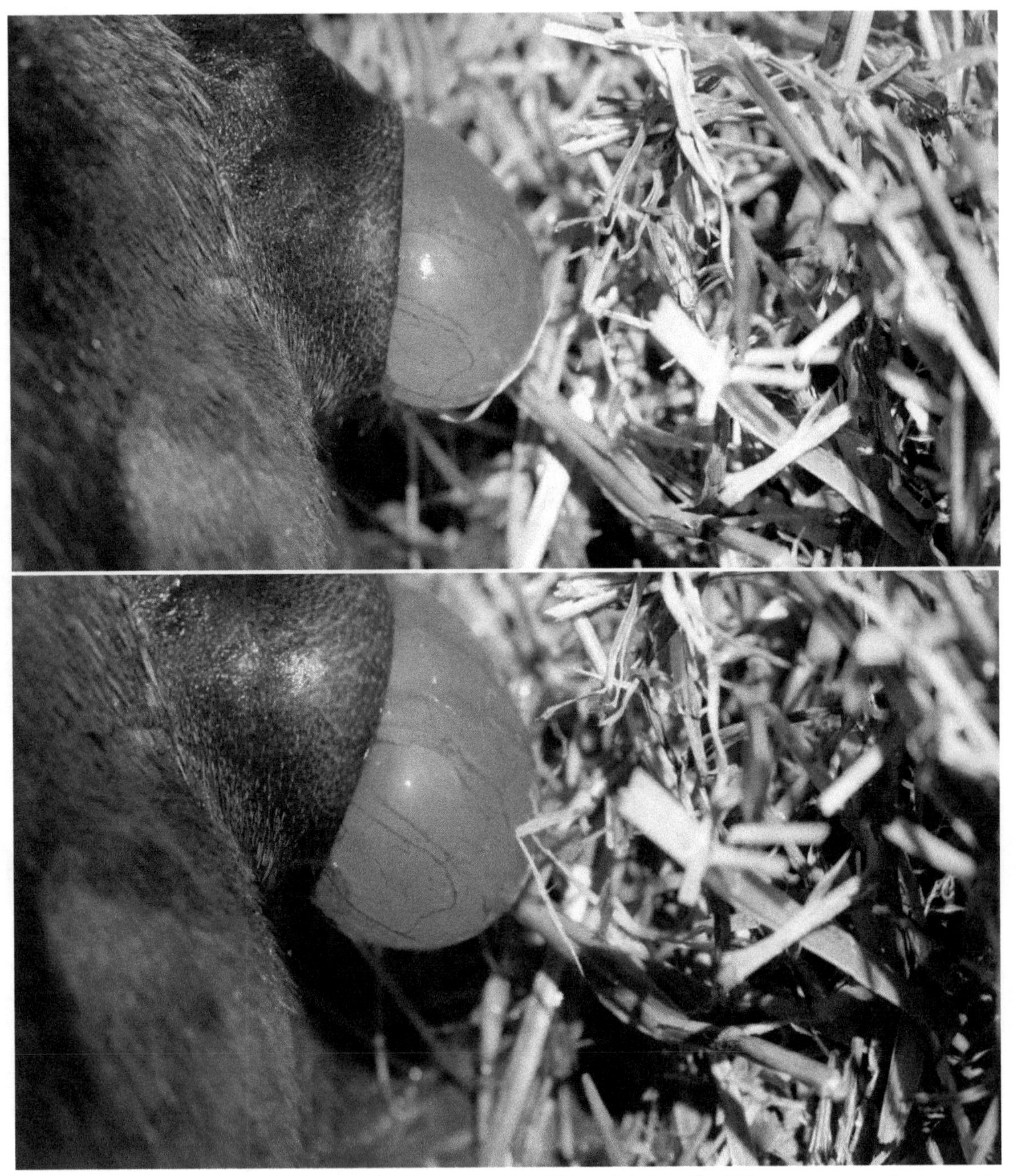

The amniotic sac continues to emerge. In some cases, it will break before the kid emerges, sometimes not at all.

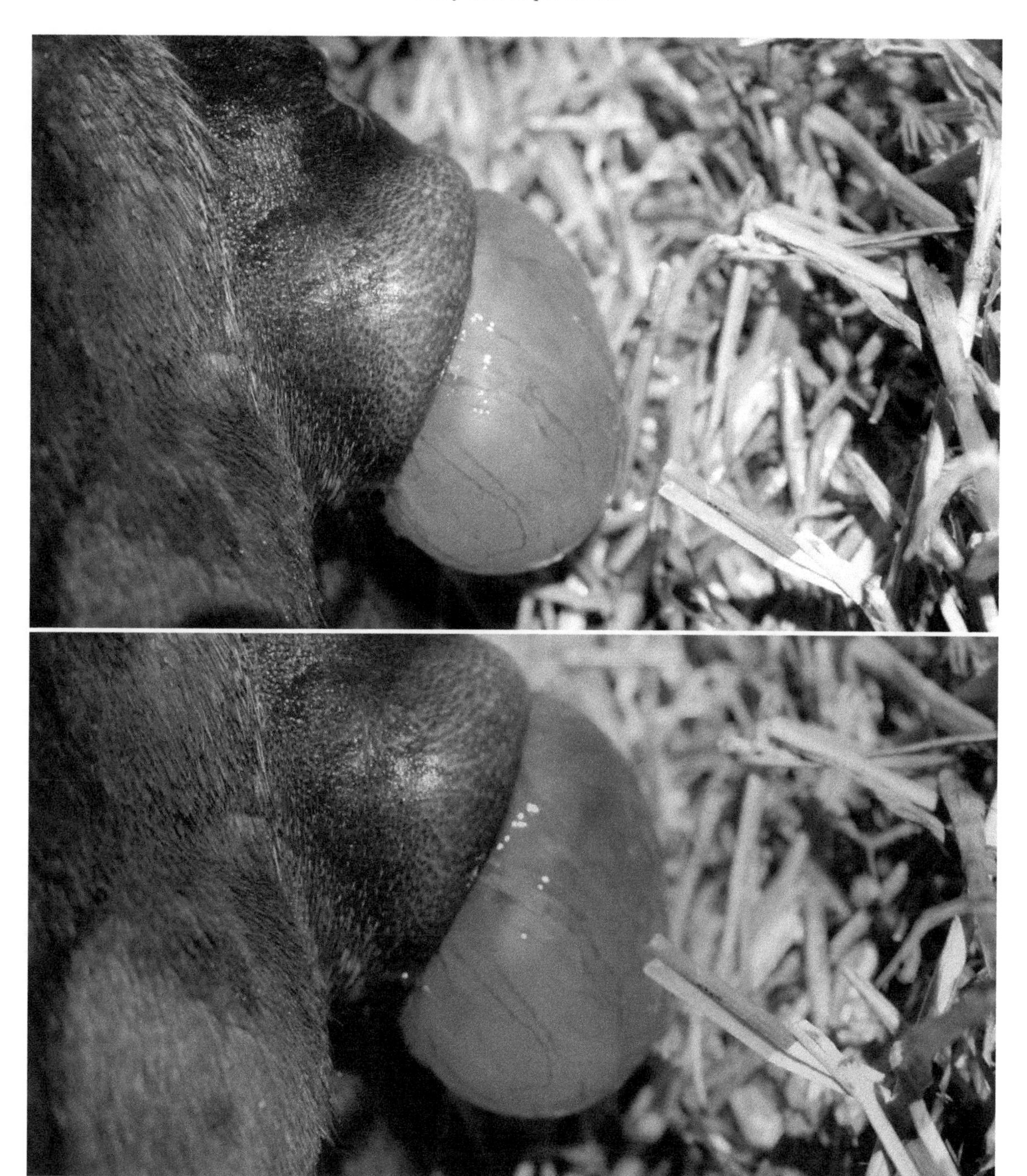

Now we can start to see parts of the kid. It can be difficult to tell what parts you're seeing before the sac breaks. At this point I break the sac myself to better see what's happening and to make it easier to clear the kid's airways after it is completely out.

Finally the kid emerges. This kid came out in a textbook nose and feet presentation. I cleared his airways and handed him to his dam.

He was followed by two sisters, and the doe cleaned everyone up.

The doe passed the afterbirth, which you can see coming out in the top picture, and the kids started nursing right away. A happy and healthy labor and delivery!

Chapter Six: After Birth

Just because the doe has given birth doesn't mean your work is over! In many ways the work has just begun. You're now responsible for ensuring the kids get the best possible start in life, and if you want milk from your dairy goats you'll be responsible for milking now, too. First let's take a look at the kids and the care they need from birth through approximately six months of age.

Newborn Kid Protocol

Immediately following birth is a good time to evaluate the newborn kids for any potential problems as well as your first opportunity to ensure they get started out on the right foot. Once everyone is clean, warm, and dry, it's time to check genders and make sure they're fed and healthy.

The Importance of Colostrum

Colostrum is the first milk produced by the doe. It is thicker and more yellow in color than normal milk, and it is only produced for the first few days after delivery. It's also the most important food your goat kids will ever consume. Colostrum is packed full of antibodies (immunoglobulins) from the doe that protect her kids from the threats of their environment. Newborns do not have a strong immune system yet; they rely on the antibodies and nutrition in colostrum to survive. It's vital for newborns to consume colostrum within the first two hours of birth. Kids are born with uniquely absorbent stomach linings that can absorb the antibodies from colostrum for only a short period of time. Their ability to absorb colostrum begins to diminish within just one hour after birth. The absorption is greatly reduced after twelve hours, and twenty-four hours after birth the window for them to absorb antibodies has closed. The chances of a kid surviving if they have not consumed colostrum within the first twenty-four hours of birth are slim.

The doe's colostrum is uniquely developed to protect her kids against threats in her specific environment. For the best possible quality of colostrum, a pregnant doe who is being sold or purchased should be moved to her new home at least two weeks, but preferably a month or more, before kidding. It's a good idea to have some colostrum in the freezer at all times to feed kids in case of an emergency, such as a doe not producing colostrum or dying during birth. Frozen colostrum can be gently warmed to body temperature and fed to kids in place of their own mothers. The first year I owned goats I purchased a half gallon of colostrum from a local cow owner from whom my family was purchasing raw milk. Cow colostrum is not as ideal as goat, but it will do in a pinch. Now I milk a bit of colostrum from my oldest does when they kid and freeze it. The older does have the best quality colostrum with the most antibodies. In a pinch, colostrum replacement gel can also be purchased for emergencies if no other options are available.

Ensuring the kids consume enough colostrum is important as well. If a kid is nursing well from the dam on its own, and each kid gets an equal turn nursing, then generally you do not have to worry that they aren't getting enough unless the doe's supply is short. For kids that are weak, do not have a strong sucking reflex, or are being bottle fed, be sure they get 10% of their body weight in colostrum or as much as they will eat. For example, a three-pound kid should consume 0.3 pounds of colostrum or 4.8 ounces. A newborn typically will not consume the full 10% at one time, so it's okay to split the meal up. Ensure that they receive 5% of their body weight in the first six hours and the remainder within 24 hours.

Newborn Kid Check

After the kids are born and all the initial care has been taken, it's time to spend a few moments observing them. Generally, if the kids are up moving around, nursing, and pooping and peeing, that's a good indication that everything is going well. Most kids will fall under this category. They'll be born normal and healthy and will be standing within minutes, nursing on their own quickly, and playing sooner than you know it. Unfortunately, some kids are not so lucky. Although rare, kids can be born with birth defects like a cleft palate or missing body part. Sometimes their anatomy isn't correct, and they may not be able to use the restroom normally—kids have been born missing their anus. It's also a good idea to check the be sure that males have two descended testicles, which will be present at birth, and that both male and female only have two teats. It's easy to check those things while the kids are little and not so squirmy.

You will also check for the sex of the kid at birth as well. It always surprises me a bit to see some of the advice given out on determining whether your new kids are boys or girls. The easiest way to check a kid is to simply lift the tail and see what's underneath, as in the picture. If there is an anus and nothing else, the kid is a buckling. If there is an anus and a vulva, the kid is a doeling. You can also check by feeling for testicles or, if you're patient enough to wait (I am not), by watching them when they urinate. Does pee by squatting and the urine flows out behind them, while bucks pee in a standing position and the urine comes out from underneath their stomach. I always end up checking under tails two or three times for each kid to be sure I'm seeing things correctly. It's possible to take a quick look under the tail and see the wrong thing, especially if your doe has kidded in the middle of the night, it's dark, and you're cold and exhausted.

It is normal for newborn kids to have soft, white-colored hooves. This is due to a protective covering of the hooves that prevent them from cutting or damaging the doe's uterus or reproductive tract. It is also completely normal for kids to have black, tarry stool for the first day or two after birth–this first stool is called the meconium. After this stage, baby goat poop becomes yellow and soft while nursing. This is normal as well and will transition to normal goat berries as the kids age and begin to eat normal food. If the stool becomes watery or diarrhea, the kid may be eating too much at one time or may have coccidiosis (see chapter eight). Usually the dam will keep the kid's bottom clean, but if she is not or if you are bottle feeding you will need to clean them up with a warm washcloth.

The kid on the left is a doeling, the kid on the right is a buckling.

A Note on Gender

Every so often the discussion of influencing gender will come up in online forums and groups. There have been many theories tossed around about ways to ensure your goats give birth to more females than males, but I have yet to find any scientific evidence of these experiments having a reliable impact. I won't go into any of those theories or recommendations, because there's no real evidence that they are effective or sound. I understand the desire to prevent the birth of excessive bucklings in favor of does, but there just isn't a good way to do it. There is emerging science in the field of sexed semen, which allows does to be artificially inseminated with semen pre-sexed to be either majority male or majority female. A study conducted in 2013 determined that sexing semen for goats is possible, and I have found at least one laboratory advertising the service, but the practice is much more expensive than standard, unsexed AI and not commonly practiced. The use of sexed semen is more prominent in cattle, but even in cattle it is still much more expensive.

The buck is the one who determines the gender of the offspring. The gender of the kid is determined by the presence of the Y chromosome which is passed on by the sire to roughly 50% of his offspring. Does only possess and can only pass on the x chromosome (xx) whereas bucks carry the Y chromosome (Yx). For every kid born you have a roughly 50% chance of it being either male or female; but of course, we know that things don't always work out that way. There is a 50/50 chance of a quarter landing on heads or tails, but it might still land on heads a dozen times in a row. Each flip of the coin resets the odds to 50%—they don't compound on each other to increase the odds of getting tails. My doe Brownie only gave me three doelings total out of ten kids before she was retired at age ten.

She had buck/doe twins, a single buck, twin bucks, twin does, and then triplet bucks. That's a 70% rate of bucklings. No one wants that, but alas, we don't get to choose. It's also worth noting that some bucks produce a higher percentage of male of female sperm, so it is possible for a buck to throw more doe kids or more buck kids throughout his life. However, it takes many, many offspring to reliably note such a predisposition. Just because a buck produced more bucklings in a single kidding season doesn't mean he will always throw more buck kids.

Another thing to consider is that the probability of getting a buckling in a litter of twins is actually 75%, not 50%, as seen by the Punnett square below. Luckily, it's 75% for getting a doeling, too, but there is only a 25% chance of the twins being either both does or both bucks. As the square below shows, you have a 25% chance for getting twin does, a 25% chance for twin bucks, and a 50% chance for getting a buck and a doe. Those odds combined equal a 75% chance at getting at least one buckling (twin bucks or buck/doe twins) and vice versa for the does. Yet again, this doesn't mean that you can expect 50% of your twin sets to necessarily be a buck doe set. Same sex twins, triplets, or even higher are not uncommon occurrences.

Male = Yx Female = xx

	Kid One Yx	Kid One xx
Kid Two Yx	Yx Yx	Yx xx
Kid Two xx	Yx xx	xx xx

Newborn Troubleshooting

Sometimes issues can arise with newborns even if the birth went well. The follow are a few things that might pop up in your newborn kids in the days following birth.

Chilled or Weak Kids

Sometimes things like a long or difficult birth or a mineral deficiency can cause problems for kids after birth. Kids may be born weak or not have a sucking reflex. You can easily check the kid's sucking reflex by sticking your finger in its mouth. A kid with a good reflex will immediately start sucking, whereas a kid with no reflex will not. Selenium deficiency can cause weak kids or kids born with retracted tendons or weak limbs. If a kid is born weak or its legs are bent at the ankle or otherwise not functioning normally, administer selenium gel (or BoSe when prescribed) and splint the legs if necessary until the tendons straighten out. Never splint legs too tightly or you can cut off circulation and damage or kill the limb. Weak kids should be assisted to get the colostrum their bodies need to survive, and if they cannot nurse from the doe or a bottle they will need to be tube fed.

If you have never tube fed a kid before, it's ideal to have a veterinarian or experienced mentor show you how to perform the procedure. There is a risk in tube feeding to accidentally place the tube in the kid's lungs instead of the stomach, as well as risk of pushing the tube too far into the kid. Before inserting the tube, measure from the mouth to approximately where you think the kid's stomach will be at the end of its last rib. Use a pen to mark that line on the tube as a reference. The kid's head should be tilted slightly back to insert the tube, and the kid should be in an upright, standing position. You will likely have to hold them in that position if they are weak. The kid should swallow the tube easily. Kids should never be tube fed if they are chilled. Always warm chilled kids first, recheck their sucking reflex, and then tube feed if needed. Colostrum should also be warm, not cold, when feeding, and should be allowed to flow using gravity by removing the plunger and holding the syringe above the kid.

Chilled kids need to be warmed quickly to prevent death from hypothermia. The finger in the mouth test is also good for checking for chilled kids, because a kid who is chilled will have a cold mouth and no suck reflex. Another good indication of a chilled kid is one who was born active and normal but is then found weak. While not the only possible cause, there is a good chance that an otherwise healthy kid who is suddenly weak has gotten chilled. Never try to feed a chilled kid, as they will not have a good suck reflex and, if tube fed, the milk will not digest properly in a cold stomach. There are a few methods of warming kids. Some people use a hair dryer blowing warm (not hot) air or hold the kid close to their own skin. I prefer immersing the kids in warm (not hot) water to warm them quickly but gently. It's important to hold the kid's head above the water to prevent them from inhaling it—they will not be strong enough to hold it upright themselves. The water should be warm to the touch but comfortable, not burning hot. Rub the kid's legs and body to stimulate circulation. As the kid warms you will be able to check their mouth again. It will be warm once more and they will have a suck reflex again once their core temperature has returned to normal. They will also visibly perk up and be able to lift their own head. After their warm bath, dry them completely and bottle feed or allow them to nurse warm milk. Kids that are not able to maintain their body heat will need additional support when returned outside such as a safely installed heat lamp or kid coat. Alternatively, you may choose to pull the chilled kid permanently and bottle feed, keeping it indoors.

Navel Ill

Navel ill, also called joint ill, results from bacteria entering at the umbilical cord and causing infection. The infection spreads through the body and causes one or more joints to swell, thus the name "joint ill." The infected joints will be inflamed, hot, swollen, and painful. They may not be able to bear weight on the limb and may not be able to stand.

Prevention of navel ill is why kid's umbilical cords are dipped at birth, and sometimes dipped daily until completely dried, as well as another reason why cleanliness is a must in the kidding stall. Treatment of joint ill requires antibiotics and is not always successful.

Rejected Kids

In some cases, a doe might reject one or more of her kids. This is more likely to happen to first fresheners than to experienced does who have given birth before. Making sure the doe is given the opportunity to clean each kid may help, but the doe might not show interest in that, either. If a doe rejects a kid, it is sometimes possible to re-establish a bond between them. First, restrain the doe and allow the kid to nurse from her. This is important for two reasons: nursing stimulates the production of oxytocin, a hormone that encourages motherly instinct and nurturing, and it also ensures that the kid will smell like the doe. Does recognize their kids by the unique smell that their milk gives them. In many cases a few forced feedings will be sufficient to make the doe accept the kid, but unfortunately sometimes it is not. If the doe continues to kick at the kid, headbutt it away, or refuse to allow it to nurse, it will need to be grafted to another doe or bottle fed.

Grafting a kid to another doe is done much the same as creating a bond between a rejected kid and its mother. The best opportunity for this to happen is immediately after the new adoptive mother has given birth when her nurturing hormones are at their peak. Applying some of the afterbirth or birthing fluids to the orphaned or rejected kid and allowing the doe to clean it can help facilitate a bond. Then, making sure the kid nurses from the doe will transition its smell to match her. In some cases, it might not be a challenge at all; I have seen some does readily allow another doe's kids to nurse without problem. Some does are more territorial about kids than others. Always be sure to never overburden a doe with more kids than she can handle. Transferring a kid to a doe who had a single is ideal, but an older doe with good milk production should be able to feed up to three kids as long as no one is being bullied off the teat. In some instances, does can feed more than three successfully, but I would not recommend grafting a kid onto a doe who is already feeding three of her own.

Some breeders have success tricking the doe's nose until the kid sufficiently smells like her by nursing as well. To do this you can use either a bit of vanilla extract or a mild essential oil such as lavender diluted in coconut oil. Rub the scent above the nose of the doe and onto the back of the kids. All the doe will be able to smell is the vanilla or lavender, and this will often facilitate bonding to the rejected or transplanted kid.

How to Tube Feed a Weak Kid

Weak kids may sometimes need to be tube fed if they are not able to nurse their dams or a bottle on their own. Follow these steps carefully to ensure the kid is tubed correctly, because mistakes in the process can cause a kid to aspirate and develop pneumonia.

1. Ensure the kid is warm and not chilled. If chilled, warm the kid in a warm bath, dry thoroughly, and check once more to see if warming has given the kid a suck reflex. If not, proceed to tubing. Never tube feed a chilled or unconscious kid.
2. Sanitize your tube feeding tools.
3. Warm your colostrum in a warm water bath. Never microwave colostrum as this will damage it and kill the antibodies. Colostrum should be tube fed at about 104 degrees F.
4. Measure your feeding tube next to the kid's body from the mouth to where you estimate the stomach should be at the end of the last rib. Mark the end by the mouth with a marker. This prevents you from inserting the tube too far or not far enough, which indicates you've gone past the stomach or have gone down the trachea, respectively.
5. Hold the kid in an upright position with the head slightly elevated as if it were standing normally. If you have no one to assist, hold the kid between your knees so that its legs dangle beneath it. Do not try to tube feed a kid that is not upright.

6. Gently feed the tube down its throat. The kid should swallow it easily, and you should be able to see the swallowing motion in its throat. You should not need to force the tube. If the kid is coughing, gagging, or violently protesting, the tube is going in the wrong place (the windpipe/trachea). A very weak or near-death kid may not react, however. The kid will be able to bleat or vocalize if tube fed correctly but will not be able to do so if the tube is in the trachea.
7. Check to be sure that the tube is in the right place. The full length of the tube to your measurement should be inserted. The kid should not be coughing or gagging. You should be able to feel the tube on the left side of the kid's throat.
8. Place the syringe with the plunger onto the feeding tube and pull back the plunger. If the tube is in the correct position it should be very difficult to pull back the plunger, and no more than one or two ccs of air should be able to fill the syringe. If the tube is in the lungs or trachea, the plunger will be easy to pull back and the syringe will fill with air. There isn't much air in the esophagus or stomach, and the pressure from the syringe will pull in the tissue and close the end of the tube, whereas the trachea and lungs will naturally have air in them and can withstand the pressure of the sucking without closing on the end of the tube. Always check this way before administering fluids to avoid drowning the kid.
9. Remove the syringe from the tube, remove the plunger, and reconnect the syringe to the tube. Hold the syringe above the kid's head and allow gravity to naturally pull the fluid into the kid's stomach. If the colostrum is very thick it might need to be thinned with a different colostrum or small amount of milk so that it will flow.
10. Do not try to feed the entire days' worth of colostrum in one feeding. Feed several smaller meals just as if the kid were bottle-feeding or nursing its dam.
11. One feeding will usually be all it takes for the kid to be able to nurse on its own. If the kid does not get strong enough to nurse after one or two tube feedings, there may be something else at play.

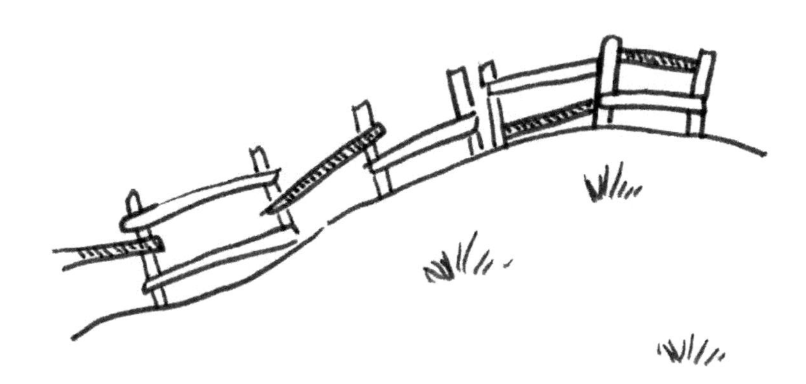

This is Granny holding a newborn goat kid. This is one of my favorite pictures of my grandmother. She raised Nubian and Saanen dairy goats before I even existed.

Dam Raising

I choose to dam raise all kids born on my farm except when it is necessary to bottle feed for the wellbeing of the kid. While some breeders choose to routinely bottle feed all kids in the name of CAE prevention (see chapter eight) or to ensure friendly kids, bottle feeding is not necessary to achieve either of those things. There are reliable blood tests now that allow you to know that your herd is CAE negative, and dam raised kids can be equally as friendly as bottle raised. My decision to dam raise is based on two main principles. First, I like to raise my animals as naturally as it is possible to do so in an unnatural environment. I believe it is healthier, psychologically and physically, for kids to be dam raised. In my experience, dam raised kids routinely grow faster and have fewer problems with health issues and parasites than bottle raised kids. Their mother's natural, raw milk, on tap free-choice is the ideal food. While kids left with the mother will nurse well into four months or more, bottle raised kids are typically weaned at three months and sometimes younger. Dam raised kids also start sampling solid food sooner, which is good for both growth and rumen development, and they also learn to better interact with the herd that they will live in. I have on more than one occasion noted bottle babies being on the lower end of the herd hierarchy when they reach maturity and less likely to fight for their spot at the hay manger. Bottle babies are what I would call "people oriented," meaning that they often seem to associate more with humans than other goats. I don't believe this is in their best interest in the long run. Overall, I prefer my kids to be raised by goats so that they learn herd dynamics, reap the benefits of their mother's milk, and generally learn to be a goat, which is something a human can't teach them.

The second reason that I prefer dam raising is about my own lifestyle rather than that of the goats. I don't enjoy the bottle baby personality in many ways. Some people prefer it, of course, but I find that they are *too* people oriented. They are more likely to cry and loudly vocalize when they see you, even from a distance, and they are more inclined to making pests of themselves by constantly being underfoot or trying to escape to find people. Bottle raised goats associate humans with food more strongly than dam raised, and that means they're constantly begging you for food (though, to be fair, the dam raised certainly do their fair share of food begging when they see you with bucket in hand). People mistake this for affection—and some of it is affection, of course—but it's largely food driven. I also do not enjoy bottle feeding, because for as cute as the bottle kids are, it takes a significant chunk of time to bottle feed kids multiple times a day and maintain their presence in your home or, alternatively, trek to the barn double the amount of times you normally would, carting bottles of milk along with you. While some don't see it this way, bottle feeding turns spending time with the kids into a chore for me rather than something relaxing and fun as it is when I spend time with dam raised kids. I also enjoy the extra freedom and convenience that dam raising allows. Leaving babies on their mothers gives you the freedom to milk only once a day in the mornings after separating the kids overnight, if desired, or to skip a day of milking if needed by leaving kids with the doe for the full 24 hours.

In addition to reducing work for the humans and stress for the goats—which occurs to dams when kids are pulled and to kids when they are reintroduced to the herd—dam raising also has a positive impact on milk production. Research has shown that allowing kids to remain with their mothers increases the milk production of the doe. Kids who are dam raised are not left with the doe all day and night to consume all of her milk but are instead separated for a period of twelve hours overnight. Does are then milked in the mornings prior to the kids nursing. Afterward, the kids are with the dams all day, drinking freely, until that night when they are separated. Typically, kids are placed in a stall nearby their dams where they can see each other but cannot nurse. Considering that milk production is a supply and demand system, allowing kids to nurse in addition to taking milk for yourself will increase the demand of milk, not decrease it. In many cases does are still milked twice daily even with kids nursing, though the evening milking will produce less due to the kids taking most of her production. Some people reverse this schedule to milk in the evenings, but personally I prefer to allow kids to be with the dams during the day. Daytime is when the kids are generally most active, and therefore they are likely to eat more often during the day than the evening.

When dam raising kids, it is still important to be sure that they are consuming enough milk. The best way to keep track of this is to weight the kids at birth and then follow up by weighing them every few days or up to a week if they are obviously growing and thriving. Goat kids should double their birth weight by two weeks old. It's also possible to notice a problem in a couple of ways. Kids who are not getting enough to eat will not grow properly; you may see one becoming a runt of the litter, for instance. I've also found that kids who are not getting enough will try to nurse much more frequently than kids who are being fed well—it might be an almost constant attempt, but the doe either will not let them or they are not satisfied after nursing due to a lack of sufficient milk. Their stomachs will feel flat and empty instead of slightly plump and full, and they will stand listlessly with their head down and back hunched. Healthy, well fed kids are active and playful. Moreover, dam raised kids who are getting enough to eat will be reluctant to take a bottle, while kids who are not getting enough will usually take it easily once they realize its food.

Making Dam Raised Kids Friendly

As I mentioned before, I don't necessarily consider bottle raised kids to be more "friendly" so much as more "people oriented" and associative of humans with food. Dam raised kids can be quite friendly, and I always prefer the personality of a friendly dam raised kid. They are easy to work with and handle, yet not constantly underfoot and in the way demanding food and attention. The main ingredient necessary to make dam raised kids friendly is simply time.

Begin spending time each day with dam raised kids from the day they're born. It doesn't require much effort to get them used to your presence. The best thing I've found to do is to simply sit in the barn with the kids. In most cases they will become curious about you and come to investigate. They'll usually climb on your legs like a jungle gym, and if it's cold they might curl up and sleep on you, too.

Doing this on a regular basis is usually enough to familiarize them with you and convince them that you're a friend rather than foe. If you're concerned that this would take too much of your time and effort, remember that bottle feeding would take just as much and likely more of your time than spending a few minutes a day with dam raised kids. If all else fails, food is the way to a goat's heart. Once the kids are old enough that they are regularly eating their dam's solid food, you can use treats such as grain or black oil sunflower seed to entice them. Many goats even enjoy things like marshmallows, peppermints, cookies, prunes, or crackers. Most goats can be swayed to accept you with time and treats. Even if you purchase a dam raised kid that is clearly wild and hasn't been worked with, you should still be able to persuade it with a little time and effort. Some goats are more naturally leery of humans than others, and some are born naturally gregarious. I respect the natural differences in personalities and don't ask that each of my goats be a social butterfly. I simply want them to be manageable. That said, for those who do want social goats, time and food is the ticket.

If all else fails and you have a wild goat on your hands, which is rare if you follow the steps above but does happen, don't despair. I've found that I am consistently able to bond with does by being at their birth and training them to milk. I no longer get stressed out about a kid or yearling that isn't interacting with me, because I know I will eventually be able to tame her when she kids. Being at the birth and being involved with her when her lovey-dovey mama hormones are flowing makes her much more receptive to accepting you in her space. I have even had previously unfriendly does lick and "groom" me after their labor thanks to those good old nurturing brain chemicals. While we may not be best friends afterward, it goes a long way toward building trust. I've also been able to train even the wildest, least-tame does to be milked without issue.

As for bucks, you might find it a relief when they are not overly friendly—it's not always nice to have a stinky, urine-soaked buck want to give you attention, nor is it necessarily safe in some instances. If given the choice between a bottle raised or dam raised male of any species—buck, ram, bull, boar—I'll always choose dam raised. Being too comfortable with people can often make intact males dangerous, because they aren't always in control of their hormones.

A Note on Mothering Instinct

I am a firm believer than mothering instincts are both genetic and learned. Mothering instinct, and natural reproductive ability in general, is one of the most valuable traits in livestock, and in my opinion the only way livestock can be sustainable on any level. While in some highly commercialized breeds it's normal for the animals to not be able to reproduce on their own, I want the livestock on my homestead to require little assistance. Of course, issues do arise, and sometimes a doe has more kids than she can feed—I don't hold this against them. However, repeated issues with kidding or an inability to properly mother a normal number of kids are grounds for a doe to be culled from my herd. I know that we can't expect total self-sufficiency from our livestock in any circumstances, but what I *can* expect is a doe who reproduces easily, gives birth with little trouble, and naturally mothers her kids. From broody hens to doting does to good mama cows, I value those instincts highly.

My rule of thumb is generally to give a doe three chances before determining that she isn't going to be an easy kidder or good mother. Having three kiddings where the birth is difficult or the doe rejects the kids is enough evidence that she does not have what it takes to be a good mother. To be a bit more specific, I do not consider minor problems part of those three strikes. For example, if I miss a birth only to find a dead kid, I don't blame the doe. It's just as likely that the kid came too fast for her to notice as it is anything to do with her mothering skills. A small deviation from the norm in kidding positions is not a big deal, assuming it doesn't cause any major issues. If a doe has such a difficult kidding that kids need to be completely repositioned, kids are getting stuck, or I have to go in farther than a finger's length, I consider that a strike. If the doe requires a C-section, that is all three strikes at once and she is never bred again.

A doe being a bad mother or not having easy births isn't an immediate indication that her doe kids will be the same way. There are plenty of reasons why an individual doe might not have luck in that department aside from poor instincts or genetics, and as we know, genes don't automatically replicate from parent to offspring. However, it can't be argued that certain traits are genetic and certain behaviors are learned. Goats learn how to be goats from living with their dams and the herd. Likewise, doelings learn about mothering by being mothered. Some of it is instinct and hormones, but I believe that not all of a goat's mothering ability can be blamed on those things alone. I have heard of goatherds that have routinely pulled all kids for bottle feeding for so long that the does largely lost the ability to mother at all after several generations of kids being raised exclusively by humans. While that is simply colloquial, I believe it is something to consider and is certainly a possibility.

Ultimately, I want to know that the does comprising my herd have strong maternal instincts and generally easy births. Selecting for those traits is important in any breeding program.

Bottle Feeding

Regardless of personal preference to dam raise or bottle feed, some kids inevitably require bottle feeding. Most often this is because the runt of a litter of three or more either does not have enough milk from the dam or is being bullied away from the milk by its larger siblings. I find that I often have to bottle feed the smallest of litters of triplets or more due to one sibling being a runt, and when goats give birth to four or more they may not be able to feed all of them depending on their age and production. In some cases, even with twins or singles, the mother may not produce enough milk due to health issues, reject the kids, or pass away from labor or postpartum complications. Whatever the reason, these kids now become your responsibility, and you act as their mother.

My dad leading two bottle babies and my Pomeranian, Lucky, to the barn.

Training a kid to a bottle is usually not difficult when the kid is still young or if it has not been getting enough milk and is hungry. The best way I've found to teach them is to force the nipple into their mouth and squeeze out a bit of milk. Usually they start to nibble a bit at the nipple, and once they realize it's a food source they will begin to nurse. Older kids who have already become accustomed to nursing from the dam are usually more difficult to train. The bottle is foreign to them, and they know it's not the same as their mother's udder. Beware of buying bottle kids from other people; be sure that the breeder has started bottle feeding the kids themselves. In some instances, breeders have sold "bottle kids" who were nursing their dam up until the point of being sold. It can be a big challenge to train those kids to the bottle, and it also places them under a lot of stress—not to mention the stress to the new, possibly inexperienced owner.

Newborn kids placed directly on the bottle should receive at least 10% of their body weight in colostrum, or as much as they will eat. They most likely will not be able to consume the entire 10% all at once but ensure that they get at least 5% in the first six hours and the remaining 5% within the first 24 hours. Ideally, they should receive their first dose within the first two hours, but receiving colostrum within the first 24 hours is critical to survival. Kids can consume as much colostrum as they will eat in the first 24 hours. After that they can be transitioned to regular milk. Kids can be fed goat milk or whole fat cow milk. I see people giving all kinds of recipes for kid milk, but I have always bottle fed with whole cow milk with no problems. The composition of cow milk and goat milk is similar enough in nature that it doesn't cause any problems. (See chapter seven for more on that.) I don't recommend using store bought formula, as it is known to cause digestive upset and failure to thrive in goat kids. While formula works in some situations, it is not the ideal food and can and does cause problems. I have never seen a goat kid suffer any ill side effects from whole cow milk, but I have frequently seen people seeking help for kids struggling with replacer. For reasons as yet unknown, goat kids simply don't do as well on formula.

Kids need to eat four or five small meals a day for the first two weeks of life. Usually it is not an issue for them to go about eight hours overnight without eating even as newborns, but particularly tiny kids or weak kids may need to be fed overnight. I do not measure out specific amounts of milk for the younger kids, but instead allow them to slowly increase their intake on their own as they grow. After two weeks of age, kids can be moved to three slightly larger meals instead of four. I do begin measuring the milk as kids reach about one month of age, primarily to prevent them from getting digestive upset from consuming too much too quickly. For Nigerians I give about 32 ounces of a milk a day and standards around 45 ounces per day. They can consume more than this, and some breeders allow their kids to free feed as much as they want, but it's important to increase their meals slowly so they don't eat too much too quickly. As they reach one month of age I also begin to transition them to twice daily meals. This is done by slowly increasing the feeding amounts at the morning and evening meals and decreasing the midday meal. Never make any kind of feed changes suddenly.

Eating too much at one time can cause scours (diarrhea) or, in a worst-case scenario, enterotoxemia. Very young kids typically don't gorge themselves on food and may take a break in the middle of eating before they're truly done. As the kids grow, however, they can and will overeat. You can prevent this by measuring out their max feeding; feeding more frequent, smaller meals; and watching for physical signs that they're eating too much. As they eat the kids' stomachs will visibly fill, and you will be able to see it getting too distended if they're overeating. I've also seen kids eat so much they start to breathe more heavily than usual (not unlike me after Thanksgiving dinner), and this is a sure sign they've downed too much milk too quickly. (Overeating isn't something you need to be concerned about with dam raised kids, because they eat frequent, small meals throughout the day.) The milk should be about body temperature for the goats so as not to burn their mouths. I heat my milk either to about 100 degrees F or until it is warm, but not too hot to touch, when dribbled on the inside of my wrist.

I have used a few different methods of feeding with success, including pritchard nipples (small red nipples designed for lamb and goat kids) attached to clean bottles, pritchard nipples on a bulk bucket feeder designed to feed multiple kids at once, human baby bottles and nipples designed for newborns, and rubber or latex lamb nipples. I prefer individual bottles when only feeding a few kids, but the bucket feeder is nice for larger groups of kids. One thing to be careful about with the bulk feeder is making sure that all the kids are getting their fair share. Usually kids will stick to one nipple once they're attached, but if some kids are dominating the bucket feeder and sucking down the milk faster than others the "runts" may still not get enough, in which case you should remove the large kids after they've had their fair share and let the slow eaters finish up. Even with bulk feeding I find it isn't hard to tell when a kid has eaten its fill, even if it keeps trying to gorge itself. Their sides will extend as their bellies get full and they will slow down nursing, even if they don't stop completely. They may also take a short break and then go back in for more; sometimes they need more, sometimes they don't. Lambar systems can also be set up with individual bottles so that multiple kids can be fed at once while still measuring individual meals. These can be purchased of built.

Kids should be allowed to continue nursing for a bare minimum of two months, with three months being better and a bit longer being ideal. If you watch the does in your herd, you will see that many does do not completely wean their kids until they around six months old. Allowing them to consume milk longer will result in better growth and general well-being. Monitor kids' growth and weight gain to ensure that they are consuming enough milk.

Note: Do not allow bottle kids to drink their milk from a bowl. The milk is intended to bypass the rumen and enter directly into the abomasum. This is achieved by a valve which closes over the entrance to the rumen when the kid's head and neck are in the nursing position. The valve opens when the kids head is lowered.

Weaning

I never wean my dam raised doe or wether kids unless selling them. Instead, I let the dam decide when her kids are cut off the tap, which usually starts around three to six months depending on the temperament of the doe. If you see the doe walk away from younger kids or kick them off after only a short time, don't assume she's weaning them prematurely. Does typically don't stand still and let their kids nurse to their hearts' content, but instead allow them small meals frequently throughout the day. I attribute this easy access, long-term nursing from the dam to the improved fortitude and growth I see in dam raised kids over bottle babies. However, when it comes to buck kids, sold kids, and bottle kids, weaning time eventually rolls around and we have to stop them from nursing.

Buck kids, especially the fast-maturing and year-round breeding Nigerian buck kids, can become sexually mature as early as two months of age. It is around this time that dam raised buck kids are usually pulled from their mother to prevent accidental breeding of dams or sisters. Bottle kids are typically weaned around three months of age, but some people choose to bottle feed for a longer period of time to more closely replicate the feeding the kids would be getting from their mother. In both cases it's important to be sure that the kids are successfully eating solid food before milk is taken away from them completely. In dam raised kids this usually isn't a problem, as they imitate their mothers and start eating solid food early on, but in bottle raised kids there is sometimes a delay in transitioning to solid food.

Weaning buck kids off of the dam is usually done cold turkey. This means when the buck kids start to act a bit too, ahem, *amorous* toward the does, they are separated from their mothers and placed in an enclosed area with other buck kids. They might yell for their dams for the first few days, but it usually dies down quickly—and sometimes they don't yell at all. When weaning bottle babies, the process can be done more gently and slowly. To start the weaning process, I start to decrease one of the feedings a bit each day until they're no longer receiving it at all. Then I will repeat the process with the remaining feeding by decreasing it until eventually there's such a small amount of milk left that it's nominal, and I stop feeding them milk all together. By adjusting their milk intake slowly, it increases their solid food consumption gradually as well and lessens the chances of digestive upset from weaning. It also helps slow down their desire to yell and beg for food every time they see you, because over time you have stopped bringing them food each time you appear. (Though in my experience they will continue to yell for some time even after being weaned, with some bottle babies still being quite vocal even as adults.)

Disbudding

Before we discuss the *how* of disbudding, I want to discuss the *why* and debunk the reasons some people use to not disbud. First time goat owners are often intimidated by disbudding. The process is foreign to them, and it seems daunting. I also see a lot of misgivings about the process because it is—momentarily—painful for the kids. Some goat owners choose not to disbud at all. While I obviously cannot control what others do with their goats (nor would I want to), I do believe that disbudding is the best option and try to educate new breeders on the virtues of disbudding and the dangers of horns. First, I want to discuss the reasons dairy goats are disbudded, then I will dive into the instructions for how to disbud your goat kids.

If you're not familiar with this terminology, to disbud means to remove the horn growth bud in goat kids so that the horns do not grow. This is done in a matter of literal seconds with a (very, very) hot iron. The iron not only kills the horn bud, it also cauterizes the area so that there is no bleeding and little risk of infection. The entire process only lasts for a few seconds, has a very low risk of complications when done correctly, and has no lasting effects other than the prevention of horn growth. Immediately after disbudding, baby goats are back to nursing mom or downing a bottle as if nothing has happened. Although the process is stressful for the kids in the moment, it is not something that causes any kind of lasting trauma. Occasionally mild localized swelling occurs, but even this is rare.

Goat Safety

The two biggest reasons to disbud are human safety and goat safety. Let's talk about the goats first. Horns are dangerous for the goat who has them, first and foremost. Horns can and do get stuck in fences, hung in hay feeders, or injured in any number of ways. It's common to hear about horned goats who have gotten their heads stuck in fencing and been injured or killed because of it. A woman my family bought raw milk from before owning our own dairy animals lost a goat when it got its head hung in the fence and was killed by stray dogs. Goats will stick their heads anywhere, and unfortunately, they don't know to dip the ends of their horns down to pass back through the hole without getting caught. I once had a disbudded, hornless goat manage to get her head stuck in a safe, well-designed hay manger, so I can only imagine the frequent trouble horned goats must get into. Considering how curious goats are, horns are simply an added liability.

Another problem with horns is their ability to be injured. One of my longest family friends owned a horned Pygmy buck whose horn was kicked off by horse, resulting in a painful, open wound and a lot of blood. Goats can break off their horns in fights with other goats or, like in the example above, by being injured by another animal. Although horns are inarguably quite strong, they are not immune to injury or breakage. Horns are vascular, so when they are broken they bleed profusely. In addition, the horns of a mature goat also open into the goat's frontal sinus cavities. Injuries to adult horns are painful, bloody, and risk serious infection.

Horns are a menace to other goats as well. When you watch goats interact, you will see them frequently headbutt each other. Sometimes this is a straight hit to the side, while other times you'll see them jerk their head back and up, a move that, if there are horns involved, could easily hook another goat with the tip of the horn. I have also frequently seen goats hit underneath another goat in the escutcheon area where the udder is and lift the other goat's backside up and away from whatever the offending goat wanted. In horned goats, these kinds of normal behaviors are a recipe for disaster and are how udders get ripped open and trauma-miscarriages are caused.

Human Safety

Human safety is also put at risk from horns. One thing that people don't often realize about livestock in general is that they don't have to be demonstrating aggressive behavior to cause injury. Because they are much tougher than humans, and we are comparatively delicate, we can easily be injured by our livestock completely by accident. I have been on the receiving end of a headbutt from a goat who was aiming at another goat, and I'm quite thankful that the goat who hit me did not have horns. Dairy goat owners work with our goats closely every day. This puts us in the line of fire for horn injuries. It doesn't have to be a goat that headbutts you; it can be a goat that simply moves the wrong way at the wrong time and hits you in the wrong place, like the face, the eyes, the chest, or what have you.

When we are bent over our goats to administer copper boluses, give a vaccine, draw blood, trim hooves, or any number of other things, we are within easy striking distance of their heads. I have held enough thrashing goats (even friendly goats do not like being restrained) to know that I don't want one with horns thrashing around me. When straddling a goat to restrain it, they often whip their head up and back in an effort to break free of the restraint. That is a recipe for disaster for a goat with horns. Worse yet, horns on dairy goats are at perfect eye level for young children. It can take only seconds for a child to move the wrong way and get stabbed by a horn, or for a goat to move the wrong way and stab a child.

Tales from the Kidding Stall: *As an example of how livestock can injure you quite by accident, let me tell you about my mom's LaManchas. I was around three or four years old at the time, and my mother owned two young LaMancha goats. One day she was working with her horse in the barnyard and I was playing nearby on the porch with the LaManchas. I bent down to look at something, and one of the goats jumped on my back. I fell headfirst into the concrete and started wailing, as children do. My mother rushed over to pick me up, and I promptly lost consciousness. Whether I fainted or was knocked out we can't be sure, but I prefer the latter because it sounds much more interesting to say, "I was knocked out by a goat." We went to the hospital and I was deemed totally fine with no concussion. Still, it's important to remember to always be careful with livestock, especially with children.*

If you look closely at these pictures you will see how the doe second from the left is butting a smaller black doe right in the area of the udder and lifting her up in the air. If the younger doe was in milk and the dominant doe had horns, this would spell disaster. This is very normal goat behavior.

Showing

Registered dairy goats cannot participate in shows if they have horns. All of the primary dairy goat registries in the U.S. require that goats be hornless for showing purposes. This includes the American Dairy Goat Association, the American Goat Society, breed specific registries, and the mini registries (The Miniature Dairy Goat Association and The Miniature Goat Registry). 4-H also does not allow dairy goats with horns to be shown. This is for the safety of the other goats and the humans involved. Although horned goats may still be registered and participate in production testing and awards, they will not be able to participate in sanctioned shows.

Dairy Infrastructure

The infrastructure we use for dairy goats does not work well with horns. While goats in the wild roam freely, away from anything like fences or barns or close quarters, that is not the case for dairy goats in captivity. Each day goats in milk must be brought into the milking room or barn, placed in a stanchion, and milked. They also eat out of hay racks and are housed in fencing, both of which horns can become caught in, as already mentioned. Horns do not fit well into milking stands and special accommodations must be set up to fit them. This causes increased cost and complicates the milking routine, especially considering that almost all herds will contain at least some hornless goats due to disbudding or the polled gene unless carefully curated to be completely horned. Considering that most serious dairy breeders will not withhold disbudding of kids for a buyer, choosing to only purchase horned goats so that the same milking setup will accommodate all goats in the herd will greatly limit your access to top quality genetics.

Marketability and Future Wellbeing

The last thing to consider is the marketability and future wellbeing of horned goats. The market for dairy goats with horns is drastically lower than those that are disbudded, for all the reasons listed above. Assuming you do find homes for horned kids, there is also the concern about the future care of a horned goat. While you may have chosen to keep all of your fencing, barn, and other structures on your farm horn-appropriate, future buyers may not. The lower value of horned goats also means that the goat may get passed around to the types of buyers you likely would not want to own your goats—the ones who just want something cheap and pay no attention to it afterward.

There's also a chance that someone down the line will decide they do not want the goat to be horned anymore. The methods of removing horns from adult goats are much more stressful and dangerous than disbudding. Horns can be banded by castration bands, which results in the horn slowly dying and finally falling off. I have done this before myself, but I don't prefer the method and would much rather disbud. As the horns weaken they may get knocked off and bleed (albeit less than a broken intact horn), and they can also become painful before they are fully removed. The other option is to have a veterinarian surgically remove the horns, and this is a major surgery and not a better option than banding the horns in my opinion. Goats do not always do well under anesthesia, and the surgery results in the front sinuses of the goat being open, providing an entryway for bacteria.

Dispelling Misconceptions

Goats are not disbudded for aesthetic reasons. I'm not sure where that idea comes from, because I can't imagine going through the trouble of disbudding just because you prefer the way it looks—nor would any serious dairy farmer make major decisions based on aesthetics alone. I did a little research, and the earliest mention of removing the horns of cows (where the practice began) in the U.S. that I could personally find was in a journal called *Bulletin of the Agricultural Experiment Station of the University of Tennessee* published in 1888. At that time the disbudding iron had not yet been invented (the electric light bulb was less than ten years old!), and cattle were being dehorned by restraining them and sawing off the horns. It was not an easy or pleasant task, and certainly not something farmers did to make the cows prettier.

One of my pet peeves is the argument that horns can protect goats from predators. It simply isn't true. While I won't say that no goat in the history of the world has used its horns to headbutt a predator, I will say that horns are not a viable prevention or line of defense against predators. First of all, horns are not designed as a defense mechanism. Goats are a prey species. When they can, they will always choose to run away from a predator to evade it. When cornered they may try to fight, but it will not ultimately save them in most circumstances. I have seen too many pictures of horned goats killed by predators to ever think that horns would do an ounce of good against a determined predator. When considering that horned and antlered animals in the wild are frequently killed by predators such as coyotes, wolves, bears, and mountain lions, it becomes abundantly clear that our domestic goats do not stand a chance. Packs of loose dogs, coyotes, big cats, and what have you are all equipped and capable of taking down prey much larger than themselves, with or without horns.

Horns are not necessary for heat regulation. Horns are vascular, which means they are capable of giving off heat. In fact, research has shown that goats from desert climates have larger horns with a thinner outer layer that allows for greater release of heat, while goats from more temperate climates have smaller, thicker horns that restrict heat release. However, goats do not need their horns to survive hot weather. If goats needed horns to survive heat, then polled and disbudded goats (and other natural polled breeds of cattle or sheep) would be dropping dead across the country in the summer. Naturally polled (hornless) goats should not exist if the horns were necessary to live in the heat, because the goats without horns would not have been able to reproduce that gene if they were dying from heat exhaustion.

Another aspect that often escapes consideration is the opposite side of the same coin: horns also distribute heat in the cold winter weather as well. While there is evidence that horns can vasoconstrict to reduce the heat released, it cannot be cut off completely. Research has even been done studying the energetic cost of large horns in livestock in colder temperatures. So, while those horns may let off a bit of heat in the summer, they're also letting heat out in the winter, too.

Some people believe that disbudding is cruel or mean to the goat kids. In reality, it's much crueler to allow a goat to get its head stuck in a fence and be killed by dogs, or to allow a goat to have its horn kicked off, or to get trapped and strangle, or to have its udder ripped open by horns, and so on. I'm not accusing people who have had these kinds of things happen of knowingly allowing their goats to suffer—accidents happen to all of us with or without horns. What I'm pointing out is that the risks of having horns are greater than the discomfort of a few seconds of disbudding.

As I mentioned earlier, disbudding done properly is extremely low risk and takes a total time of a few seconds. Thousands of goat kids are disbudded each year with no issues or problems. In my experience, the kids complain just as much or more about being restrained and having their heads shaved as they do being disbudded. Disbudding is not the only thing we do to livestock (and other domesticated animals) that causes a short period of pain and discomfort. Things like castration, tattooing (or ear tagging or branding, as is done in cattle), giving a shot of medication, and so on all cause a level of pain. We also routinely spay and neuter our dogs and cats; this requires anesthesia and surgery (major abdominal surgery for spaying) and is not only is stressful and painful for the animals but also carries a risk of complications or even death. My family lost a cat due to a routine spay surgery, for example. Likewise, some research shows that spaying and neutering dogs, especially at a young age, increases their risks of joint issues and certain other health problems down the road. Comparatively, disbudding is a much faster procedure with low risks and no negative long-term effects when done properly. Personally, I've observed more lasting discomfort in castrated male livestock than I do in disbudded kids.

Ultimately, we do these things because the long-term benefits outweigh the short-term discomfort that the goats will not even remember later in life. The same can be said for disbudding. A few seconds of discomfort is a worthy trade for a lifetime of increased safety and wellbeing.

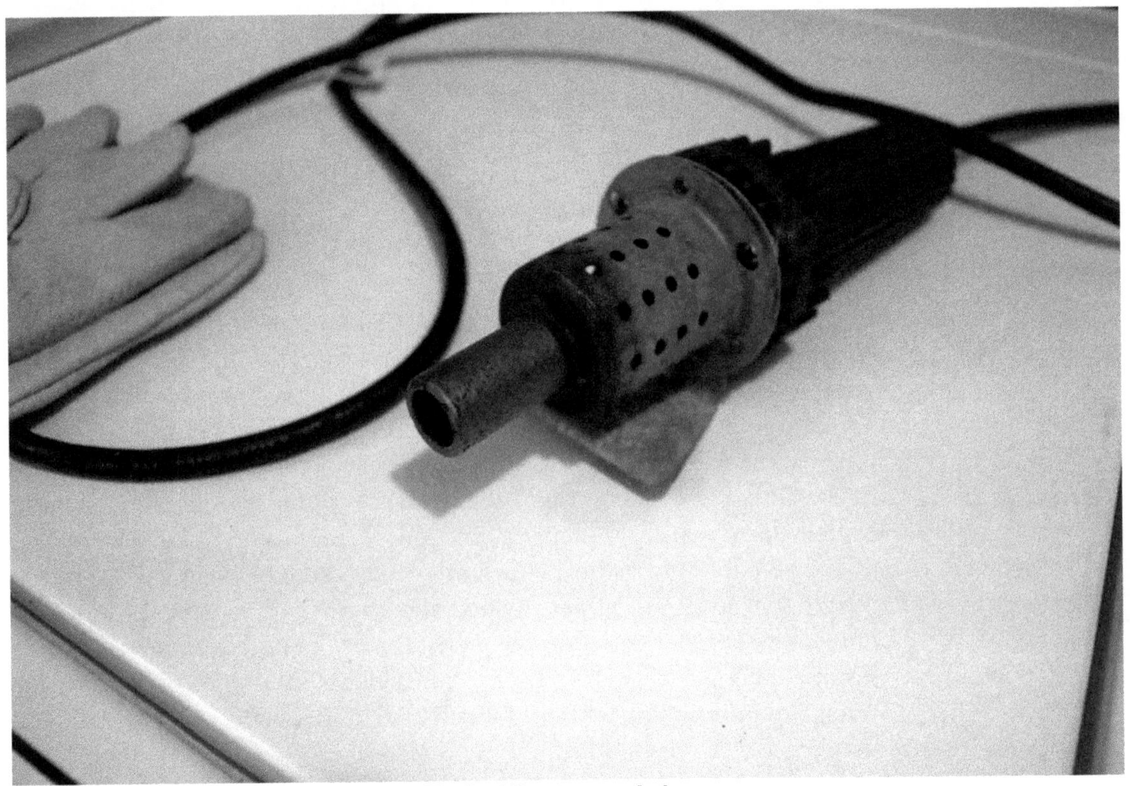

Disbudding iron and gloves.

How to Disbud

Disbudding requires the use of a specially designed electric iron with a cylindrical tip that goes over the horn bud to kill the growth bud and cauterize the wound with no loss of blood. As mentioned before, disbudding is an incredibly short process. It generally takes only about ten seconds total per horn bud. The entire process usually takes about two minutes or so per kid, because frequent breaks are provided to allow the iron to maintain the appropriate heat level and to give the kids a break. The maximum time I hold the iron to the kid's horn bud at one time is five seconds. For smaller kids, I will do a count of three seconds. For larger buck kids I will count to five. After my count, I break for a few seconds and blow on the kid's head. It is also important to allow the iron to rest for a couple of minutes in between kids to allow it to reheat back to its maximum heat. The hotter the iron, the less time it takes to disbud and the faster the kid is happily nursing from its mother (or bottle) once more.

It's important to wear thick leather gloves while disbudding to avoid burning yourself with the iron. It's also a good idea to have an experienced breeder show you the disbudding process if possible before attempting it yourself. Seeing the process done is quite helpful. I advise to find a breeder to show you, or disbud your first kids for you, rather than a veterinarian. While most vets are familiar with the process, they do not practice it nearly as frequently as a breeder. A vet may disbud only a few—or even zero—kids in a given year, whereas a breeder will be disbudding several (possibly dozens or even a hundred or more) kids each year. I will also mention that many veterinarians do not have much experience with goats in general, simply because they are not as common or as profitable as animals like cows, horses, dogs, or cats. Some people unfortunately cannot find vets experienced with goats at all in their area.

I will offer a word of caution on disbudding as well. First, be sure to only use a disbudding iron with a tip for goat kids, not calves. The calf tip is far too large for goat kids and can cause injury. I use the Rhinehart X30 with a ½" tip. The smaller pygmy tip is not large enough. Don't skimp on choosing a good iron, because a higher quality iron will heat faster and stay hot longer, resulting in a shorter disbudding process and lower likelihood of scurs. Also, do not hold the tip on the kid's head for longer than five seconds, because prolonged exposure may also cause the kid to overheat. Be sure to also allow the iron plenty of time to reheat between jobs, because a cool iron will not work as well and will cause scurs. I like to rest the iron about five minutes between kids and check its heat on a piece of scrap wood. Lastly, do not use caustic disbudding paste for goats. Not only is it not effective for goats, but it is also dangerous. The paste takes several minutes to "work," and if the kids are released they can rub it on their ears, in their eyes, on their dam's udder, your own skin, etc. Paste is not an effective or safe method to disbud goat kids.

Kids are disbudded between three days and two weeks of age, and the earlier they are done the better. Disbudding should take place as soon as the horn bud becomes apparent.

The smaller the bud is at the time of disbudding, the less time it takes, and the less likely scurs are to develop. I will hold back the tiniest kids from disbudding for a few days to allow them to grow, but I never wait longer than two weeks. I also don't recommend disbudding kids if they are ill or weak; wait for a full recovery before disbudding. Most kids are ready to be disbudded when their horn buds emerge. The disbudding iron cauterizes the area, so there is no bleeding and no need to use antiseptic. Kids should be securely restrained before disbudding to prevent them jerking and causing you to hit yourself or the wrong part of the kid with the hot iron. Many people use a disbudding box to restrain them; these can be purchased or made by yourself. In addition, a pair of socks with the toes cut off can hold back the ears for you to keep them out of the way and prevent them accidently hitting the iron. Don't be alarmed: Kids will likely yell when restrained and sometimes when being shaved. They will also yell when being disbudded, but this stop when the iron is removed. I've also had kids stop yelling after the first couple of seconds of the iron after it has killed off the nerves in the area. Below, follow along the step by step guide for disbudding.

1. Preheat the iron for about 30 minutes or so until it is red hot. Test it on a piece of scrap wood to be sure it is ready—it should easily burn a solid ring in the wood.
2. Shave the kid's head. Shaving the head allows you to clearly see the horn buds and helps reduce smoke. Burning hair creates a horrible odor and a large amount of smoke.

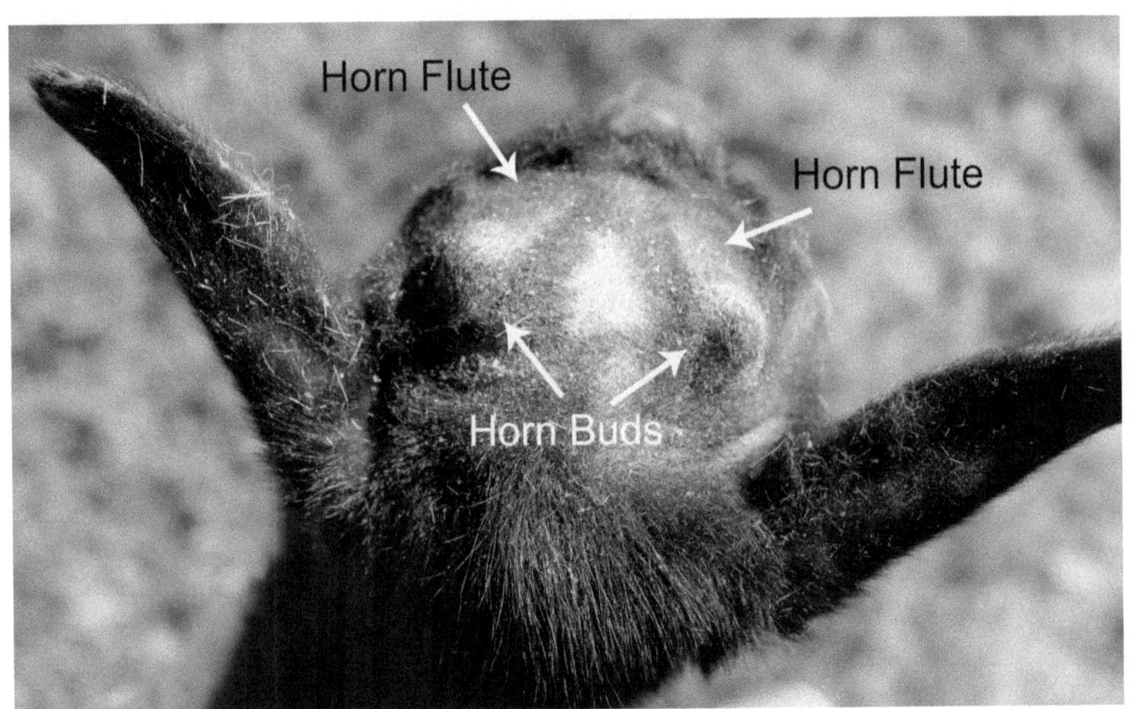

Shaving the kid's head lets you clearly see the horn buds and the horn flute that is often present on bucklings.

3. Restrain the kid in a disbudding box or by having someone hold the kid. Hold the kid's head firmly with a gloved hand, covering their eyes and holding the ears out of the way.
4. Center the iron over one horn bud so that the bud is inside the hollow tip. Apply the iron with even contact and twist it on its vertical axis for up to five seconds. This does not require much pressure, so let the weight of the iron do most of the work.
5. Remove the iron and blow on the horn bud. You should see a copper ring, and the "cap" of the bud should be well burned and loose. Let the kid rest for a few seconds.
6. Repeat step 4 on the other horn bud.
7. Repeat step 4 on the first horn bud again.
8. At this point the copper ring should be close to a white color. Using the iron or a disinfected pocket knife, pop off the cap of the first horn bud—it should release easily. The area under the cap will be open/raw, so apply the iron one more time for just a couple of seconds to cauterize the area.
9. Repeat steps 7 and 8 on the last horn bud.

When disbudding a doeling, you are done at step 9. If you are disbudding a buck, I recommend one more step to help prevent scurs. Due to the testosterone in bucks, their horns are much more aggressive than does and more difficult to fully disbud with no scur growth. In most cases, bucks will have horn flutes that need to be disbudded as well. Continue to step 11 for bucklings.

10. Look at the kid's head and locate the horn flutes. These will be two distinct lines extending from the main horn bud. They will be located in front of and usually slightly to the center of the horn buds. We need to disbud these flutes as well. The iron will need to be applied in a figure eight pattern now, with the front rim over the horn flute and the back rim sitting in the middle of the main horn bud.
11. Apply the iron to horn flute by centering the edge of the iron over the center of the horn bud with the other edge centered over the horn flute. This will not take as much time as the main horn bud, usually only about two to three seconds. Flick off the released cap and quickly cauterize the area by briefly applying the iron once more.
12. Repeat steps 11-13 for the other horn bud.
13. Take the kid back to mama or give it a bottle.

Occasionally you will see mild localized swelling. I have only seen this once personally. When this happens, you can apply an ice pack wrapped in a kitchen towel to the area for up to thirty minutes. Note: If you see severe swelling, you (or your disbudder) may have applied the iron too long or used an inappropriately sized iron. Seek veterinary help.

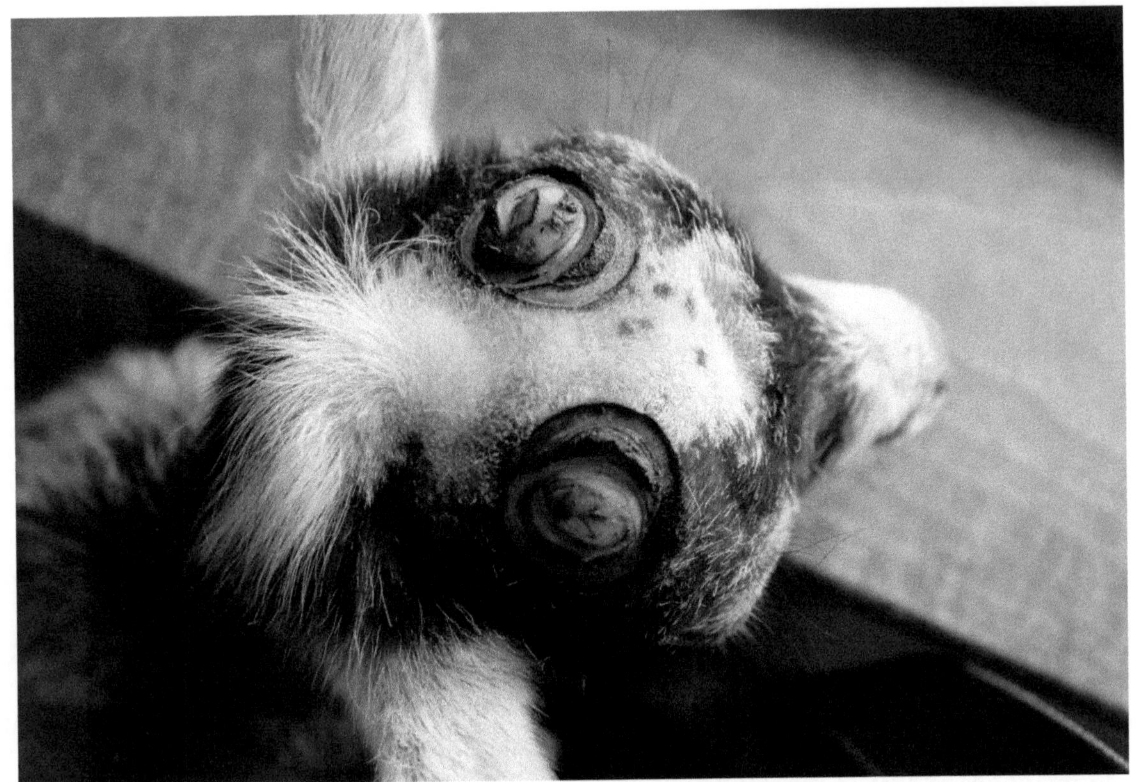

This is the figure eight burn done for buck kids to capture the horn flute area. The iron centers on the horn bud so that the edge overlaps the area of the horn flutes.

Identifying Polled Kids

Some goats are naturally hornless. This is called "polled" and means that the goat will never develop horns at any point in their life. The polled gene is dominant, so only kids born from a polled parent will be polled themselves, and any goat that carries the polled gene will be polled themselves. Unlike some livestock species like cows and sheep, there are no breeds of goats which are entirely polled. A kid born to a heterozygous polled goat has a 50% chance of being polled themselves. Homozygous polled goats are fairly rare, because of the stigma of breeding polled to polled, but if you do happen upon one it will produce only polled kids. A goat producing even only one kid with horns is not homozygous polled.

Sometimes people believe that two of their "disbudded" goats have produced a polled kid. What has actually happened is that one of the parents was errantly disbudded as a kid despite being polled. Believe it or not, this does happen. Polled goats often have bony knobs on their skulls that can resemble a horn bud. Misidentifying these knobs can result in accidently disbudding a kid that was never going to have horns in the first place. It's important to be sure of the horn status of kids born to polled parents. So how do you determine if the kid is polled?

First, if you have any doubt about a kid's horn buds, wait. Although it is best to disbud as early as possible so the whole process takes less time, it's more important to be sure the kid is actually horned first. If there is even the smallest chance that the horn buds you think you're feeling are actually polled knobs, simply wait it out. If they are actually horn buds, the horn itself will eventually emerge from the skin. Then there will be no doubt as to whether the kid is polled or not. The horns emerge slowly, so you will still have time to disbud at this point. Just be certain to check every day, because you do not want to disbud a kid whose horns have grown.

Often you will be able to tell without waiting for the horn to emerge. There is a difference in appearance and feel of horn buds versus polled skulls. Horn buds are shiny under the skin and are pointy. Typically, polled knobs are flatter, wider, and not shiny under the skin. There is also a difference in the hair growth pattern on a polled goat's head. A goat with horns will have two little cowlicks in the hair above their horn buds, whereas the hair on a polled goat's head will lay flat over the head and sometimes come to a little point off to the side. Judging the hair on the kid's head is the first way I identify a polled kid versus a horned kid, followed by feeling the area to make sure. Then, if I'm still in doubt, I will shave the head for a closer look and wait a few days.

This doe is naturally polled. You can see the "giraffe knobs" on her head. Polled goats often have these points on their head where horns would have grown.

Gemma before her horns were banded for removal.

Tales from the Kidding Stall: *Gemma and her brother Rubino were the only two kids I've ever missed disbudding. The reason for this comes down to my own mishaps. I only use the disbudding iron once per year, and in complete keeping with my incredible ability to misplace thigs, I could not find my disbudding iron during the short timeframe where Gemma and Rubino could be disbudded. To err is human, I suppose.*

At first, I thought I could withstand having one horned doe, but as her horns grew I knew I couldn't. I cringed internally every time I saw her stick her head in a hay manger, headbutt another goat, or put her head down near another doe's eyes. I waited until Gemma's horns were a few inches long and banded them, as well as Rubino's, to remove them. While banding horns is not ideal, I was able to do hers while they were quite small and during the winter while flies are not a concern. Personally, I believe banding is the better option than dangerous surgery. In a fun twist of irony, Gemma hit me in the left eye with a horn the day I banded them. As I picked her up off the table, she thrashed her head back for balance, and it connected with my face. Luckily it was a glancing blow that only left me with watery eye and a tiny bruise, but it was a reminder of the importance of disbudding. This was, after all, not the first or last time I would handle Gemma with my face close to her head.

Jack the wether, after his dangerous scur was banded to no longer grow toward his face.

Scurs

Scurs are partial horn growths that occur when the disbudding job doesn't completely kill the horn bud. These are typically only one or two inches in length, and sometimes they are tiny little horn bits called "button scurs" on the top of the head. When showing goats, a large scur is a defect. The cause of scurs is most often a poor disbudding job. This happens when the iron is too cool, the disbudder too timid, the placement incorrect, or the bud not burned long enough. Bucks are especially prone to scurs due to their excess of testosterone, and it seems that scurs in bucks are sometimes inevitable no matter how skilled the disbudder, though burning the horn flute in the figure eight shape helps. Certain breeds are known to have very persistent horn growth as well, such as Nigerian Dwarf goats. Nigerian kids are known to have horn buds that appear earlier and grow faster, and Nigerian bucks have a high incidence of scurs. In terms of overall safety, scurs are typically not an issue. They are much smaller and shorter than horns, so they do not get caught in fences and infrastructure the same way that horns do. They also have blunt ends rather than pointed, which, combined with their short length, makes them much less dangerous for humans and other goats.

In most cases, scurs are only an aesthetic issue. Occasionally a scur will get knocked off in a fight between goats and bleed, but this is not usually anything to be overly concerned about. In some cases, however, particularly large scurs can turn and grow toward the goat's head. In this instance, scurs must be trimmed to prevent pain and, eventually, death of the goat as the horn will continue to grow into the goat's skin and face or head. Small scurs growing toward the face may be snipped off using hoof trimmers, but larger scurs will require cutting with a wire saw designed to cut PVC pipe. You will need to restrain the goat, usually using a headstall or milk stanchion, and trim off only a bit of the scur at a time. The horns of goats, including scurs, are vascular and will bleed profusely if cut too deeply. For that reason, only cut off a half inch or so at a time. When you see a pinkish tone—not unlike the quick of a dog's nail—stop cutting to avoid causing bleeding and pain. In addition to the blood flow in the horn, goat also have nerves running through the horns as well.

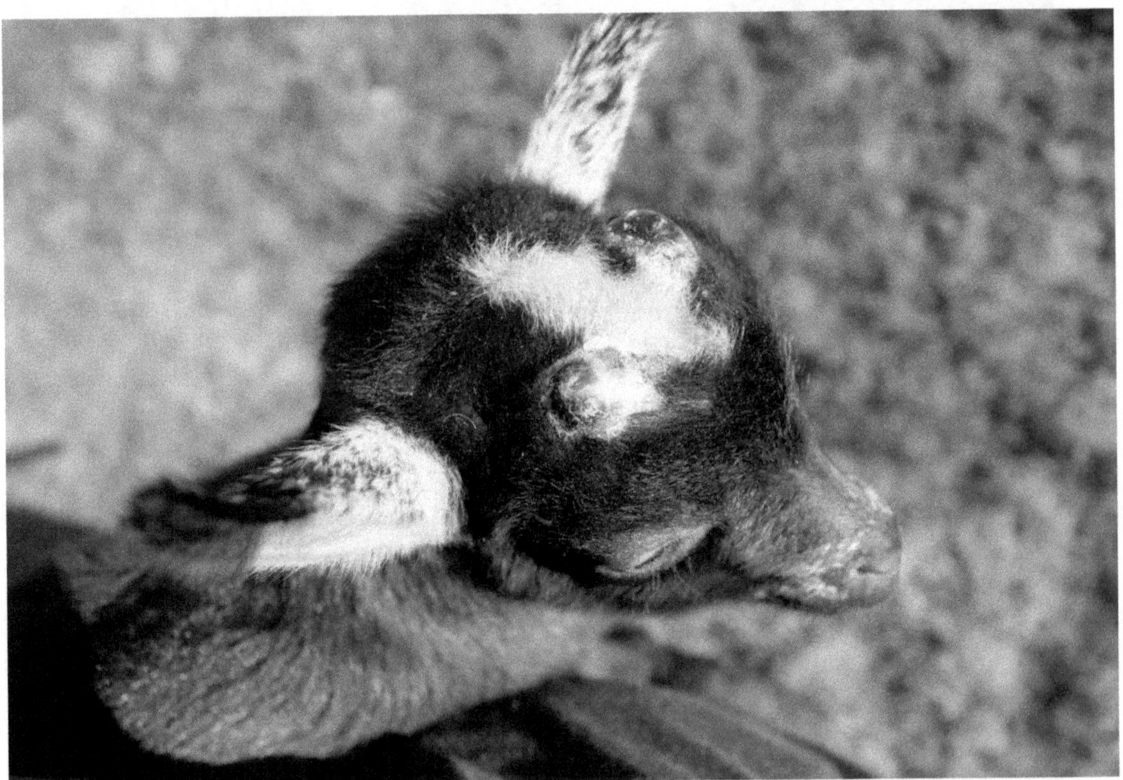

This kid is developing scur growth after being disbudded. After the disbudding scabs fall off, kids should show no signs of horn tissue growing. If you see black or gray growth, that is an indication that the kid is growing scurs. When caught this early, the kid can be disbudded a second time to stop the remaining growth. Unfortunately, even experienced disbudders will sometimes have scurs develop, especially in buck kids.

Tales from the Kidding Stall: *I have had only one goat with a scur that grew toward its head, and it was a wether born early on in my goat raising venture. Jack's scur was about two inches wide, and it was growing in toward his face. At first, I opted to cut the tip off to prevent it growing into him, but the scur grew quickly and as it grew it widened. Because of the shape of the scur, it was not only curling the tip toward him, but also widening into his head near the base where it could not be cut. I weighed my options and chose to band his scur. We notched the base of his horn, and I applied the castration band. It took several weeks, but the scur did eventually weaken. It was knocked off during a sparring match with another wether. There was a bit of blood involved, but after cleaning and applying antiseptic there were no other issues. However, the scur did grow back—this time smaller, weaker, and upright rather than curved toward him. This smaller scur also got broken during a sparring match, and after that incident it did not grow back at all. I was able to comfortably sell Jack to a pet home, knowing that his scur would no longer be a danger to him. Given the choice, I prefer to prevent scurs through proper disbudding than to deal with problematic scur growth.*

Removing Horns or Scurs

I've mentioned banding and surgically removing horns or scurs. To elaborate on these two options, I will first explain the process of surgical removal. A veterinarian sedates the goat and cuts the horns off, which results in quite a bit of bleeding as there are veins and arteries running through the vascular horns. Then the horn base is cut out of the goat's head, leaving behind an open wound into the frontal sinuses of the goat. The frontal sinuses are packed with gauze. This is a major surgery, the recovery process is long, the procedure itself is risky, and the open wound presents a risk for infection. There is a high incidence of complications from surgical horn removal, though usually they cause no lasting ill effects on the goats. This is not an option I would personally choose for horn removal.

In the rare instances in which I have needed to remove a horn or scur, I have opted for removal via castration band. This is not ideal due to the time it takes, and because sometimes the weakened scur/horn can be knocked off prematurely in sparring matches, but I personally prefer it over the surgical process. Disbudding is obviously the best method to prevent horn growth, but there are sometimes instances where disbudding was not done or done in correctly for whatever reason. There are a few steps to remove horns this way. First, the hair of the goat's head should be shaved around the horn base to allow better visibility. Restrain the goat in a headstall or have someone hold them. I recommend wearing protective glasses or goggles as you will be working with your face close to the goat's horns. Use a round rasp (called a bastard cut rasp) to file a notch on the front and back of the horn near the base. This is not painful for the goat; it's like filing your fingernails. Use the elastrator, fitted with a green castration band, to place the band at the base of the horns beneath the notches. Check the bands daily to ensure they have not fallen off, to watch for injury, and to keep an eye on progress. The band constricts blood flow to the horns which causes them to gradually atrophy and fall off. The width of the horns or scurs will determine how long it takes for them to die.

Keep blood stop powder or cayenne pepper on hand in case the dying horns/scurs are knocked off in a sparring match and bleed. Flour may also work in a pinch. It's best to do either of these removal processes during the winter when flies are not a concern. Although banding the horns is not initially painful, the dying horns may become sensitive as they begin to atrophy or if they are injured. If broken off or injured, treat with a wound protectant as well after bleeding is stopped. Goats should be given a tetanus vaccine prior to either surgical or banding removal of horns, regardless of whether you routinely vaccinate, due the potential for introduction of bacteria.

LaManchas have tiny ears called either gopher ears (less than one inch long with little or no cartilage, pictured) or elf ears (less than two inches long). They must be tattooed on the tail web.

Tattooing

Dairy goat kids who are registered are assigned tattoos to identify them. If you have any intention of showing or participating in programs such as DHI or linear appraisal, it's important that your goat kids have clear, easy to read tattoos. Tattooing is usually done around eight to twelve weeks of age or prior to sale. There isn't a minimum or maximum age, but the kids need to have enough space in their ears or tail webs to allow comfortable tattooing without stretching the skin. It's also worth noting that there are laws in the United States requiring goats and sheep to have a permanent form of identification as part of the Scrapie Eradication Program. I won't go into detail regarding scrapie or the laws surrounding it, but tattoos accompanied by registration are considered an approved form of identification by the USDA.

Tattoos are applied in the ears for eared breeds, and LaManchas (a breed with tiny ears) are tattooed on their tail web. When registering with ADGA and other prominent registries for dairy goats, you will choose a sequence of letters attached to your herd which will go in the *goat's* right ear (or right side of the tail web). If you register with multiple registries, you will want this tattoo sequence to be the same in each registry. For example, my herd tattoo sequence is TRMF; each kid born on my farm is tattooed TRMF in the right ear. A unique identifying letter and number are placed in the *goat's* left ear (or left tail web). ADGA suggests a specific letter for each year, omitting the easily confused letters G, I, O, Q, and U. The letter for the year the kid is born is combined with a number designating the birth order of the kid. For example, the ninth kid born on your farm in 2018 would have K9 in its left ear. The unique tattoos for each goat are recorded on their registration papers.

Tattoo supplies can be purchased online through goat supply websites; be sure to not mistakenly purchase a tattoo designed for calves, as it will be much too large. There are tattoo tools designed to auto-release the ear; however, these will not work well for tail webs and therefore should be avoided if you are breeding LaManchas. Ink is available in both green and black, and I recommend the green ink. Black ink can be difficult to read or even invisible in goats with dark skin, whereas green ink will show up on all skin types. I recommend having one tattoo tool permanently set up with your herd sequence so that it does not have to be changed. The second tattoo tool will hold the year letter and birth number, which will change with each kid. Always check the tattoo on a piece of paper before tattooing the kid to ensure you've aligned the letters and numbers in the right order and with the right letters. The tattoo letters are small and can be hard to read. You will need a clean toothbrush to apply the ink, and you will want to wear a pair of gloves as the ink will dye your hands (and pretty much anything else it touches).

Follow these step by step instructions to successfully tattoo your goat kids:

1. Clean the kid's ears or tail web with rubbing alcohol to remove dirt and disinfect.
2. Test your tattoo on a piece of paper to ensure it is correct.
3. Restrain the kid.
4. Look at the kid's ear or tail and choose a location for the tattoo that avoids freckles, bumps, or obvious blood vessels.
5. Rub the ink over the area you will be tattooing.
6. Position the tattoo tool and clamp it down quickly and firmly. Remove the tattoo tool.
7. Immediately use the toothbrush to rub additional ink into the skin for fifteen seconds. This works ink into the punctures of the letters. Don't skip this step!
8. Keep careful records of the tattoos of each kid so that registration information is correct.

9. Do not apply any salve, ointment, or medication to the tattoo. Leave it undisturbed until fully healed.
10. Tattoos can be read by placing a flashlight behind the ears or tail web.

Castration

Excess male kids who are not going to be kept as bucks will need to be castrated. Ideally castration should not be done early on in life. The male urethra is stimulated to grow by testosterone, so when he is castrated the urethra stops growing. Castrating too early can cause the urethra to be narrow, which increases the chances of dangerous urinary calculi becoming trapped in the urethra. Castration is the main reason why wethers are more prone to having problems with calculi. Likewise, it is important that wethers not be fed unnecessary grain; wethers, unless sick or malnourished, should not be fed grain and will thrive on a hay and forage-based diet. While some breeders choose to wait until buck kids are close to six months of age for maximum growth, this is not practical for most breeders. I personally castrate at two months of age—the earliest age that Nigerian Dwarf bucklings are potentially capable of impregnating their dam and siblings—so that I can keep wethers with their dams. If castrating later or keeping buck kids intact, they should be separated at two months of age.

There are three methods of castration: surgical, banding (elastrator), or burdizzo (emasculatome). Surgical castration is done by a veterinarian. The benefit of this method is that buck kids are immediately testicle-free. There are several downsides to surgical castration, however, and it is the option I personally recommend the least. Surgical castration is usually done using sedation or anesthesia, to which goats can have negative reactions. Anesthesia is never without risks, especially for goats. In addition, the surgery leaves a wound and puts the goat at risk for infection and attracting flies. There is also the consideration of cost—the price of castration greatly increases when choosing surgical castration over other methods. I do want to note that simply because goats are sedated does not make this method "painless" as some may think. There is residual pain and soreness at the wound afterward as one would expect with any surgery.

Banding is one of the most common methods used to castrate. This method is bloodless, very inexpensive, and easy to do at home. The specially designed castration bands, applied with a tool called an elastrator, cut off the blood supply to the testicles. Over a relatively short period of time the testicles and scrotum atrophy and fall off. The downside of this method is that it takes a longer period of time and, from my own anecdotal experience, it seems to cause greater discomfort due to the time it takes for the blood supply to be completely cut off to the testicles. Some buck kids act as if nothing has happened at all after banding, while some show signs of discomfort for up to thirty minutes afterward. There is also a potential of the banded location attracting flies or creating an anaerobic environment that may allow for infection, though this is rare. I personally do not like the idea of those tiny rubber bands falling off in the pasture, either. If you choose to castrate via banding, you must be certain that both testicles in their entirety are below the band, and that the goat's nipples are not under the band.

The burdizzo is my preferred method of castration. The burdizzo, also called an emasculatome, castrates by crushing the spermatic cords leading to the testicles. This cuts off blood supply and atrophies the testicles. This method is completely bloodless and does not create an opening for infection like surgical castration or banding. The goats do protest the most vocally with this method; however, the discomfort afterward appears shorter than banding in my experience. Like with banding, it takes some time for the testicles to atrophy and die. Unlike banding, the scrotum itself does not die and fall off. This can lead to some confusion for people unfamiliar with the burdizzo, but rest assured if the process has been done correctly the scrotum will be empty. Because you cannot visibly see that the castration was successful, it is important to be very precise with this method. To castrate with a burdizzo, each cord must be clamped individually from the side, as shown in these photos; do not try to crush both cords at once. Pull the testicle down with one hand and feel for the cord. Once you have found the cord, hold it carefully in place and clamp with the other hand. The cord is slippery and may slip out of the burdizzo if you do not hold it in place. The burdizzo must be clamped fully until it "locks." It will take both hands to reopen the burdizzo. Repeat with the other side. Some sources recommend clamping each cord twice; however, I have always clamped only once without issues. I do find that I sometimes have trouble completely clamping the burdizzo with only one hand, so it can be helpful to have a helper hold the cord for you while you clamp. I don't recommend commissioning a male friend as they seem to take the process personally. (All joking in good fun, male readers!)

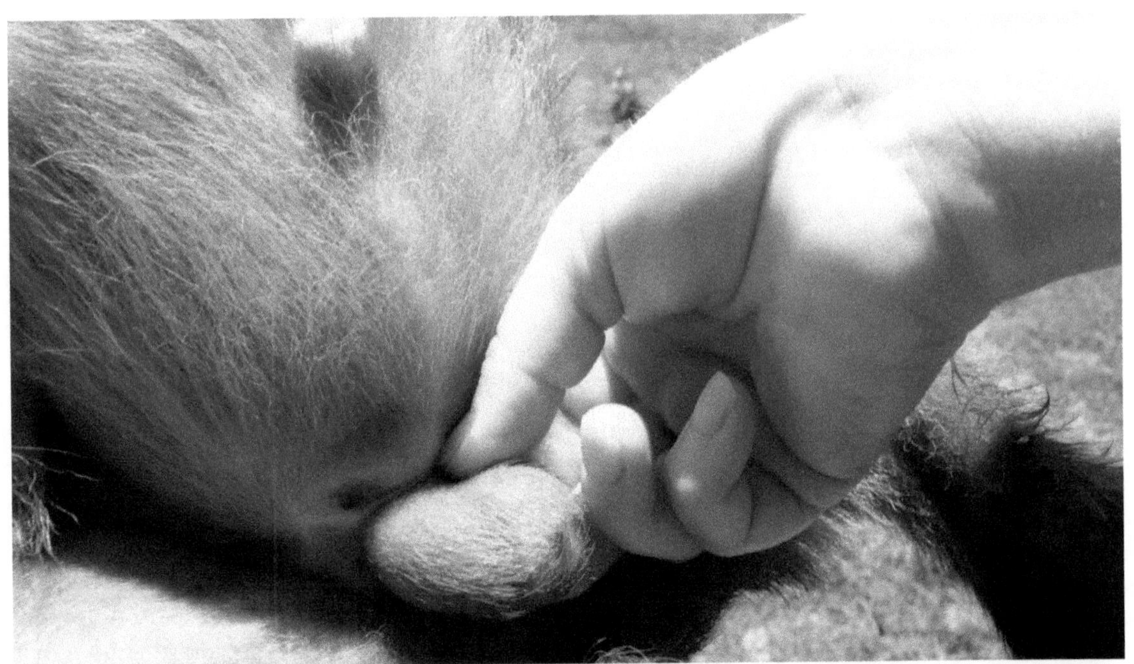

When castrating by burdizzo, you must first feel and locate the spermatic cords. These feel like thick elastic bands connecting to the testicles.

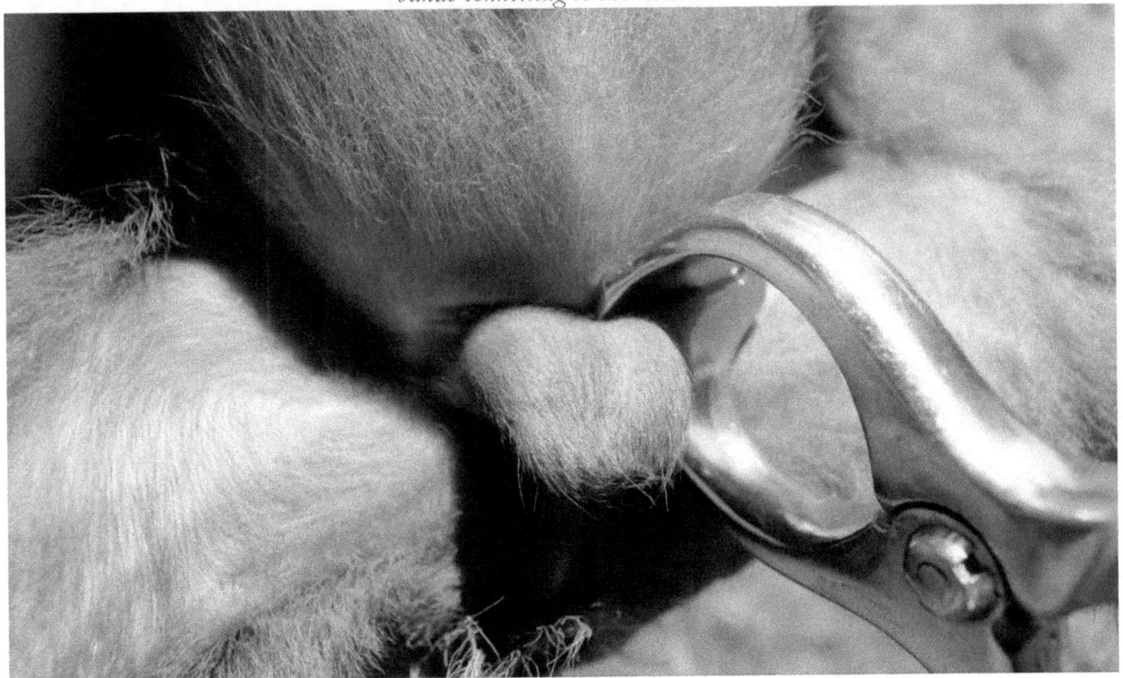

After locating the cords, clamp them one at a time from the side. Never try to clamp both cords at once. The emasculatome must close completely into a locked position.

Naming Kids

Naming kids can be a really fun part of the goat breeding experience, but it can also be a bit overwhelming. Let's say you have ten does kid in one year. That means you could have twenty or more kids to name all at one time. It can be a bit difficult to think of that many names all at once. I've found it's extremely helpful to have a certain naming structure set in place to follow both in naming kids and keeping up with bloodlines. Different breeders develop different strategies—and some just wing it—but I'll explain my process for you. Barn names, which are what you call your goats, may or may not be the same as the registered name.

The first part of a registered kid's name is always going to be your herdname. The herdname for my goats is "Tiramar," so each goat of my own breeding is registered as "Tiramar [Goat's Name]." When you buy a goat from another breeder, the goat will have their herdname even if you register and name the goat yourself. Likewise, kids born from doe you purchased already bred will carry the original breeder's herdname and not your own. You will choose a herdname when you initially join your registry and set up your herd tattoo and register your animals. Registered animals are only allotted a certain number of characters and spaces for each registry, so I recommend keeping your herdname short and sweet. It should also be as unique as possible, because a herd name that has already been used with the registry cannot be used by you. Relatively common or generic things like "Oak Hill" or "Jones Farm" will likely be taken already. A short herd name will give you the maximum space for naming your goat, and making it something unique and uncommon will help ensure you get the name you want.

I like to use a naming system that helps me keep track of genetics and parentage as well, so that I can remember who is the offspring of who with just a quick glance at their name. This is a common practice, and different breeders follow different techniques. In my own herd, I choose an abbreviation for my bucks' names to stick in front of their offspring's' names immediately following my herdname. For example, I gave my buck Bazinga the abbreviation of BZ, therefore his daughter was named Tiramar BZ Mattie Ross. Looking at that name, it is obvious who the sire was based on the BZ. For does, I pick a particular theme to follow that goes along with the dam's name. For example, Brownie's kids were named after desserts. Some of her kids were named Cookie, Oreo, Count Chocula, Lord Licorice, Rocky Road, etc. An added bonus of following a theme is that it gives you something to go off of if you can't think of a good name for the kid. Some people feel these systems are limiting, but I find they encourage greater creativity and help with organization.

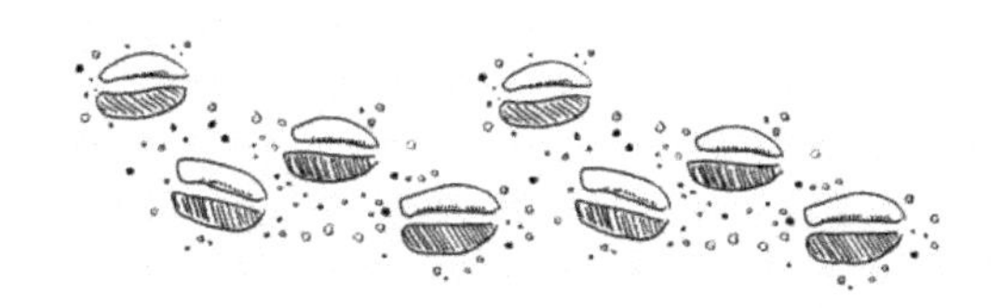

Selling Kids

As much as the kids born on your homestead are adorable, precious, amazing little things—you can't keep them all. Prepare yourself now for the inevitable fact that some of your goats will need to be sold each year. Doe kids typically sell fairly easily, but bucks and wethers can be more of a challenge to place. In either case, adjusting to selling kids and determining which ones to keep and how to set prices can be a challenge. I suggest knowing ahead of time what kids you want to keep from which doe. For example, you may want to keep doe kids from your best does, or you may want a buck kid out of your highest quality doe bred to your highest quality buck. Whatever the case may be, knowing ahead of kidding will help prevent impulsive decisions. Impulse decisions can go either way—you might impulsively decide to keep a kid you don't actually need or you may impulsively decide to sell a kid you really should have kept because someone made an offer. All of your decisions don't need to be set in stone, but having a general idea of your goals up front can be quite helpful.

After your kids hit the ground, it's time to choose specific kids to keep. I make my decisions for keeper kids based on the merits of their parents. Parents with a strong history of production, resilience, good conformation, and all other desirable traits are the ones whose kids you want to keep. Sometimes, though, you will find yourself blessed with an overabundance of kids. Maybe you wanted one doeling out of a certain litter, but lo and behold, the doe had quad doelings. Lucky you! So how do you decide between them all? First of all, look at their conformation. Unfortunately, this is somewhat of a guessing game, because kids can change drastically over time as they mature. There are some things that will be evident even early on, though, and you can make an educated guess. If the kids are all fairly even in conformation, move on to judging things like personality, vigor, and aesthetics. Many times it will simply come down to choosing the kid that you like the most based on nothing more than personal preference or a gut feeling.

When it comes to buck kids, most should become wethers. It can be tempting to leave a majority of buck kids intact due to their higher monetary value and the fact that they are generally easier to sell, but this is irresponsible. The fact is that there are always more bucks born than are needed in the dairy goat industry, and only the best of the best should be kept intact. As I mentioned earlier in this book, bucks are half of the herd. While a doe can only produce one litter a year, a buck can produce an almost infinite number of kids in a single breeding season. Buck kids should be kept intact only when both of their parents are proven to have the production, conformation, and other desirable traits to warrant keeping their male offspring; their parents should also have proven themselves to be able to pass on their qualities to their offspring as well. In my own herd, I now castrate the majority of my buck kids and only keep bucks intact that I would use in my own herd. In fact, I am most likely to keep a buckling intact for the sole purpose of using him in my own herd and not to sell.

Pricing can also be confusing for new goat owners. Our instinct is to sell the offspring of our goats for the same price we paid for their parents, but sometimes this isn't actually warranted. Knowing the base market value is helpful, but prices vary tremendously by quality of the animals and the reputation of the bloodlines. Pricing also needs to be adjusted based on the individual merits of the parents. For example, you might buy a doeling from a first freshening doe sold for $350. However, if that doe's mother goes on to earn a production award, high linear appraisal score, and permanent show title, her kids will be worth more than you paid for them as the offspring of a first freshener. Likewise, if your doe goes on to prove herself, her kids will be worth more than you paid for their dam. On the other hand, if you happen to purchase an expensive kid out of a highly awarded doe only to find that the goat you purchased isn't as impressive, your offspring might be worth less than you spent on their mother. In general, every accomplishment of the parents increases the price of the kids, and registered kids will always bring more than unregistered. To give you a rough guide, I often see unregistered goats going for $100-200 for doelings, registered goats whose parents have no accomplishments for $300-400 for doelings, and registered goats with proven parents for $500 and upwards. Remember that markets fluctuate, and depending on demand, market saturation, and a million other possible influences, prices might rise or fall.

Advertising goats for sale is necessary in order to move the excess kids. After all, until you've built a hefty reputation, people will not know about your herd until you tell them. Social media is a very helpful tool for advertisement, and being active in online groups and forums, building a platform with a dedicated page for your farm on the various social media websites, and building your own personal farm website with a bit of information about you and high-quality pictures is extremely helpful. Nothing will sell your goats better than providing two things: details about the accolades of their ancestry and beautiful photos. You can also post in places like Craigslist or online farm sales websites, but these limit you to a localized audience. It may be surprising, but people are willing to travel or pay for shipping for the right animal. I have sent animals as far away as California from my little homestead in Tennessee, and I have driven as far as the Chicago area to bring in the right bloodlines for my herd. You will never reach that kind of broad audience if you rely on local advertisements alone. I also encourage you to be active in the online goat community, even if you only do so as a reader. While you may need to sift through a bit (okay, a lot) of drivel and blatant misinformation, there's good advice and information to be found. Just be certain to use discernment—not everyone who can type advice online knows what they're talking about.

Selling goats can be a difficult process for some, and I can sympathize with that as well. I personally almost never sell an adult goat, because I become too attached to them by that point to sell them. It's also difficult at times to sell a goat without really knowing what kind of home they will be going to or what kind of care they will receive. Unfortunately, a lot of misinformation and old fashioned "it's just a goat" attitudes are still prevalent, though there are many good homes as well. It never hurts to ask a few questions if you are uncertain about a potential buyer—and remember, you have the right to refuse to sell one of your goats if you don't trust the potential buyer. Goats should never be sold to a buyer who will not house them with at least one other goat. Also look out for potential red flags that demonstrate a lack of understanding of goats and, more importantly, an unwillingness to learn about them. Potential warning signs include things like haggling on price (because no way are goats worth more than twenty-five bucks!) or mentions of unsafe housing or living conditions. It is more helpful to listen to people than it is for you to try to educate them or ask them a thousand questions. Often people will tell you who they are if you only listen. Meanwhile, people also often know the right answers even if they don't actually practice them.

It goes without saying that you shouldn't be too paranoid or intrusive to your buyers, either. Follow your gut instinct if something tells you a sale isn't right, but at the end of the day your responsibility ends when the goat leaves your property. I have had negative experiences where an animal I sold did not end up in a good situation. This eventually happens to everyone who sells any kind of animal. We can only do our best as breeders to place excess kids in the best possible situations. After that, we are not responsible for the actions of others. There is no sense in dwelling on something outside of your control. The best advice I can give you is to truly release yourself from guilt or responsibility if something negative happens to a goat that is no longer in your care. First, bad things happen even when owners are being responsible and caring for their goats appropriately. Secondly, you cannot know if a situation is a bad one. You can only go by what you know, and what you know is only what the buyer tells you. When you let a goat go, truly let it go. It's not your burden any longer.

Tales from the Kidding Stall: *I made the decision to sell a wether once on bequest of a friend. They were selling a doe and the buyer needed a companion, so I agreed to let them sell one of my wethers. I regret selling without speaking to the buyer myself, and would never do so again, but at the time everything my friend was telling me—which the buyer was telling her—seemed on the up and up. We found out less than two weeks later that both our goats had "run away" into the woods, and the buyer blamed my wether for "leading the doe off." They claimed my wether escaped each day, ran off, and then came back until he finally convinced the doe to follow him. While my wether wasn't extremely friendly, their doe was; she was a bottle baby and would not have run away and refused to be caught. Even if their story was completely true, that only means the buyers didn't have appropriate fencing for goats, knew there was a problem with it, and did nothing to fix it. The fact that the goats ran away into the woods meant they most likely became food for coyotes. I was angry, but my friend's children were heartbroken. Looking back, there were red flags that I might have caught had I spoken directly to the buyer, but my friends were less experienced than me and didn't pick up on them.*

This incident was one of the biggest reasons I decided to stop selling wethers. I will only sell wethers now under special circumstances and typically only to buyers with whom I have previous experience. While I've had good experiences with buyers purchasing pet wethers and caring for them well, the risks of the bad outweighs the good for me. Wethers are more likely to be neglected or inappropriately cared for because buyers have less invested in them and they serve no real purpose other than to be a companion. Wethers are also highly susceptible to being literally spoiled to death, as they are the most likely ones to develop urinary calculi and so many pet homes want to "pamper" their goats and thereby kill them with kindness—quite literally. Unfortunately, even well-meaning people often do not listen when warned, and many people must learn the hard way before they will accept advice. The saying may be "buyer beware," but unfortunately there are bad buyers out there as well. So, I say to you "seller beware," especially if you're selling pet wethers—and even if you're not.

This is an old picture of me (the short blond one) with my mom's LaManchas. I'm the third generation to own goats on my maternal side of the family and a fourth generation farmer on my paternal side.

Chapter Seven: The Milk Parlor

The primary goal of raising dairy goats is to collect and use their milk. After long months of waiting, it's incredibly exciting to finally get to collect that beautiful liquid gold. It's easy to put on a pair of rose-colored glasses and imagine a picturesque scene with a well-behaved doe calmly munching her feed while you aim streams of pure white milk into a silver bucket. The birds are singing, the sun is shining, and you might as well be in *Heidi*. In reality, it takes a bit of time and practice for milking your goats to become an enjoyable experience.

Training a Doe to be Milked

If you're quite lucky, you may be able to procure a doe who is already trained to milk. These aren't as commonly available as doelings, but they can be found when breeders are choosing to downsize their herd or feel a doe no longer fits into their program. In most cases, you will need to train your does to milk yourself. Sometimes even experienced does will need a refresher course in proper stand etiquette after a dry period, and some does do not like to be milked by strangers. My grandmother had a Saanen goat, many years ago when my mother was a child, who would only stand to be milked by my grandmother; Fanny Bird ran away from any other person who tried. Likewise, I once farm sat for a "well mannered" bottle baby who needed to be milked. Her owners could milk her without so much as putting her in a headstall (which they did not own). Meanwhile, I couldn't milk her without walking away covered in spilled milk and feeling like I'd been in a rodeo. Each doe's personality is different, so you won't really know what you have until you start milking.

I always recommend being at the birth of your goats for several reasons, one of which is because it helps strengthen the bond you have with your does. I consider this the first step in training a doe to be milked. Immediately following her birth, assuming the doe is doing well and did not have a traumatic delivery, she is highly receptive to bonding due to the maternal hormones surging in her system. If a doe has a capacious udder and enough milk, I will milk a bit of colostrum from her the same day of her delivery after her kids have had their fill. I have yet to encounter a doe who puts up any kind of fuss at this the day of delivery, no matter how wild she was before. If I don't feel comfortable taking any colostrum, I will still interact with her udder so that she becomes familiar with the sensation of having her udder handled. It is important to follow appropriate hygiene just the same as you would on any normal milking day to prevent mastitis. Hygiene is discussed later in this chapter.

Training your doe to the milk stand prior to milking her will make your life easier as well. A milk stand or stanchion is a must have for milking, because it helps you to control the goat while milking. These can be purchased or made yourself. The stanchion holds the doe's head in place and holds a bowl of feed for her to eat while you milk. Goats are usually quite food motivated, and a little bit of grain or alfalfa pellets is your ticket to training your doe to jump onto the stand. Does will associate standing on the milk stand with eating and will jump on willingly for a snack. While training your doe, acclimate her to being touched on her udder and, if she isn't naturally friendly, being touched in general. While not strictly necessary, this can help you establish the milk stand as a normal, happy place that the doe will be happy to visit when it's time to milk her.

More difficult does will take a bit more time to train. You can expect spilled milk and feet in buckets from most of your does as they initially learn to be milked. In some cases, even very friendly does will be fidgety on the stand and prone to sticking their feet where they don't belong. Flies also do not help matters and will cause even the most well behaved does to kick. There will also be incidences when you may need to further restrain the doe until she becomes acquainted to being milked. If you have a friend willing to help, they may lift one leg of the doe for you. This will prevent her from kicking her feet. You can also set a bowl beneath the doe and milk her with one hand while the other hand lifts one of her legs. There are also hobbles designed to restrain does on the stand; however, I have not had luck when attempting to use them.

The most effective way I have found to restrain the most difficult of does is to use curb straps designed for horses' bridles. These are short chains that have a small nylon or leather belt and buckle on either end. These are the perfect size and length to easily and painlessly restrain your doe's legs. Attach one end to your milking stand in the proper place to hold her leg in place without overextending it. Then wrap the opposite belt around the doe's hock, above her hoof. Do the same to the other side. These allow a couple of inches of room for the doe to move her leg, but she will not be able to move it any further. Difficult does will kick at these at first, but they soon realize it is futile to continue fighting it. In my experience it only takes a few times of using them before the doe will stop fighting and simply stand still, happily eating her food and not moving her legs. In many cases you can discontinue their use, but some does may need the sensation of having the "bracelet" on her legs to prevent her trying to kick.

No matter what, don't give up on your does. My first experience milking, which you can read about in the following *Tale from the Kidding Stall*, was extremely discouraging and prevented me from trying to milk again for a couple of years. If I'd known then what I learned later, I would not have given up on the doe so quickly that year. The same doe who put me off from milking—the primary reason I'd wanted goats in the first place—ended up being the doe who taught me how to milk and, more importantly, taught me how to train a doe to be milked. The most important tool you need to train even the most difficult doe is simple patience and perseverance. Even the orneriest does can learn to be milked willingly.

Tales from the Kidding Stall: *Brownie was my first doe, and she was far from tame. In my naivety, I believed that milking her would be simple and easy. Call it rose-colored glasses or the simple optimism of youth, but eighteen-year-old me didn't know any better. Oh, but I learned. The first I time I tried to milk her it was a downright rodeo. I tried to milk her while my mother held her without any luck. Then we switched places, and I restrained her while my mother tried. Instead of getting milk, what we got was blood. Brownie kicked my mother's hand so hard with her hoofs that she cut it open. Needless to say, we called it a day.*

It wasn't until a couple of years later that I tried milking her again. I had a milking stanchion by this point, and I'd determined that I wasn't going to fail. This was also the first year I finally witnessed Brownie give birth. I missed her first two kiddings, but by this time I'd learned the signs and was able to attend. This was one of the turning points of our relationship. I was able to train Brownie to the stand for food, but she still kicked with a vengeance. She kicked so hard that it was impossible to milk her or to hold her legs still. Sometimes she would even jump with both legs at the same time, all the while eating her food as if nothing was going on behind her. At last I had the idea to restrain her legs and realized the curb straps on my horses' bridles would work perfectly.

It took about two weeks of Brownie fighting the restraints, and then suddenly she settled into her new routine. This go around there was no blood—human or goat—and it felt like the biggest accomplishment in the world to succeed at taming her for milking. From then out she stood almost perfectly still on the stand while I milked. Then it was time to learn my next lesson, which was that hand milking is painful—not for the goats, but for humans. My hands cramped fiercely as I learned to milk, and it didn't help that Brownie had small teats with small orifices. Oh, the torture!

Yet my little "Brown Cow" and I became friends, and I milked her until she was retired at the age of ten. If you had told me that first day I tried to milk her that she would become a cooperative, well-

mannered doe, or that we would develop a friendly relationship later on in life, I probably wouldn't have believed you. Yet my experience with Brownie is proof that even unfriendly goats can become well behaved does on the milk stand with time, patience, a few tricks, and a little bit of food.

Brownie, aka Brown Cow, the doe that started my herd.

Milking Supplies:

- Udder wash (I use gentle soap and water with a few drops of essential oil, but you can also purchase udder washes or wipes)
- Teat dip (I use an iodine dilution)
- Clean rags
- Stainless steel milking pail/bucket
- Stainless steel or glass lidded jars/containers
- Milking machine (optional)
- Bleach
- Electric clippers with a fine blade (to trim hair around udder)
- Milk filters, coffee filter, or fine muslin cloth
- Glass storage jars/jugs

- Milking stand or stanchion
- Milking room or stall
- Strip cup (optional)
- Stainless steel funnel
- No return flow dip cup

Hand Milking

Most new goat owners start milking by hand at first and may or may not transition to a milking machine later depending on their circumstances. Like any new skill, learning to hand milk is a process. You may not have great success the first day—or even the first week—but over time you will learn to milk quickly and efficiently. Be prepared for your hands, and possibly your arms, to cramp and be sore as you learn to milk. You will be using brand new muscles that you likely haven't worked before. Milking also becomes more or less difficult depending on the quality of the udder. Never underestimate the importance of a good udder, even for a simple home milker. A meaty udder with small teats, tiny orifices, and poor teat placement is much more difficult and time consuming to milk than a buttery soft udder with good sized teats and open orifices.

Because learning to milk takes time, you likely will not actually empty the doe's udder as you are learning to milk. This is why I don't recommend buying a doe in milk who does not have her kids with her. Although you can do this—and I've done it myself—it can be an extra challenge for a new milker. You may find that you can't empty the doe out completely, either from inexperience, difficulty with the doe's cooperation, or muscle fatigue. When this happens, milk is left in the udder after milking. Because milk production is based on supply and demand, leaving milk in the udder will cause the doe to slow in her production. Does typically drop in production upon moving anyway due to the stress of being moved and placed into an unfamiliar environment. When you have the doe's kids in your possession as well, they will clean up any milk left over after milking and help keep production up.

The first and most important thing to know about hand milking is that you should never yank or pull on the teats. This does not express the milk correctly, and it is also uncomfortable for the doe. To properly milk the doe, first trap the milk in the teat by sealing the top of it either between your first finger and thumb or in the crook of your thumb and palm, depending on the size of the teat. Then press the milk out by closing your middle, ring, and pinky fingers in succession on the teat. This will push the milk out of the teat and into the bucket in a steady stream. Then release the teat to allow more milk to flow inside and repeat the process. In most cases, you will be milking with both hands and alternating streams—left, right, left, right.

It's important to always follow the appropriate protocol for hand milking, both to ensure the safety of the doe's udder (preventing mastitis) and to keep the milk clean and safe for consumption. All milking supplies should be kept clean, including your own hands and the doe's udder. The udder and the area surrounding it should be kept shaved so it's easier to keep it clean. Immediately before milking, clean your hands and the doe's udder. Then milk into a clean container, and if you are pouring off milk, be sure that secondary container is clean as well. If milk is contaminated by anything, such as a hoof going into the bucket, it should be discarded.

The overall process of hand milking is as follows: coax the doe onto the stand with food, brush her down to release her loose hair, clean your hands and wash the doe's udder, milk out a few squirts from each teat into a strip cup or onto the ground, milk into a clean container, dip the doe's teats one more time, and strain and cool the milk as quickly as possible. Brushing the doe down and cleaning her udder and your hands helps preserve the cleanliness of the milk. The udder shouldn't be sopping wet when cleaned; a damp cloth is fine. Allow it to air dry before milking. A few squirts from each teat are sent to a strip cup or the ground to clear the doe's orifice and ensure only the freshest, cleanest milk is being collected. You can also check these squirts for clumps or discoloration, but you will also be checking milk later when it is strained. After milking, the doe's teats are cleaned one more time to remove bacteria and she is sent on her merry way. Quickly straining and cooling the milk prevents the growth of bad bacteria and ensures a clean, fresh tasting milk. This should be done as quickly as possible. Milk should always be strained, no matter how clean it appears, to remove any hair that may have fallen in and check for clumps that might indicate mastitis.

One you have perfected it, the whole process can be done in a very short amount of time. Does also enjoy routine, so if you are milking more than one at a time, you should develop an order in which they are milked and stick to it. You will want your milking area to be separate from the other goats both for sanitation and sanity—they will steal food, hop on the stand with you, and cause all manner of disruption if allowed to run amuck. The does will wait their turn in a space adjacent to the milking parlor and then happily walk in and jump on their stand for their turn to be milked and eat breakfast. Note that does will behave best when the food bowl is kept full at milking time; many will put up a fuss if they run out before milking is done. To avoid overfeeding grain to the does, simply fill the bottom of the bucket with alfalfa pellets or hay to give them something to munch on after her grain portion has been emptied. Multiple does can be milked at once if you are machine milking, but of course you can only milk one doe at a time when hand milking.

Keeping the milk clean while hand milking is a bigger challenge than when machine milking. A fussy doe, or a doe plagued by flies, will kick over the bucket or stick her foot in it. The milk is also open to the air during hand milking, which means hair and such can fall into it. While I personally don't worry about the errant hair here and there—which will be removed when the milk is strained—any major contamination requires the milk to be tossed or fed to the pigs, if you happen to have them. I once had a cow sling a clod of mud from her *front* hooves into the nearly-full milk pail—talk about frustrating! Those who say not to cry over spilled milk have likely not hand milked a goat or cow before. That said, there are a few tips and tricks for keeping the milk pail clean. General sanitation practices are a must, but preventing the milk from being spilled is important as well. If your doe is moving too much, I recommend milking with one hand and holding the milking pail with the other. This does make the process take much longer, but in the end it can save you a lot of spilled milk. I recommend milking into a jar instead of a pail for the most difficult does; the smaller size and smaller opening makes it easier to keep it clean and out of the way. I also highly recommend periodically breaking to pour off milk into a secondary, lidded pail. I do this routinely even with well-behaved does. Milk into one pail or bucket and then pour the milk off into a jar or milk pail with a lid after a decent amount collects, then continue milking. That way if the milk gets spilled or contaminated you haven't lost all of it.

Natural Fly Repellent Spray

Flies are a huge annoyance at milking time, and they will plague both you and your animals as you go about your chores. The worst time for flies is during the dog days of summer when the weather is hot and humid. There are many ways to help deter flies—fly traps, keeping bedding as clean as possible, using fly predator bugs, and the like—but sometimes you need a little something on the goats themselves, too. I like to avoid the use of chemicals when I can, so I make my own fly spray using essential oils. Mix the follow ingredients together and a glass spray bottle (preferably amber colored) and store in a cool dark place away from direct sunlight and temperature extremes. Shake well before each use, and spray the goats just prior to milking to help deter flies.

- Two cups apple cider vinegar
- Two cups water
- 15 drops each rosemary, cedarwood, oregano, peppermint, and melaleuca essential oils
- 1 tbsp mild dish soap of choice

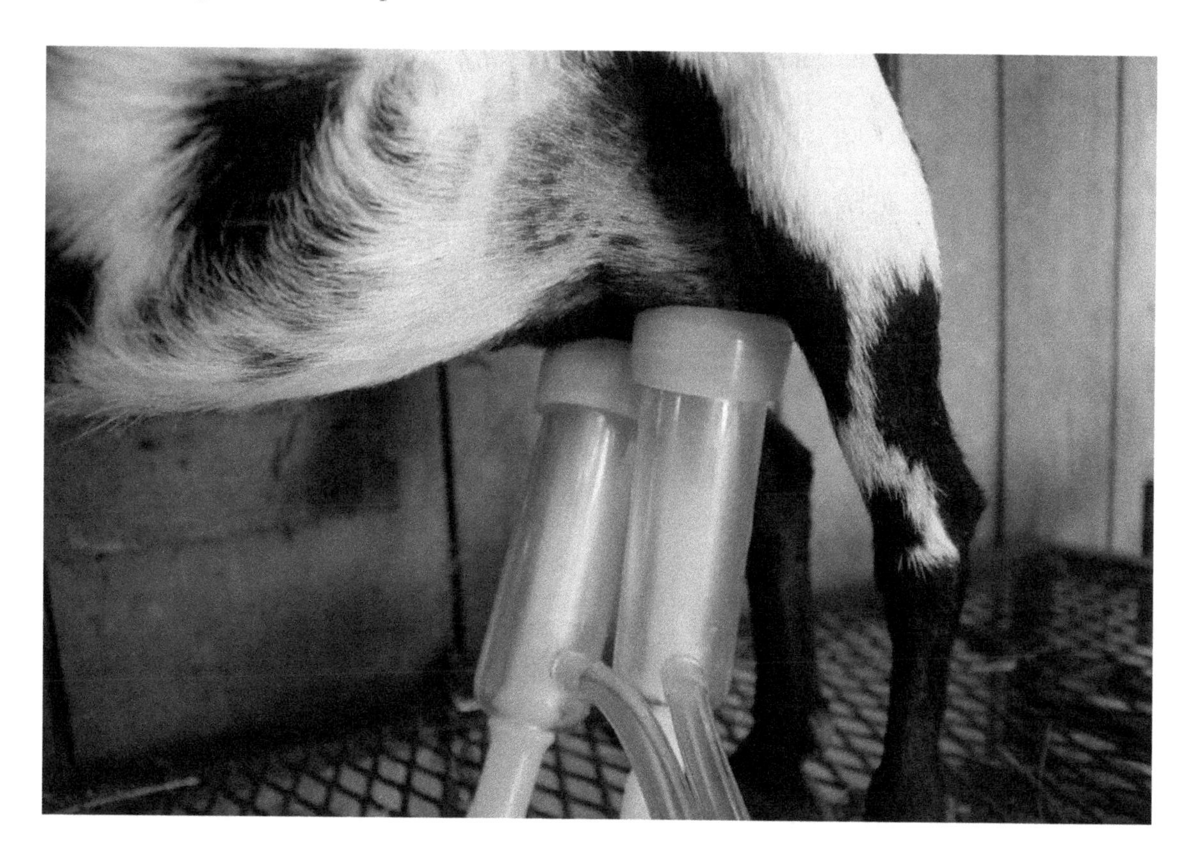

Machine Milking

Machine milking can speed up the process if you are milking multiple does at once. If you are only milking one or two does, a machine will likely *add* time instead due to cleaning process for the machine. The milk machine must be thoroughly cleaned after each use so that milk does not dry inside the lines or components, making it difficult to remove and promoting the growth of bacteria. Cleaning the machine takes place immediately following milking and is a three-step process. First, the machine is rinsed with hot soapy water—the hotter the better. Make the water boiling, if you can. You can rinse by filling a five gallon bucket with the soapy water and submerging the claws to allow them to suck it up. After pumping through the soapy water, you will run through a disinfectant mixture. There are commercially available disinfectants you can purchase for this purpose, and some people use a bleach solution. The disinfectant is run through the same way as the initial rinse. Next you will rinse once more using plain hot water to clear out the system. Boiling is best if you can manage it. You want to let quite a bit of that hot water run through to ensure all chemicals are cleared. Then you can hang the system up to dry until the next use.

The primary benefits of the milking machine, aside from time management in a large herd, is the increased protection of the milk. When using a milking machine, the milk bucket can't be stepped in or knocked over. The milk is kept in an enclosed system from start to finish and therefore is not exposed to contamination. If you have any intention of creating a herd share or selling your milk commercially, you will want to use a milking machine for this reason. While hand milking is fine for home use, the improved sanitation and protection of the milking machine makes it essential for milk that is going to be sold or shared. Another benefit of machine milking is that more than one goat can be milked at once. To do this, you will need the same number of milk stanchions as does you intend to milk at one time and a milking system that supports multiple does at once. All the does are walked in and prepped for milking at the same time, then milked all at once (usually into a bulk tank, though some people choose to milk into individual jars for each doe), and then cleaned and released at the same time.

Preparing the doe for a milking machine is essentially the same as preparing her for hand milking. Her udder and your hands should still be cleaned and the first few squirts of milk wasted. After this, you will affix the machine claws to the doe's teats and allow the machine to milk her. Be sure to test the suction of the milking machine—it should be firm enough to stay on the teat but not so firm as to be uncomfortable for the doe. It's important to use a **pulsating** milking machine. A steady suction like is seen in some of the less expensive, non-motorized milking "machines" is damaging to the teat and painful for the doe. I wasted money on such a device early on in an attempt to get some milk from Brownie, my difficult little doe, and I realize at the first use that it was *not* a good idea. The pressure continues to build and squeeze the teat until it forces milk out with no break to the doe's teat. It was obviously painful, and Brownie let us know it. You will still need to milk out the udder the rest of the way after machine milking, because typically the machine will not get it all. Once the milk stops flowing through the tubes, remove the claw from the udder and empty the udder the rest of the way, dip the teats as per usual, and send the doe back out to pasture.

When is the Udder Empty?

Knowing when to stop milking can be confusing at first. In many cases a doe's milk flow will lessen before she is actually empty, and sometimes it will seem like her milk never completely stops. As the doe's milk flow slows, gently massage or bump the udder. This will cause another let down and you can continue milking. Do this each time the flow slows, and each time you will see a burst of new milk until the doe is at last truly empty. As it slows dramatically, you may only get a couple more squirts after each massage. At this point, I will massage with one hand and empty with the other until milk either stops coming out completely or I am only getting a dribble. Because the doe's body is constantly producing milk, you may not get to a point where the milk completely stops altogether, and that is okay. However, you want to be sure to get the udder as empty as possible to promote the best possible milk production from the doe.

Some people promote a process called "stripping" the teats. Stripping the teats involves supporting the udder with one hand and using your thumb and forefinger to pull down over the teat to get out the last few drops. This is not something I have ever done, and it is not something I personally feel is necessary. Pulling on the teats can be uncomfortable, but more than that I do not see a great benefit for getting out the last drop of milk. The doe's body will begin producing milk again right away, which will result in milk once again entering the teats quite quickly after milking. If you are dam raising, the kids will also get every last drop out after you milk should you happen to miss any.

Milk Handling, Safety, and Sanitation

Many goatherds choose to consume their milk raw. I'll be discussing the differences between raw milk and pasteurized later in this chapter, but for now we'll assume you will be using your milk raw. Really, all milk should be treated as if it were going to be consumed raw. Pasteurization is not an excuse to be lackadaisical or skimp on sanitation. Introducing bacteria to the milk at any stage can cause premature spoilage and food safety risks regardless of pasteurization. Don't forget that keeping things clean is also important for the health of the doe and preventing mastitis; sloppy milking habits can introduce negative bacteria to the doe's udder. That said, let's talk about safe milk handling principles.

First, it's vital to keep things clean. The doe's udder, your hands, the milking machine if you're using one, and everything that comes into contact with the milk or the udder needs to clean and disinfected. As mentioned earlier, cleaning can be done with disinfectants specially designed for this purpose or you can choose to use your own preference. I personally use warm soapy water with a few drops of essential oil and a clean rag to clean the doe's udder. I also use an essential oil soap to wash my own hands immediately before milking. The doe's hair should be clipped around her back legs, udder, and stomach immediately in front of the udder. Clipping keeps dirt, debris, and hair away from the milk bucket and makes the doe easier to clean. Brushing the doe with a soft bristle brush prior to milking sweeps away loose hairs and dirt that might fall into the milk bucket.

In addition to cleaning the milking machine as described earlier in this chapter, if you're using one, all other supplies that will be touching the milk need to be cleaned and sanitized. Stainless steel and glass are the best materials to use to handle and store milk because they are easily sanitized and nonreactive. I do use plastic lids for storage jars, and the tubes of milking machines are food grade plastic or silicone. I personally use bleach and heat to sanitize my supplies. A 10% solution of bleach water can be used, as can boiling water or a dish washing machine that has a setting for sanitizing with heat. Buckets, jars, lids, funnels, and the like should be allowed to air dry. Any reusable cloth that is used with milk (cheesecloth, butter muslin, etc.) can be washed as normal, then dipped into boiling water to sanitize, and hung to air dry after cleaning.

It's important to keep milk clean for consuming, but it's also important to keep all supplies sanitized when making milk products. Failing to do so can cause early spoilage as well as complete failure in certain cultured dairy products. Dairy foods like yogurt, kefir, cultured buttermilk, certain cheeses, and other cultured or fermented dairy products rely on the growth and development of beneficial bacteria. If the milk is inoculated with negative (bad) bacteria alongside the good, the bad bacteria may take over and cause your creations to spoil, not develop, or taste bad. It's important to keep milk cooled and cool it down quickly as well, because bacteria thrive at lukewarm temperatures. In some cases, people will blame an off flavor in milk, especially goat milk, on the goat itself when most often the blame lies on poor milk handling (failure to keep it clean or cool it fast enough) or poor nutrition in the goat's diet. The bottom line for milk safety is to keep it clean and keep it cold.

One last thing to consider about milk safety is this: an unhealthy animal cannot produce healthy food. There are certain zoonotic diseases (diseases that infect multiple species, including humans) that can be transmitted via raw milk. These include diseases like caseous lymphadenitis (CL), tuberculosis, brucellosis, and others. Thankfully modern scientific advances allow us to test goats and other livestock for these communicable diseases and know that our animals are free from any dangerous illnesses that could be transferred to us in their milk. I talk more about these diseases in the Troubleshooting chapter of this book, as well as how to prevent and test for them to be certain your milk is a healthful, nourishing food for you and your family—whether it is consumed raw or pasteurized. Unthrifty animals that are deficient in minerals or undernourished will not reach their full production potential, and their milk may present an off flavor as well. Always take care of your livestock and they will take care of you, too.

The Milking Room

Once you know how to milk, you'll also need an appropriate place to milk. While I am not above milking out in the open air—and have done so many times—it's undeniably less sanitary and exposes the milk to more potential bacteria. On top of that, you are also at the mercy of the elements. That means you'll develop a typical farmer's tan, but you also won't be able to milk when it's raining—or at least not be able to *keep* the milk when it's raining. Even if you're not in the open air but still milking in a general barn area, it's still exposing the milk to more potential bacteria and yourself to more potential hassles. At the end of the day, you can make whatever situation work that you need to, and it is up to you what standards to uphold for your milk. Like I said, I've milked in many less-than-ideal situations myself. Sometimes we're forced to make-do. Ideally, though, you will have a designated space solely for milking.

The milk room does not need to be fancy or large. It can be an independent building unto itself, or it can also be a separate room within your existing barn. Some of the classic features of a milk room include an easy to clean floor (preferably concrete or rubber), easy to clean walls, a table or counter space, storage, a sink, and one or more stanchions. Milking rooms can be customized completely to fit your individual needs. Some may be quite simple and not feature all these elements, while others may have space for milking a dozen or more goats at one time. Typically, a home milking room won't have more than two to four headstalls for goats, as most home milkers do not buy the expensive industrial milking machines that allow for milking more than four animals at once. Most often you will be milking one goat at a time or maybe two, unless you aspire to commercialize your dairy.

Although some milking rooms do not have them, I recommend keeping a sink to wash your hands immediately before milking. To reduce waste, I prefer to wash my hands traditionally with soap and water rather than wiping them down with disposable wipes. If you don't have running water at your barn, you can make an inexpensive substitute using a camping table and a water hose. It's much cheaper to buy a long water hose or two and a table than to run underground plumbing for running water. Camp tables with a hose attachment and sink can be found online or in outdoor specialty stores that carry camping goods. These tables function by attaching a water hose underneath to the faucet. The water hose is turned on at your house, and then the valve is turned on at the table so that the water can flow when the handle is activated just like a normal sink.

The milking room should be kept clean, although it does not need to be sterile. Goats will sometimes poop or pee on the stand, so being able to clean the floor is helpful. Goats need to eat while being milked; this makes it easy to ensure each doe is getting her full ration without being bullied off her feed, and it also keeps them occupied while you milk. Some stanchions are elevated up off the ground so that the does walk up a ramp and are at standing height. Other stanchions are elevated only a small amount so that you can sit by them to milk. In both cases, keeping them above the ground is important so that the milking bucket is not sitting on the floor, but instead is on an elevated surface which can be cleaned. Stanchions can be made yourself out of wood or purchased, in which case they are typically metal. The two most important features for the stanchion are a place to put feed for the doe to access and a head stall that prevents the doe from jumping off the stand. The headstall should be loose enough so that she can easily raise and lower her head as she eats but not so loose that she can pull her head through.

Some milking rooms are fully enclosed and equipped so that all milking supplies—including machines—can be cleaned and stored within the milking room. Although convenient, such an extensive milking parlor isn't necessary for the home milker. The ability to keep all supplies stored in the milking room is a nice luxury, but they can also be toted to and fro to be cleaned in your own kitchen. If you want to go an extra step, the milking room can even be converted into a full-fledged milk house with space to filter and store milk or even make cheese. Most people do not go through the extra expense and trouble to make such an extravagant system unless they intend to commercialize, but one can always dream!

How Much Milk to Expect

The question of how much milk to expect from your goats always comes up for new dairy goat owners. The truth is that it can vary wildly. One of the most important things to do to ensure good production is to buy from herds who milk. There are many pet herds for goats, especially in certain breeds that carry a higher "cute factor" or more color varieties, and these herds are not where you want your goats to come from. The two primary influences on your goats' production will be genetics and management. We've talked about how important mineral requirements are for goats, and we've also discussed nutrition. Does in milk should receive an average of one pound of grain for every three pounds of milk, adjusting according to the individual, alongside their free choice hay, alfalfa (hay or pellets), and free choice minerals. She should be kept in optimal body condition—neither over or underweight—and her parasite load should be well managed to produce the best possible production. That management will account for approximately 60% of your does' production abilities, and the remaining 40% will rely on their genetics. The best managed, highest producing Nigerian Dwarf doe in the country will never eclipse the top Saanen doe. Two goats receiving identical care can have vastly different production levels depending on their genes, even within the same breed. Proper management ensures your does reach their full potential, but it can't make up for poor breeding.

Assuming you are managing your does for peak production, the rest relies on the genetic potential and the quality of the individual doe. Evaluating the female ancestors of the doe, on both her dam and sire's lines, will give you an idea of how well she may produce. DHI records are extremely helpful for assessing the genetic possibilities for your doe. A long line of proven production in the form of registry-awarded production awards is a good indication that the doe's genetic history supports production that at least meets the minimum requirements for her breed to star with ADGA. You can also access detailed records to see how many pounds of milk a doe's dam and granddams produced in a year. This can give you an idea of whether the production history is merely adequate, average, above average, or bucket busting. Through ADGA's website you can also access the records of the Top Ten producing does for each breed each year. Although demand for kids from those does will be high—as will the prices—following these records can show you what the best of the best are producing as well as which herds are making the cut. A little trick I've learned to get top genetics at a slightly lower price is to buy kids from first freshening does that are descendant of the genetics you want. Generally, though not always, kids out of first freshening does are priced a bit lower since the first freshener has not yet had a chance to prove herself. Keep in mind, however, that genetics can vary wildly even just two to three generations down from a specific goat. A Top Ten milker four generations back in the pedigree may mean nothing at all depending on several factors, particularly breeding practices.

Genetics and management are not the only deciding factors. Sometimes an individual doe either does not produce in accordance with her family history or produces above and beyond her family history. Likewise, sometimes an exceptional doe may not pass on her qualities to all her offspring. Evaluating those aspects is important and gives you a good basis from which to start, but all goats are individuals. Some pairings don't work as well as others, and some individuals are more or less flukes in comparison to their relatives. If getting desirable traits were as simple as pairing two genetically ideal goats and getting a perfect kid as a result, showing and milk competition would be a bit less interesting. Always evaluate your animals on an individual basis as well as a genetic basis. Look at the production of their offspring as well as themselves to see how they are passing on their traits.

As for general production, there are breed averages, and I will share them with you now. Just remember that actual production will vary wildly based on the many factors we discussed. Some individuals will be well under average, and some may exceed the average, Below are the breed averages based on the 2016 DHI averages recorded through the American Dairy Goat Association:

Breed	Pounds of Milk Produced in 305 Days
Alpine	2588
LaMancha	2261
Nigerian Dwarf	741
Nubian	1973
Oberhasli	2217
Saanen	2772
Sable	2316
Toggenburg	2203

Encouraging Milk Let Down

Some does will withhold their milk and resist letting it down for you. "Letting down" refers to the doe releasing her milk and making it easily available for you to milk out. If you observe kids nursing, you will see them "bump" the udder to cue their mother to release her milk. The kids do this by headbutting the udder, sometimes quite firmly. This tells the doe to let down her milk so that it's available for them when they nurse. If you find that a doe with a large, capacious udder is not giving you much milk—yet still feels full—you may need to encourage her to let down her milk for you.

To encourage milk let down, you can replicate a similar behavior to the kids by lightly bumping the udder by bouncing it up and down with your hand. If that doesn't produce the results you're looking for, you can also gently massage the udder as well. In addition, some does may have a congested udder, especially immediately after giving birth. In this case a warm compress massaged on the udder can help the doe let down and break up the congestion. It's also important to know that the doe's udder may be swollen a few days after kidding as well, so it might appear full even after you've milked her out completely.

In many cases you can bump the udder a few times as you're milking when the stream starts to slow and encourage another, smaller let down. Although this isn't strictly necessary, the more milk you encourage her to give at each milking, the more she will continue to produce. Though each doe has a maximum capacity, milking is also a supply and demand system. The more demand there is for milk, the more the body will produce, up until the maximum capacity is achieved.

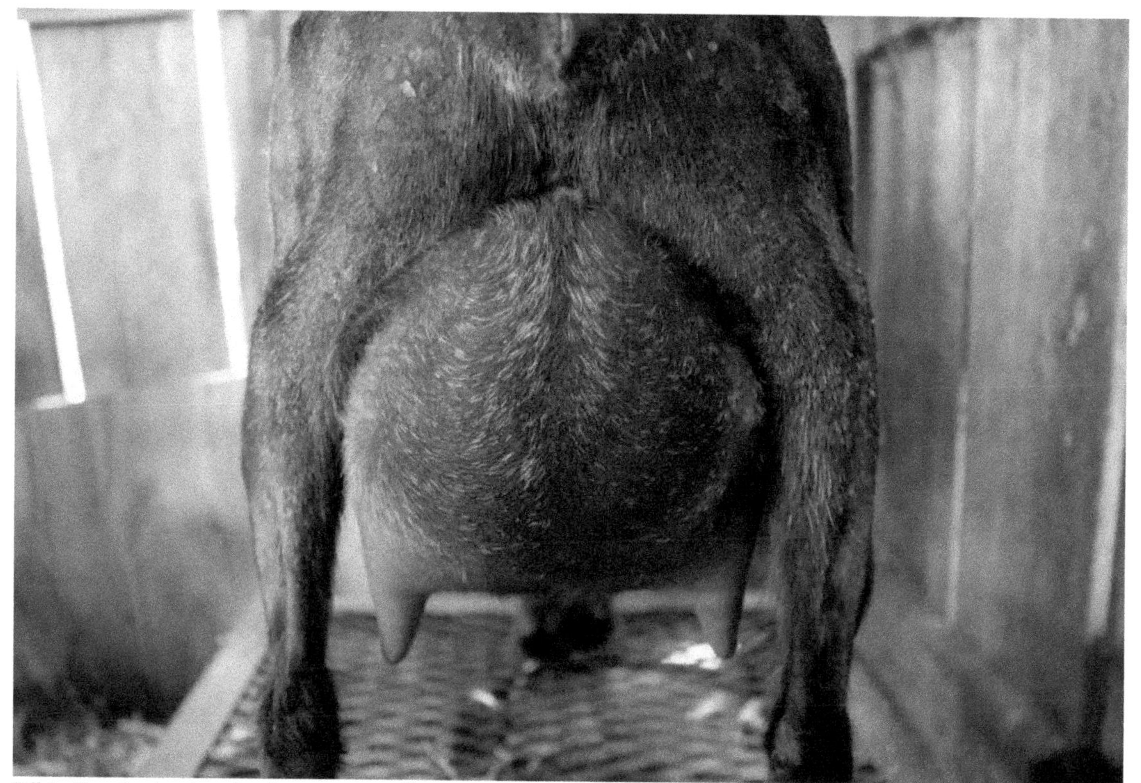

This first freshening doe has a very well attached udder. You can see the wrinkles of skin at the side where the attachments are located. She also has a nice u-shaped escutcheon and her teats are decent size. However, the teats should ideally be placed more inward so that each is centered on its half of the udder.

Evaluating the Udder

Understanding the parts of the udder and how they should look, feel, and function is one of the most important aspects of breeding dairy goats. While milk production is the ultimate goal, we cannot forget that milk production and ease of milking are both influenced by the quality of the udder. A poorly attached, undersized, hard or meaty udder will not produce like a velvety soft, capacious, well attached udder. Likewise, differences in the udder can make a doe difficult to hand milk or put her udder at greater risk of mastitis. The good news about udders is that they can be improved through selective breeding just like any other trait. I have seen a doe with a meaty, poorly attached udder with small teats and tiny orifices produce a doe with a soft, milkable udder. Choose your breeding bucks based on their dam's udders and milk production, because they can go a long way toward improving your doe herd.

So why do you want a lovely udder and not an ugly one? It's much more than aesthetics! First take note of the attachments. There are three points of attachment for the udder—the rear udder attachments at the escutcheon, the foreudder attachment, and the medial ligament. Attachment is one of the most important features to an udder. A poorly attached udder will sway back and forth, be knocked around by the goat's legs, sag low below the hocks, increasingly sag over time, and be at greater risk for injury and introduction of bacteria that may cause mastitis. The udder should be attached high and wide on the escutcheon; there should be a narrow gap between the top of the udder and the bottom of the vulva; and the side attachments, where the udder ends next to the legs, should be wide and horizontally. The ideal rear attachment forms a 'U' shape rather than a 'V' shape. The floor of the udder should be above the hock (hind knee). The lower the udder, the more likely it is to be kicked or stepped on and the closer it is to mud, dirt, manure, and bacteria.

The medial ligament is the ligament that separates the two halves of the udder, and it supports the udder and prevents it from sagging. This ligament should be well defined and centered in the udder, with both udder halves being symmetrical. In some instances, a single kid may cause the udder to become uneven due to the kid favoring one side; in this case, be sure to milk out the side the kid is not nursing to keep the halves more even in size. A poor medial ligament will not support the udder and will allow it to sag over time. The medial ligament also shouldn't be too severe so as to split the udder in two, because that would allow the halves of the udder to move freely of each other and expose the udder to more abuse in the process. Remember that while the rear udder attachments impact height and capacity of the udder, the medial ligament is the main support for the weight of the udder. It's also worth noting that a poorly attached udder is harder to milk as well, because you may find yourself needing to support the weight of the udder with your hands or arms as you milk to bring it high enough.

The foreudder attachment is important as well, especially for capacity and cleanliness. Foreudders with poor attachments will have a "shelf" or "pocket." While this pocket won't singlehandedly destroy the doe's capacity or function, it allows dirt and bacteria to hide in a hard to clean space. A smooth foreudder attachment that blends into the doe's stomach is easier to clean, supports the front end of the udder, and provides more space for milk.

The capacity of the udder can be partially evaluated by sight and feel, though only actually milking the doe will reveal her true capacity. The udder should be capacious, which means that it should appear large for the doe's size. Although not technically a part of udder anatomy, the width of the doe should always be considered alongside the udder. A doe with a high and wide escutcheon, followed by a naturally wide stance of the rear legs, will be able to carry a large, capacious udder without difficulty. In other words, a doe with good width of body will have plenty of space for her udder to fill. The udder should also have a soft, smooth texture. A hard, lumpy, or meaty texture is an indication of disease or illness (CAE, mastitis, congestion) or poor udder quality. After being milked out, a doe's udder should appear visibly empty as well as feel empty. A meaty udder can give the appearance of being capacious without providing much room for milk. Some swelling and congestion is normal immediately following kidding, so withhold judgment on the meatiness of the udder until the doe is a couple of weeks fresh.

The teats are the last element of the udder to consider. The placement of the teats should be centered on each half of the udder, neither too narrow nor too wide, and they should point down rather than forward or sideways. Teats pointing in random directions makes aiming while milking a chore, and teats that are too close together or too far apart give less room for your hands. The most important elements of the teats, however, are the size and length of the teat and the size of the orifice. Teats should not be so small as to be difficult to grasp for milking, and they also should not be so large as to be cumbersome for milking. Short, tiny teats will give a workout to your hands as you try to milk and may not hold the claw well when being machine milked. Huge, blown out teats are uncomfortable to grasp, hard to completely empty, might not fit well in the claw, and can make it hard for kids to latch onto. The orifice size of the teat should be large, but not huge. It takes twice again the amount of time to milk out an udder with tiny, pinprick orifices that let only a minimal stream of milk out at a time. A good-sized orifice is one of my favorite teat qualities. Too large, however, and the doe might leak milk. Worse, huge orifices are an open door for bacteria to walk right in.

Lastly, there are a few particularly undesirable traits you absolutely want to avoid in your dairy does. Does should only have two teats, never more. Does with extra teats or "fish teats," which are double teats that are attached to each other like a fish tail, should be culled from your breeding program. If a mating of two goats produces offspring with an extra teat, that buck and doe should not be bred to each other again. Double orifices (two orifices on one teat) are also a fault. A teat with no orifice, called a blind teat, is not only a fault, it is also painful for the doe because her udder will produce milk into that half without any way for the body to release the pressure. Lastly, a blind udder half, meaning a side of the udder that does not produce milk, is a major fault and disqualification. In some cases, a doe may lose half of her udder to severe mastitis, in which case she could still be a productive brood doe but would no longer be eligible for showing. She would not be able to continue to produce if she developed a blind teat but the udder still functioned.

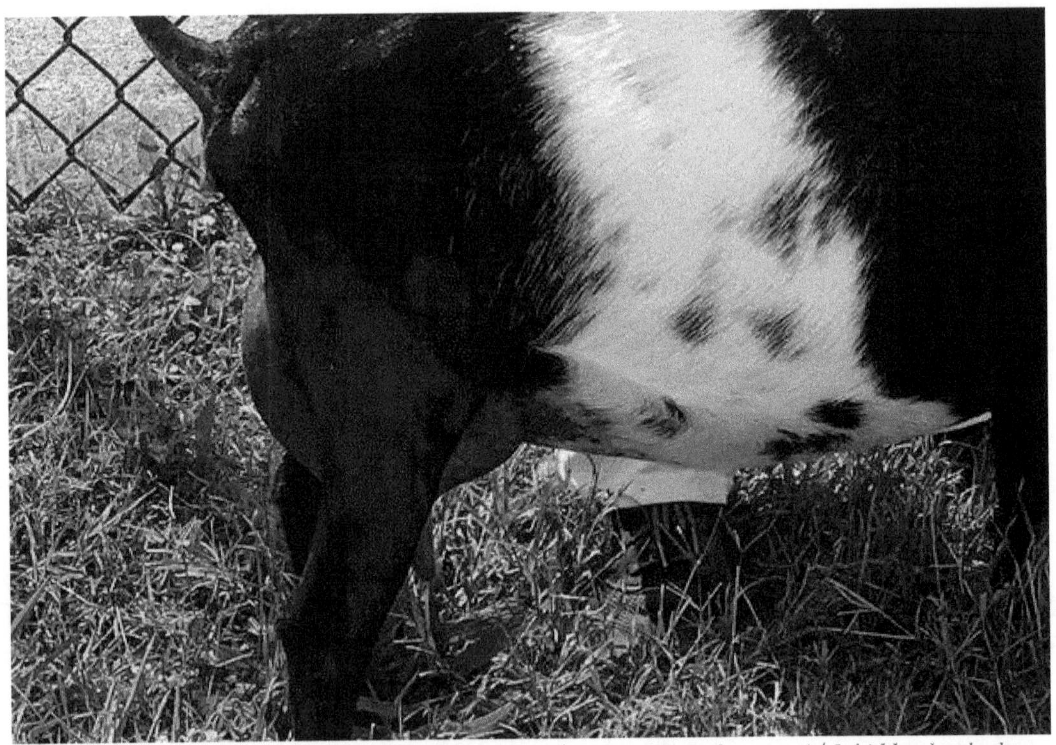

This doe shows a proper side view of the udder with 1/3 showing in the rear, 1/3 hidden by the leg, and 1/3 showing in front of the leg. Her teats are a very nice size with open orifices, her udder is capacious, and the texture is soft and buttery. Although not pictured, she also has a very nice medial ligament and good rear attachments. Overall this doe has my favorite udder in my herd to date.

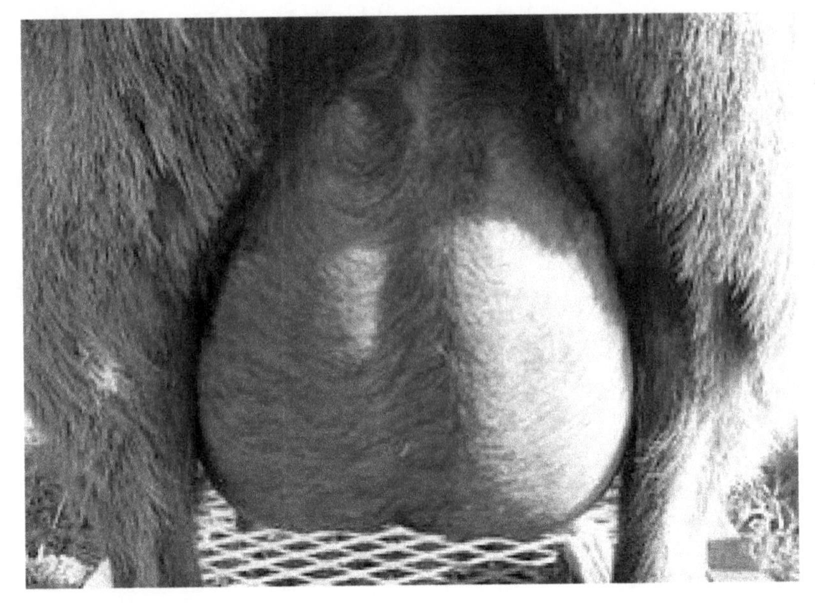

This is an example of a poorly attached udder. Note the attachment at the top of the udder is narrow and more V shaped than U shaped. This udder also had small, poorly placed teats (which is why they can't be seen from the rear) and small orifices. The front of the udder had a small pocket. It also lacked capacity and had a meaty texture. Overall, this was one of my least favorite udders in my herd.

The Milking Schedule

Does are most often milked twice per day at twelve-hour intervals. This means that a doe milked at eight in the morning will be milked again at eight in the evening. The exact time you choose to milk is not as important as establishing a routine and sticking to it. Goats are creatures of habit, and they respond best to a steady routine. Don't milk at eight one morning, ten the next, six a.m. the next day, and so on, or you will hurt the doe's milk production. Failing to milk on schedule will also cause the doe physical discomfort due to an overfilled udder. If milking twice a day does not appeal to you, you can milk once per day. Once per day milking is discussed later in this chapter. Regardless of which schedule you choose, consistency is the key to getting the results you want.

Does are usually milked for a standard lactation of 305 days. This means that a doe is bred once per year, usually in the fall, kids once per year five months later, and is then milked until she is three months pregnant. This schedule allows for the doe to have a two month break to rest her body and build colostrum before she kids again. Some people choose to breed their does so that they are all on nearly the exact same time frame for milking, but some goatherds choose to stagger their breeding so that does are in milk year-round. There are other options for this as well, such as milking through, and both year-round milking and milking through are discussed later on in this chapter as well. Lactations can be cut short if you choose not to milk the full 305 days; however, allowing a doe to have a short lactation—especially on her first freshening—can set her up for short lactations from that point forward. A doe's body will often learn how long her lactation should be based on how long she is milked, and her production may drop at the same time each year if she is milked for a short season.

Does can be milked as early as the same day of freshening, depending on their production levels. Indeed, a doe with a heavy production and full udder will benefit from having some excess colostrum milked out in those first days after kidding, and her production levels will as well. This is also the ideal time to train the doe to being milked. However, kids are typically not separated from the doe overnight until they are two weeks old. That allows the kids to take as much milk as they want as frequently as they want, and the humans are only taking the leftovers. This is also a period in which the colostrum remnants will still be present in the milk. In most cases the colostrum is replaced by normal milk after about 48 hours, but in some instances trace amounts of colostrum will continue to be present for up to two weeks. Most people do not care for the flavor of colostrum and instead save it in the freezer for future emergencies.

Milking Once a Day

One reason many people do not stay in the dairy world is due to the added work of milking. In fact, the average life expectancy of a goat dairy is only three to five years. Milking is a daily chore, and no livestock require more care and commitment than dairy animals. Neither wind nor rain nor any other inconvenience can keep you from your appointed milking post if you intend to keep your doe's production up. The traditional method for milking, and the schedule used by commercial dairies, is to milk twice a day. Some dairies even milk three times a day to boost production. For the home milker, especially one that works outside of the farm, milking twice a day can become a burden. Luckily it is possible to milk only once per day, and this is the route many people choose to take.

I often choose to milk my goats once per day for a majority of their lactation. The easiest way to milk once per day is to keep the kids with the doe and dam raise them. When the kids are two weeks old, they are old enough to be separated from the doe overnight so that you can have a full twelve-hour fill on the doe for morning milking. In a once a day milking operation, the kids are then released to nurse the doe for the rest of the day until they are separated at night. This gives the goatherd the freedom of only milking once per day. As a bonus, the kids can also function as relief milkers if something comes up that prevents a morning milking; for example, a family emergency, illness, or short vacation. That can be a huge relief to a milkmaid or milkman who does not have an alternate milker who can be employed to milk the does while the owner is away. The caveat to this plan comes in if you are participating in milk production testing. As the kids age and start to wean naturally or are sold, the doe will need to be milked twice a day at twelve-hour intervals to keep her production up for testing. If you do not mind a drop in production and are not on DHI tests, then does can continue once a day milking even after the kids are weaned.

Does can also be transitioned to once a day milking from a twice a day milking schedule without kids nursing. To do this, you will gradually adjust your milking time to wean the doe off being milked twice per day. Most does cannot stop milking twice daily cold turkey, because their udders will be full and painful if not milked. Instead, slowly move the time of the second milking closer to the time of the first milking over a period of several days. Depending on how heavily the doe produces, the milking may be moved up anywhere from one to three hours at a time. So a doe being milked at eight in the morning and evening would be transitioned to six in the evening, then four, then two, then noon, then ten, and then once a day milking. How quickly you can make the transition will depend on the doe's body and production; some does will slow down production more quickly than others. Heavy producers may take additional time to work down without risking causing the doe discomfort.

For those who are participating in milk test and dam raising, while only milking once per day, milk test day will present a different schedule than your normal milking routine. Kids will be separated from their dams the night before milk test day, and they will not be allowed back with their dams until the end of the day, after the second milk collection test is done. Kids who will be nursing dams participating in DHI should be exposed to bottle feeding early on so that they will accept both a bottle and nurse the doe. This is best done when the kids are very new, because the older the kids the less likely they are to take a bottle if they've been nursing the doe. Older kids not exposed to bottles will usually not accept them on test day. If this happens, you can allow them to nurse immediately after the morning milking—you would be surprised how quickly the doe starts to produce milk again after being milked out—and then separated again until the final test of the day is complete. While not ideal, the kids are already used to waiting twelve hours in between meals overnight, and older kids will already be sampling hay and grain as well.

Milking Year Round

Many people want to be able to milk their does year-round with no gaps in milk production. After becoming accustomed to the incredible fresh milk from your own barnyard and all the delicious dairy items you can craft with it, a two month spell without fresh milk can feel like a drought in a desert. Store bought products just don't compare to what you can produce at home. That said, milking year-round or not is a personal preference. Some people choose to take time off from milking each year for various reasons, such as time to take a vacation or time to simply relax. I personally prefer to take time off from milking for the simple reason that I do not like to milk in ice, snow, or bitter cold. For that reason, I avoid milking in January and February—the heart of winter in my locale—and plan for most does to kid in March or April.

On the other hand, many people who are less influenced by cold weather than I, want to milk every month of the year no matter how frigid. There are two primary ways to do this: breed for year-round milking or milk through. Seasonal breeders are more difficult to breed for year-round milking, but it can be done. Typically, they will come into heat beginning in fall and ending in early winter, roughly September through January, though some does may vary. This still provides quite a bit of wiggle room, as does can be kidding from February through June. Non-seasonal breeders such as Nigerian Dwarfs and sometimes Nubians offer the greatest flexibility, because does may freshen during any month of the year. Still, goats do not always cooperate with our plans. Even under ideal circumstances with proper mineral supplementation and planning, does still may not conceive as planned, thereby delaying their freshening.

Another option for year-round milk is to milk through. Milking through means to continue milking the same doe past the normal 305 day lactation and through the next season. This way the doe only kids every other year and has a two year lactation. This is popular for smaller herds who do not want their does to give birth every single year. However, not every doe is physically capable of milking through. While some does will happily keep milking two years or even more, others will naturally start to dry off on their own toward the end of a normal lactation cycle. You may try to extend a doe's lactation only to find that she tapers off and leaves you with no milk until her next kidding season. One other consideration for milking through is that does may sometimes become overweight during this time. Does commonly become overweight if they are held dry for an extended period as well. Overweight does are prone to fertility issues and are more likely to experience metabolic problems or dystocia.

Raw Milk and Pasteurization

The debate over raw milk continues to rage. I am happy to admit my bias as a longtime supporter and consumer of raw milk. I first became aware of raw milk, its benefits, and its controversy when I was still quite wet behind the ears at eighteen years old. My first experience with raw milk was buying a gallon from an Amish farm while on vacation in a little rural town. The Amish milkmaid dipped her milk bucket down into a cistern in the ground and pulled up a gallon of milk which she then poured off into our jars. While I now question the sanitation of that particular set up, the milk was delicious and rich and creamy—and it did not make us sick. From that point forward, I have obtained raw milk by whatever means I could whenever I could. I knew I wanted to raise my own dairy animals and purchased my first two goats the following December. During times when my own animals were not in milk—which was often during many years, as I was still in college—-my family and I purchased from milk shares or pet milk whenever we could.

Although I am undeniably biased in favor of raw milk, I do value honesty and will do my best to clearly define both the positives and negatives of raw milk. Let's start with the cons and get those out of the way. Naturally you must know that any raw food—be it raw milk, raw eggs, raw meat, or raw broccoli—carries with it an increased risk. The Federal Drug Administration asserts that raw milk and raw milk products are inherently unsafe to consume. The process of pasteurization kills most bacteria in the milk—both beneficial and harmful bacteria that may be present—and thereby lowers the risk of consuming negative bacteria in your milk. We are all familiar with the frequent recalls from bacteria such as e. coli and listeria contamination such foods as raw vegetables, processed foods, or pasteurized dairy products like ice cream. Unsafe handling of raw milk, or obtaining raw milk from animals infected with certain diseases, can introduce dangerous bacteria into the milk. Pasteurized milk is brought to a minimum temperature of 145 degrees F and held there for thirty minutes (low temperature pasteurization), brought to 161 degrees F for 15-20 seconds (high temp, short time pasteurization—most common in regular commercial milk), or brought to 280 degrees F for a fraction of a second (ultrapasteurized). Pasteurization is designed to extend shelf life and decrease risk by inhibiting bacterial growth, but it does not necessarily kill all bacteria.

On the other side of the coin, I would like to politely disagree with the FDA. Raw milk in and of itself is not inherently dangerous, in my opinion. Raw milk is a traditional food that is widely consumed, both by a growing number of Americans who are learning about raw milk and choosing to consume it, as well as a good chunk of the world where raw milk is not treated like radioactive goo. Raw milk and raw milk products, including soft cheeses, are legal and common in many developed European countries and elsewhere in the world. Many US states also allow for the sale of raw milk and raw milk products under varying degrees of restriction, though many continue to outlaw it as well. Because raw milk laws are subject to change, I will not include any details on raw milk legality in specific locations; I encourage you to research the laws in your own state or country to fully understand them and ensure you are following appropriate protocol if you intend to provide raw milk for others from your own farm.

The benefits of raw milk are many. Raw milk is milk in its most natural state. While the process of pasteurization denatures the milk proteins, raw milk proteins remain in their original state. Raw milk also contains beneficial bacteria, enzymes, and probiotics not found in pasteurized milk. Raw milk also contains its own protective elements designed to protect it from bad bacteria. Of course, these elements can be overwhelmed, particularly if not handled appropriately, but they are a part of the milk's natural protective state. Some of these elements, which are greatly reduced by pasteurization, include lactoferrin, leukocytes, macrophages, immunoglobulins, and antibodies. These elements, and others, support immunity and act against negative bacteria and pathogens. Pasteurization completely deactivates or greatly reduces all of these processes in milk. The same cooking that kills harmful bacteria also kills the beneficial bacteria. In short, raw milk is a living food, while pasteurized milk is a dead food. Nearly every live thing in it has been killed. I highly recommend the resources provided by the Weston A. Price Foundation and the Campaign for Real Milk for more information on the health benefits of raw milk.

We are really beginning to delve into the benefits of healthy microflora in our digestive systems. It is fascinating to me the role that the beneficial bacteria in our microbiome play. Healthy gut flora impacts our immunity, supports healthy weight maintenance, helps digest our food, and protects us against harmful bacteria. We have been taught that we should keep our environments, our food, and our bodies sterile, when in fact we should be encouraging the friendly bacteria to populate our digestive systems, our food, and our homes. We can't forget that everything we do to kill bad bacteria harms our vitally important beneficial bacteria. Studies have shown that the digestive systems of people in developing countries with more traditional diets and fewer processed foods have higher rates and greater diversity of good bacteria than those of people in the United States. Naturally fermented or cultured foods, as well as unprocessed foods in their natural states, are traditional foods that have been enjoyed for centuries. They are whole, nourishing, and complete; no parts of them have been damaged or negatively changed by processing. While we absolutely should adopt some modern food safety protocols and practice careful handling of raw milk and other foods to prevent contamination, we should stop fearing the word *bacteria*. Many of these tiny microorganisms are our friends!

When it comes to raw milk safety, there are two keys: safe milk handling and healthy animals. I discussed safe milk handling earlier in this chapter, but as a quick review, all containers or tools coming into contact with raw milk should be clean and sterilized, hands should be cleaned, udders should be cleaned prior to milking, and a closed milking system by machine is safer than hand milking. If purchasing or legally selling raw milk, one should only use a milking machine and not hand milk. Appropriate cooling and storing of milk is vital as well. Raw milk should also come from healthy goats. Unhealthy animals cannot produce healthy food. Dairy animals should be healthy and free from disease for the raw milk to be safely consumed. There are certain diseases that can be transferred via raw milk. Thankfully we can test for and prevent these diseases. In fact, according the United States Department of Agriculture, as of November 2017 all fifty states in America are considered to free from bovine and swine brucellosis and bovine tuberculosis. All dairy animals, particularly those used for raw milk, should be tested for and free from any such diseases. I discuss these diseases and others in the Troubleshooting chapter.

Ultimately the decision to consume your milk raw or to pasteurize it is your own—as it should be. Only you can weigh the benefits against the potential risks and come to that conclusion. Unlike certain regulatory entities, I do not believe in policing the food you choose to consume.

Goat Milk versus Cow Milk

Goat milk and cow milk have more similarities than we may realize. This is the reason I suggest feeding whole cow milk, even if it is store bought, to goat kids in lieu of milk replacer when goat milk is unavailable to supplement. The chart below, provided by Cultures for Health, shows you just how similar goat and cow milk is nutritionally. Despite the similarities in nutritional content, there are distinct difference between cow and goat milk. Some of these differences should be considered when you're choosing whether to keep goats instead of cows on your farm, in conjunction with other considerations such as cost, infrastructure, and space as well. One interesting thing to note is that it takes about five to ten goats to produce the same amount of milk as a cow depending on breed and individual production; you can expect to need more miniature dairy goats to make the same equivalent.

Composition per 100 grams	Goat Milk	Cow Milk
Protein (g)	3.1	3.2
Fat % (g)	3.5	3.9
Calories/100 ml	60	66
Vitamin A (IU/gram fat)	39	21
Thiamin (B1- UG/100 ml)	39	21
Riboflavin (UG/100 ml)	210	159
Vitamin C (mg ascorbic acid/100 ml)	2	2
Vitamin D (IU/gram fat)	0.7	0.7
Calcium %	0.19	0.18
Iron %	0.07	0.06
Phosphorus %	0.27	0.23
Cholesterol (mg/100 ml)	10	14
Sugars (lactose)	4.4	4.8
Saturated fatty acids (g)	2.3	2.4
Monounsaturated fatty acids (g)	0.8	1.1
Polyunsaturated fatty acids (g)	0.1	0.1

One of the first differences that often comes to mind for people who have never tasted fresh goat milk is the taste. Store bought goat milk often tastes "goaty," but this is due to the age of the milk and how it is processed and handled. Some brands are of a higher quality and better tasting than others, and quality is the key. The milk from your own herd, if it is handled correctly, will taste so similar to cow milk that you may not even notice the difference. My grandmother used to trick her children, including my mother, into drinking goat milk by not telling them it was any different. They assumed it was cow milk and drank it readily, despite "not liking" goat milk. Depending on the breed of goat, you may even find that it is richer, creamier, and sweeter than cow milk due to a higher amount of butterfat. The average butterfat for both cows and most goats is around 4%, but some breeds of goat are known for producing a higher percentage of butterfat. Nigerian Dwarf goats and Nubians are two examples of this averaging about 6% and 5% butterfat, respectively.

Goat milk and the products made by it are nearly pure white except when colored by annatto (a natural cheese coloring derived from the seeds of the achiote tree). This is because goats are better adept at turning beta carotene into vitamin A than cows. The fresh cheese made from goat milk, called chèvre, is known for having a tangy yet mild flavor distinct to itself, but other cheeses can largely be made interchangeably with either cow or goat milk. Some cheeses are traditionally made with a specific type of milk; for example, feta is traditionally sheep or goat milk, Roquefort is traditionally sheep milk, and mozzarella is traditionally made using the milk of Italian water buffalo. Despite this, you will have no trouble making mozzarella with your goat milk!

One way in which cow milk is structurally different from goat milk is the size of the fat molecules. The fat molecules in goat milk are much smaller than cow milk. They stay suspended in the milk, and only a small portion of the fat will rise to the top. Cow milk is not naturally homogenized; its larger fat molecules easily rise to the top where they can be skimmed for making butter, cream cheese, and the like. Store bought cow milk is almost always homogenized—meaning the fat molecules have been broken apart mechanically—unless otherwise stated. Cream can be taken out of goat milk by a cream separator. Goat milk also contains lower levels of lactose (milk sugar) than cow milk. This combined with the smaller fat molecules, which result in a smaller and softer curd, and the increased levels of short and medium chain fatty acids in comparison to cow milk, make goat milk easier to digest than cow milk for some people.

Chapter Eight: Troubleshooting

In this chapter of the book, I am going to give a brief synopsis for several ailments and complications related to reproduction. It's important to remember that this is *not* a comprehensive compendium of all potential illnesses, diseases, or problems that might arise in your dairy goats. I am also only including a general description and synopsis; if you think that your goat is suffering from one of the issues listed here, please do additional research and work with your experienced goat mentor and small ruminant veterinarian to establish a method of action.

Infertility

Infertility in goats can be caused by many different things. One cause of infertility that we have already looked at in the earlier chapter on Nutrition is mineral deficiency, specifically copper and selenium. Deficiency in either of these minerals can cause low birth rates, sterility, failure to maintain pregnancy, and many other complications.

Infertility can also be caused by hormonal imbalances that prevent a doe from retaining a pregnancy and cycling normally. If you have a doe who frequently cycles, acts "buckish," and mates but fails to ever conceive, she might be suffering from a hormone imbalance. Does, particularly does who are overweight, may develop cysts on their ovaries. This is often called "short cycling" or being "cystic." Does who are overweight are much more likely to suffer from infertility than does kept in proper condition. Does who are held over to milk through two cycles are prone to becoming overweight and may have trouble breeding back because of it. Does can also have a subclinical uterine infection that prevents conception, and goats born with abnormalities such as hermaphroditism can experience infertility as well.

Bucks may be infertile or have a low sperm count as well, and it is usually attributed to poor nutrition or mineral deficiency. Infertility in bucks can also be caused by physical deformity such as cryptorchidism. Infertility in bucks is less common than in does. Thankfully infertility is rare in both sexes and is commonly able to be resolved by addressing mineral deficiencies.

Tales from the Kidding Stall: *I once owned a doe named Abby. She came to me as a middle-aged doe who had already had a few litters of kids. As luck would have it, Abby never conceived for me in the several years I owned her. I addressed any possible mineral deficiencies, attempted breeding her to different bucks, left her with bucks for months at a time, and treated her with prescription medication from the vet, all to no avail. Abby showed classic signs of being cystic; she cycled more often through her heat cycle than she should have (sometimes seeming to always be in heat), acted very bucky when the other does were in heat, was a bit overweight, and would breed with bucks readily when cycling but never conceived. Unfortunately, I have no words of wisdom or piece of advice for dealing with such a doe, because nothing I attempted ultimately allowed her to conceive.*

Hermaphroditism, Monorchidism, and Cryptorchidism

Goats can be born with physical deformities that prevent mating and conception. Goats can be born as hermaphrodites, meaning that they are born with physical features from both sexes. A hermaphrodite might be a "true" hermaphrodite and contain both ovaries and testes or they may be a "pseudohermaphrodite" and have either ovaries or testes but be malformed in other ways. For example, a doe might appear almost normal, perhaps with a small deformity on the vulva, but not have the appropriate reproductive tract. In both cases the goat will experience infertility.

Monorchidism refers to a buck who has only one testicle descended into the scrotum, whereas cryptorchidism refers to a buck who has neither testicle appropriately descended. Cryptorchid bucks are infertile due to the increased heat from their body affecting the sperm; testicles are descended away from the body to prevent overheating the temperature-sensitive sperm. Monorchid bucks may be fertile due to the one testicle being descended, but they should not be bred to avoid reproducing the negative gene that resulted in the other testicle not being descended. In both cases bucks will continue to display normal reproductive behavior, and castration must be done surgically. Typically, these bucks are raised or sold for meat, but sometimes they may be kept as a teaser buck to help detect heat. Monorchid bucks will need their one descended testicle removed to be a teaser buck.

Note: Twin heifers in cattle who share the womb with a bull calf have a high chance of being an infertile "freemartin." There is no such correlation with male-female twins in goats, which is a good thing considering that goats most often have more than one kid!

Retained Placenta

The placenta, or afterbirth, should be expelled shortly after the doe gives birth. In my experience, the placenta typically expels within an hour or two after the last kid is born in a healthy doe. If the doe does not expel the afterbirth normally, it is considered retained. I experienced multiple incidences of retained afterbirth in my herd before I started supplementing with selenium; after addressing the mineral needs, I no longer see placentas being retained by does.

In my experience, retained afterbirth typically comes out part way but continues to dangle and does not release fully. This can wick bacteria into the uterus. The placenta can be tied into a knot to prevent it dragging the ground and to add more weight; the gentle addition of weight often helps the doe's body release the remainder of the placenta. A small plastic bag with water may also be tied to the afterbirth to add just a small amount of weight to help continue the release. *Never* pull on the placenta to remove it. Doing so can cause a tear in the doe's uterus and cause her to bleed internally. If you miss a birth and do not see the placenta, don't assume that the doe has retained it—it's more likely that she has eaten it.

If the placenta is retained and knotting it does not allow the doe to release it, a veterinarian can prescribe oxytocin to encourage the doe's uterus to expel the afterbirth. It's important to be sure that the doe is done kidding, because giving oxytocin to a doe who has a stuck kid will only result in her pushing more and still getting nowhere. There is also a short window of time in which this is effective, because the doe's cervix will eventually close and no longer allow the placenta to pass.

Metritis (Uterine Infection)

A uterine infection can be clinical (causing symptoms) or subclinical (asymptomatic). Uterine infections can be caused by the death of a fetus prior to birth or the introduction of bacteria to the uterus. Bacteria can be introduced any time a doe is internally assisted in birth and even if care is taken to prevent exposure. A retained placenta may also cause an infection. Uterine infection may be accompanied by a foul-smelling discharge or other symptoms such as a fever, lethargy, or lack of appetite. In subclinical cases, the doe may not have any overt symptoms but may have trouble conceiving in future attempts. Does with a uterine infection may be prescribed antibiotics or anti-inflammatory medications.

Mastitis

Mastitis is an infection of the udder and can occur in one or both halves of the udder. These infections can be subclinical, meaning the only evidence of the infection might an "off" or salty taste to the milk or a drop in production. Mastitis can also cause lumpy or discolored milk, high somatic cell counts in the milk, discoloration or hardening of the udder, an udder that is hot or cold to the touch, pain in the udder, fever, and in the worst cases gangrene (tissue death) or septicemia (widespread infection throughout the body stemming from the original infection in the udder). There are a number of different bacteria that can cause mastitis, and in some cases mastitis can be chronic and recurrent. Does with chronic mastitis should be culled from the herd.

Mastitis is caused by the introduction of bacteria into the udder via the orifice of the teat. Does with poor udder attachments that allow the udder to be kicked, stepped on, or drag the ground and does with orifices that are too large are more prone to mastitis, but any doe can contract it. Does can even contract mastitis while dry. Mastitis prevention is one reason that kidding stalls should be kept clean; does laying down with an extremely full udder, digging a nest into the bedding, and sometimes with orifices opening and losing their waxy plug in preparation for kidding are exposed to bacteria more than usual. After losing a doe to gangrenous mastitis that became septic, I always dip the doe's teats in an iodine solution immediately following birth. Care should also be taken during milking to thoroughly clean the teats before and after milking.

Mastitis can be detected by certain tests, such as the California Milk Test, that can show the presence of bacteria. The milk can also be cultured to determine the exact cause of infection. The treatment for mastitis depends on the severity and type. In some cases, udder congestion can be mistaken for mastitis, and in those cases a warm compress and massage may be beneficial. Milk can also taste "off" for reasons other than mastitis, mentioned below. It's a good idea to determine for certain that you are dealing with mastitis prior to treatment. Treatment can include udder infusions, frequent milking out, and antibiotics. In cases of suspected gangrene or septic mastitis, it's important to act quickly and seek veterinary advice. The udder tissue might slough off or rupture. Does may require full or partial mastectomy. If the mastitis has become septic, intravenous antibiotics and other supportive care may be administered by a veterinarian.

Unfortunately, the gangrenous and septic form of mastitis moves quickly, and death is not uncommon. The veterinarian at the University of Mississippi Starkville who treated my doe with gangrene mastitis told me that he once had a client whose cow contracted mastitis the day she gave birth (a very common time for mastitis to be contracted) and was dead within three days.

Off Tasting Milk

Milk can have an off flavor for several reasons. Mastitis can certainly cause ill flavored milk, but it is not the only possible reason. If you are certain that your milking hygiene, handling, and storage are up to par and the milk is being cooled quickly and consumed while still fresh, the flavor may be indicative of another cause. Subclinical mastitis may be at play, but nutritional imbalances and deficiencies as well as what the doe is eating can cause bad tasting milk. Cobalt deficiency, discussed in the Nutrition chapter, is known for causing off flavored milk. Diets high in molasses (sweet feed) can cause poor tasting milk as can poor diets in general. If the goat is eating something strongly flavored, such as wild onions or garlic, this flavor can also sometimes transfer into the milk.

Tales from the Kidding Stall: *In instances where I suspect mild, subclinical mastitis, I have had luck treating it naturally before it progressed. If a doe's milk tastes salty but shows no other issues, I will prepare an udder balm using olive oil and fresh garlic. I finely mince several garlic cloves and allow them to infuse in two cups of olive oil. Then I rub the oil and garlic on the doe's udder after milking and do not wipe it off. I do this until the milk returns to a normal taste. In one instance it only required one day of rubbing the udder with garlic oil for the milk flavor to return to normal.*

Abortion and Stillbirth

Miscarriage, or loss of pregnancy, in livestock is called abortion. Abortion can happen very early in the pregnancy—before you even know the goat is pregnant—or so late that the kids were nearly developed. Stillbirth, which is when full-term kids are born dead, can occur as well. It's important not to automatically assume that a dead kid was stillborn, however. Kids that have died in utero will show signs of decay, such as hair slippage or weak, easily torn skin. Kids may die during the process of a difficult labor as well. Kids that are found dead after an unwitnessed labor are most likely to have died due to not being cleaned quickly enough, resulting in suffocation or hypothermia. If the kids appear otherwise fully formed and normal with no signs of decay, and the doe was full term, then they most likely died after being born or possibly during labor.

The causes of abortion are numerous, and this is not a comprehensive list. However, abortion is usually quite rare, so the majority of pregnancies will end with successful, live kids rather than tragedy. That said, all aborted material should be treated as a biohazard. Many causes of abortion are zoonotic and can be transferred from goats to humans or other livestock species. The doe should be quarantined away from other animals, and all the fluid, tissues, or fetuses from the abortion should be handled with caution. You should always wear gloves and avoid touching aborted materials. Pregnant women should avoid handling the aborted materials or the goat who aborted. The doe or the aborted fetus should be tested to determine if a disease was the causative agent. Washington Animal Disease Diagnostic Laboratory offers abortion screening services both of blood or an aborted fetus, and your veterinarian should know of other local options for diagnosis as well.

Hormonal Problems

Hormonal issues may cause the doe to abort early in the pregnancy, likely before you even realized the doe was pregnant. If the doe's body does not produce the appropriate pregnancy hormones or produces the hormone prostaglandin which signals she isn't pregnant, the body may continue to cycle through and not hold onto the pregnancy, despite a fertilized egg(s) being present. This would cause a very early loss which would not produce any fluids or tissues. These losses are called early embryonic death, and unless you have a doe who repeatedly fails to conceive, you likely will not even know they have occurred.

Physical Trauma

Though rare, a doe can lose a pregnancy due to trauma. This typically happens when a particularly aggressive goat in the herd headbutts the doe in the stomach. You may or may not see the trauma occur. In an abortion caused by trauma, only one doe would abort in the herd, not several. The doe would also test negative for any of the infectious causes. Extreme environmental stress may have an impact as well. Personally, I would not assume trauma was the cause until all other reasons had been ruled out, but it is certainly a possibility. If multiple does have aborted at once, sometimes called an abortion storm, trauma is not the likely culprit.

Ingestion of Toxic Plants or Medicines

Certain medications and dewormers can cause abortion or fetal deformities if given to pregnant does. Some hormonal medications are also specifically used to cause abortion in case of accidental breeding or to induce labor. Always check the safety of a medication for use in pregnant does before dosing.

Certain plants and foods are also abortifacient. Mycotoxins in moldy feed can cause abortions, as can certain toxic plants such as ponderosa pine, lupine, hemlock, and plants that produce cyanide, alkaloids, or nitrates such as those found in fertilizers. Fungi such as ergot, which grows on grains, can have an impact as well. While some toxic plants will kill the adult goats themselves, some may be consumed in small enough amounts or have a lower toxicity that harms the fetus but not the doe.

Mineral Deficiency

Mineral deficiency, which is discussed in the Nutrition chapter, can cause abortion as well. The most likely culprits are copper or selenium deficiency. Both minerals are essential for healthy reproduction. Deficiency may cause low birth rate, infertility, difficult labors, retained placentas, or abortion. Copper deficiency is associated with early term abortions, whereas selenium may cause preterm labor or stillbirth.

Toxoplasmosis

Toxoplasmosis is caused by a protozoan parasite known as toxoplasma gondii. Toxoplasmosis causes abortion or stillbirth, because the infection spreads through the bloodstream and causes necrosis of the cotyledons. Cats are the vector for toxoplasmosis. Cats contract the disease by eating the raw meat of rodents, and then they pass on the T. gondii in their feces. Eating raw meat infected with T. gondii or accidentally ingesting infected cat feces is the only way to contract toxoplasmosis. Barn cats are commonly kept for mousers, and stray cats often wander into farms. When those cats defecate in the pasture or barn the disease can be contracted by goats. This doesn't mean you should never own barn cats, as they can be quite useful for keeping rodents out of feed stores. Kittens and young cats are most likely to pass on the infection. Once they have been initially infected and shed the disease, the cats develop an immunity and no longer shed. Likewise, once a goat has contracted it they develop an immunity as well and will not have another abortion. New cats and kittens should be quarantined away from goats for at least a month before introduction.

There is no treatment or cure for toxoplasmosis other than the natural immunity that infected animals develop.

Tales from the Kidding Stall: *The only abortion I have thus far experienced in my herd at the time of this writing was caused by toxoplasmosis. I remember that day quite clearly, and it was a rather hard day on the farm. I can't remember all the details now—we never can, can we?—but it was one of those days where nothing seems to go right. Then when I went down to the barn to tend to the goats, I saw that a pregnant doe's backside was bloody. She was too early on in pregnancy for any tissue or fetuses to be passed, but I knew what was happening. I sat on a haybale and cried. Naturally I was filled with fear as well, anxious that whatever she had was contagious, and all my does would lose their kids. Since I had no fetus to test, we drew blood and sent it to WADDL for the abortion screen. Thankfully all the contagious diseases came back negative, but toxoplasmosis came back positive.*

I did a bit of research and learned that our barn cat, Mickey, was the most likely culprit. I had caught him once using the bathroom in the dirt floor of our barn. The area he was in was not where the goats lived, but they passed through that area each day to go out to pasture. I didn't think anything of his behavior at the time, other than to be annoyed, but now I know that's most likely how the toxoplasmosis was contracted. Thankfully I have not seen any of our barn cats do that again, and have not experienced any more abortions, either. I will always have barn cats to help keep the mice at bay, but I know now to keep younger cats quarantined and to discourage them using the barn floor as a restroom. Of course, our own barn cats or strays may use the ground in the pasture as well, so prevention isn't foolproof.

Coxiellosis (Q. Fever)

Q. (Queensland) fever is the common name for coxiellosis, and the name for the disease when it infects humans. Coxiellosis is zoonotic and infectious; it can affect humans, other livestock, wildlife, and even domestic pets like cats. It can cause an abortion storm in a herd, with up to 50% or more of the herd being affected. Coxiellosis often causes late term abortions or stillbirths, and the aborted placenta will be covered in a gray-brown exudate. Coxiellosis is caused by coxiella burnetii. It can be transmitted to humans via inhalation or contact with the aborted fluids. Ticks can transfer the disease between goats, but they are not thought to play a role in human infections. The disease can also be secreted in milk, urine, and feces. Infection can be subclinical, and shedding of the organism is much lower in subclinical infections than when abortion occurs.

There is no cure for coxiellosis. After an initial abortion, does develop an immunity to abortion, but they remain subclinically infected and may spread the organism.

Chlamydia

Chlamydia, caused by chlamydia abortus, is the most common cause of abortion in goats. Chlamydia is another possible cause of abortion storms, with up to 60% of the pregnant does aborting or giving birth to stillborn or weak kids. The does may abort at any time, but abortions in the last month of pregnancy are most common. Does who abort from chlamydia become immune to abortion. It's not known for certain whether chlamydia infected does continue to shed after their contraction of the disease, but ewes (sheep) with the infection do remain infected for life and shed the organism at ovulation, even after developing their immunity to abortion. The aborted placenta may have a reddish-brown coating on the cotyledons.

Chlamydia is zoonotic and may be contracted by humans.

Brucellosis

Brucellosis is caused by infection with brucella melitensis. Brucellosis causes abortion, most often in the fourth month, but can also cause mastitis or lameness. The aborted fetuses and placenta appear normal. Brucellosis is zoonotic and can be passed on to other livestock and humans. Brucellosis is also secreted in the milk. There is no cure for brucellosis, and does who contract it are infected for life and should be culled. The United States has developed an eradication program for brucellosis, and because of this the infection has become rare in the United States. As of the November 2017 report, all 50 states are considered free from brucellosis and tuberculosis in domestic livestock herds according to the USDA. However, that report could change at any time with the report of an infected animal, and brucellosis is still present in wildlife herds, so it cannot be considered completely eradicated.

Listeriosis

Listeriosis can present in different forms, one of which causes abortion. Listeria can be contracted from contaminated feed, the soil, feces of infected animals, and other sources. In one version, listeria causes a rapid encephalitis that can result in death in 24-48 hours and only has a 30% chance of survival with treatment. In the abortive form, abortion usually occurs later in the pregnancy. Herd wide abortion storms are rare with listeria but may occur. Does are typically subclinical until abortion, but afterward they may develop metritis (uterine infection). The encephalitic version is not contagious to other goats in the herd because the infection is confined to the brain, but the form of listeria that causes abortion can be spread from the aborted materials.

Listeriosis may be treated with antibiotics. Listeriosis is zoonotic and can infect humans, but human infection is relatively rare. Listeria can also contaminate milk. Infected does may shed the disease for a month or longer after infection/abortion.

Caprine Herpesvirus 1 (CpHV 1)

Caprine herpesvirus 1 is related to bovine herpesvirus 1 (BoHV 1). It can be contracted via the mucus membranes of the respiratory and reproductive tracts, and is responsible for abortion storms. Abortions are most often late-term, and they may present without other clinical signs of infection. CpHV1 can also cause stillbirth of full term kids. Outside of abortion, it can also cause vulvovaginitis (inflammation of the vagina and vulva), balanoposthitis (inflammation of the penis), or respiratory disease, although adult goats are usually subclinical. Goats can be infected and shed the disease without showing symptoms. Stress and anything that lowers the goat's immunity can result in renewed shedding in asymptomatic goats. There are no cures or vaccines for CpHV 1.

Cloudburst (False Pregnancy, Pseudopregnancy)

Although rare, does sometimes experience a false pregnancy. These are often called cloudbursts. Cloudbursts are more common in older does, and they result when the doe's body behaves as if it is pregnant when it has not actually conceived a pregnancy. This can happen in does who have not been exposed to a buck at all, or to a doe who was exposed to a buck and did not conceive or lost the embryos early on. The does corpus luteum produces progesterone and her uterus will fill with fluid as well (called hydrometra). Sometimes this fluid can cause the doe to look pregnant even though she isn't. The doe may also develop an udder in preparation for her "kidding" as well.

If you suspect a pseudopregnancy in one of your does, a veterinarian can diagnose the doe via ultrasound. The ultrasound will show the fluid in an otherwise empty uterus, indicating the false pregnancy. The false pregnancy can end on its own, when the doe's body stops producing the progesterone. This causes her to go into labor and "give birth" to the empty fluid. This is what led to the term "cloudburst." Does can also be treated with prescription hormonal medication from your vet that will cause the corpus luteum to stop producing the progesterone and the doe's cycle to return to normal.

Pregnancy Toxemia and Lactational Ketosis

Toxemia and ketosis are metabolic diseases. The primary difference between the two is only that toxemia is the term used when it occurs during pregnancy and ketosis is the term used when it occurs after pregnancy in lactation. The primary cause of ketosis is an issue in feeding: either underfeeding or overfeeding. Toxemia most often occurs in the last few weeks of pregnancy, and ketosis typically occurs early in lactation shortly after birth. Multiple kids in pregnancy increase the risks for toxemia due to lack of proper nutrition. As the kids grow the space of the rumen shrinks. If the doe is eating poor quality hay or forage, she may not be able to consume enough of it to meet her needs. Having high quality, nutritious hay is extremely important, especially during late pregnancy. High multiple pregnancy in and of itself does not mean a doe will develop ketosis; it is when this combines with other factors that toxemia can occur. With proper management and nutrition, does carrying quadruplets or more can remain completely healthy throughout pregnancy.

Overfeeding of grain can cause pregnancy toxemia as well. Overweight goats are more prone to toxemia due to their fat stores shrinking the rumen's space as well as the impact of the hormone leptin, released by adipose (fat) cells, lowering their appetite. Does fed too much grain and eating little forage are more likely to go off their feed and not consume necessary roughage late in pregnancy when they need it most. Rumen acidosis may also contribute to toxemia. Pregnancy toxemia is more common than lactation ketosis. Symptoms of toxemia are subtle at first, and may include lack of appetite, general listlessness, lethargy, dull eyes, or isolation from the herd. As it progresses the doe may start teeth grinding, have swelling in her lower legs, grow weak, or exhibit neurological signs such as star gazing, blindness, tremors, coma, and death. Does who survive pregnancy toxemia are more likely to have a difficult labor, weak or stillborn kids, and lactation ketosis.

Prevention of toxemia and ketosis includes making sure that does have the ability to exercise, not allowing unbred does to become overweight, feeding high quality hay and forage, and not overfeeding grain. Hay should also be available in such a way that dominant "herd queens" cannot bully the subordinate does off the feed. Treatment in early stages includes increasing feed quality and gradually introducing or increasing grain. For more severe cases or does who are off feed, propylene glycol is administered via drench or, in some cases, intravenously. Does are given B vitamin injections as well, and your veterinarian may suggest inducing labor if the doe is known to be close enough to her due date. Does are also often treated for hypocalcemia alongside toxemia because the two diseases present similar symptoms and sometimes occur together.

Hypocalcemia (Milk Fever)

Hypocalcemia results when the doe's demand for calcium exceeds what her body and diet can support. Hypocalcemia occurs most often in early lactation right after birth, but it can also sometimes happen in late pregnancy. Hypocalcemia can also occur alongside or secondary to toxemia as well. Does who are heavy producers are more likely to suffer from milk fever than others. There is a misconception stemming from old preventative practices in cattle that does should be fed a low-calcium diet in late pregnancy, but feeding alfalfa or other foods that contain calcium has not shown to increase the chances of does contracting hypocalcemia. Alfalfa is a safe food source for does both in late pregnancy and during lactation, and is a good source of calcium and protein for a lactating doe. In fact, a low-calcium diet may actually cause hypocalcemia in goats.

Symptoms of hypocalcemia are similar to those of toxemia: listlessness, lack of appetite, weakness, and eventual death. Does may lay down on their sternum with their head and neck curved back over their shoulders. Does with hypocalcemia may also have a low body temperature or shiver. Because the doe is off feed, she may develop ketosis as a secondary illness to her milk fever. For that reason, does who exhibit one or the other illness are often treated for both. Treatment for hypocalcemia includes administering a supplement called CMPK, which stands for Calcium Magnesium Phosphorus Potassium. Proper levels of magnesium, phosphorus, and potassium are essential to calcium absorption.

Prevention of hypocalcemia is focused on a proper diet with plenty of high quality forage, proper levels of calcium and magnesium, and prevention of any sudden changes in diet that may upset the doe's digestion. Some people recommend feeding does human antacid medications containing calcium as preventative, but the type of calcium in those supplements is not readily absorbed by goats.

Urinary Calculi (Urolithiasis)

Urinary calculi are stones that develop in the urinary tract of male goats. These are most common in wethers due to the smaller urethra, but intact bucks can experience blockages caused by calculi as well. These urinary stones, which consist of phosphate salts, can block the end of the urethra, preventing urine from escaping the bladder. Goats will have trouble urinating, may have bloody urine, dribble urine, have an extended abdomen, and show signs of pain such as vocalization while urinating, kick at the stomach, stand hunched, and go off feed.

Urinary calculi is most often caused by diets high in grain and low in roughage (hay, browse), but can also occur due to mineral deposits in the drinking water. Overfeeding grain to males is the most common cause. This causes an imbalance in calcium:phosphorus ratios. The best prevention is to avoid feeding grain to male goats except when necessary to maintain condition. When feeding grain, ensure the proper calcium to phosphorus ratios, at least 2:1 and up to 4:1 calcium:phosphorus. It is a good idea to feed bucks alfalfa when they are consuming grain. Bucks should also be encouraged to drink plenty of water—keep minerals available, especially in cold months, and ensure the goats are drinking water during winter. Ammonium chloride can be added to the diet of male goats when consuming grain as well.

Treatment requires a veterinarian to surgically remove the pizzle (end of the penis) of the goat, but more severe cases may require further intervention using a catheter, muscle relaxants, or surgery. Without treatment the bladder will burst and kill the goat.

Vaginal or Uterine Prolapse

Prolapses occur when the doe's body begins to essentially turn itself "inside out." The interior of the vagina or the uterus extrude from the vulva. Overweight does are more prone to vaginal prolapse, and calcium deficiency, lack of exercise, and genetic predisposition can be a contributing factor as well. Vaginal prolapse occurs during pregnancy before delivery, but full uterine prolapses occur during or immediately after kidding. The rectum may also prolapse in conjunction with or independent of vaginal or uterine prolapse, and in vaginal prolapse the cervix may prolapse as well, and the bladder may enter the prolapsed vagina. Vaginal prolapse can be mild and intermittent with a small prolapse occurring when the goat lays down, or it may be severe and persistent. A veterinarian can correct the vaginal prolapse by cleaning and reinserting the prolapse, draining the bladder first if needed, and holding it in place either with a special type of stitches (which must be remove before kidding) or with special devices designed to prevent prolapse. Applying sugar to the area can help reduce swelling.

Vaginal prolapse does not necessarily increase the chances of a difficult delivery or uterine prolapse. Uterine prolapse happens after delivery while the cervix is open. However, the contributing factors are similar: calcium deficiency or hypocalcemia, overweight, lack of exercise, genetic predisposition, or a difficult delivery. Uterine prolapse is quite serious, and quick response is necessary to save the goat. The prolapse should be kept as clean and moist as possible, and the goat should be brought to a veterinarian (or vice versa) as quickly as possible. Prolonged prolapse can damage the uterus and result in infection or necrosis (death) of the tissue. The veterinarian will clean and attempt to replace the uterus. It may be necessary for the veterinarian to perform surgery or provide certain medications to increase uterine tone. As with vaginal prolapse, the bladder or intestines may also collapse into the prolapsed uterus. Prognosis depends on many factors, including the quickness with which the condition is treated.

Common Communicable Diseases

While there are many diseases and illnesses that goats may contract, some of which are communicable or zoonotic and may be tested for preventatively, there are three primary diseases of goats that all responsible goat breeders should test for and avoid: Caprine Arthritis Encephalitis (CAE), Caseous Lymphadenitis (CL), and Johne's Disease (pronounced yo-knees). These are chronic, incurable, contagious diseases of goats that you do not want to enter your herd. Strict biosecurity, disease testing, and careful selection of herds from which you purchase are important to keep your herd free from these diseases Reputable goat breeders will be able to show you negative test results for these diseases, be willing to test any goat in their herd for the disease at request, and keep their herd free from these diseases. Some breeders who have maintained closed herds for several years may cease testing, and some breeders may choose not to test yearly for certain diseases due to decreased reliability of the test (discussed further below), but in these instances, they should still be willing to pull a test for a potential buyer.

Unfortunately, there is a lot of misinformation about these particular diseases, and there are also still people who do not see them as important or do not care if the disease is in their herd. It's important to be careful who you purchase from to avoid bringing a diseased animal into your herd who can infect all of your other goats. New goats should always be quarantined a minimum of thirty days, with a longer period of three months preferable, and retested before introduction to your own herd, regardless of prior test results while within another herd. Ideally you would pull an initial test upon receiving the goat and again at the end of quarantine before introduction. Kids under six months of age will need to be quarantined longer, because tests results are not reliable at a younger age. Avoid allowing strange goats to come to your farm, or your goats to go to a strange farm, to avoid potential exposure to disease.

As I have mentioned elsewhere in this book, unhealthy animals cannot produce healthy food. These diseases can be devastating to your herd. While I don't advocate panicking or losing sleep over these diseases, it is important to take them seriously and err on the side of caution.

Caprine Arthritis Encephalitis

Caprine Arthritis Encephalitis, or CAE, is one of the most well-known infectious diseases in dairy goats, and thankfully it is also one of the most easily tested and prevented.

CAE infected goats, referred to as CAE positive, may be asymptomatic for many years or even a lifetime, but they are still capable of transmitting the disease. CAE is most often passed from goat to goat through infected milk, but it can also be transmitted through aerosol transmission from goats with the pneumatic form, or possibly through blood or mating, though this has not been confirmed. The most common means of transfer is from dam to offspring through milk, but in some instances kids or even adults may nurse on an unrelated doe. In addition to the spread from the pneumatic spread, does can also contract it during the milking process. Contaminated hands or milking machines, or open or spilled milk in the parlor can spread the disease. There is no cure for CAE.

The symptoms of CAE may present in multiple forms: arthritic, pneumatic, mastitic, wasting, or encephalitic. The arthritic form is most often seen in adults, and it causes arthritis-like symptoms that vary in severity. The joints of the animal will swell and become painful, most often in the knees, and they may walk on their knees due to a loss of range of motion. Severe cases are debilitating to the infected goats. The goat will be inactive and lethargic, will not stand and walk normally, and body condition may decrease over time. Mastitic CAE will affect milk production and can cause hard udders with little or no milk production. This symptom can sometimes be mistaken for chronic mastitis when it is in fact CAE. These may occur together or individually of each other.

In cases resulting in pneumonia, CAE causes a chronic pneumonia and can be transmitted via aerosol particles from the lungs. Again, this may occur concurrent with other symptoms or on its own. CAE can also cause chronic wasting, alone or with other symptoms. Despite receiving adequate feed and not being under a parasite load, the goat will continue to lose body condition over time until it ultimately wastes away and dies. Both the wasting and pneumatic forms are most likely to occur in adults. It's important to remember that goats with CAE may not present these symptoms for many years; it's important to always use disease testing and not simply a healthy appearance to determine the CAE status of a goat or herd.

The encephalitic or neurotic form most often affects kids under one year of age. It causes swelling in the spine which leads to lameness that develops into paralysis over a period of days or weeks. Inability to stand and weakness in joints in an otherwise healthy kid are the first signs. Note that selenium deficiency also causes leg weakness; however, selenium deficiency will usually cause the kid to be born with weak limbs and the condition will improve with treatment (selenium and splints), whereas CAE will get worse rather than improving. Eventually the kid will succumb to the illness and die.

CAE is preventable. There is a very reliable ELISA test for CAE that tests for antibodies in the goat's blood. The test can be done through BioTracking, WADDL, or another laboratory offering the ELISA test. As stated above, reputable breeders will have negative test results for CAE and other diseases. Yearly retesting is advised for most herds, and testing of new incoming goats should always be done prior to introducing them to your herd. There is a variable incubation period for CAE, so in some cases a goat testing negative may seroconvert and test positive at a subsequent test. If you are visiting another herd, even one with negative test results, look for warning signs such as swollen, painful knees and goats with limited mobility or wasting. Although goats may be asymptomatic, no goat should be purchased from an unhealthy-looking herd under any circumstances.

If a goat in your herd should have a positive test result, don't give up hope. CAE can be eradicated from a herd, and you may be able to keep the kids to replace infected goats if you follow appropriate protocol. To keep kids from an infected dam and prevent them becoming infected themselves, kids are pulled from their dams immediately at birth. The does are not allowed to touch their kids, and kids are bottle fed with milk that has come from negative goats, pasteurized milk, or cow milk from the store. Keep in mind that kids fed pasteurized milk from CAE infected dams may still test positive themselves for several months; withhold testing the offspring until they are six months of age or older. In order for this to be successful, you must be present at the birth and prevent the kids from nursing their dam. The infected doe will then be culled from the herd after a replacement is produced.

CAE does not contaminate the environment.

Caseous Lymphadenitis (CL)

Caseous lymphadenitis, or CL, is a chronic, highly contagious, zoonotic disease affecting goats. It is caused by the bacteria Corynebacterium pseudotuberculosis. It can be transmitted to humans and other livestock, especially sheep and camelids, via the exudate from abscesses, which may be external or located in the udder (contaminating the milk) or the lungs (resulting in aerosol transmission). There is no cure for the disease in goats or people. It is prevalent in pet and meat herds, because in pet herds there is a lack of knowledge and in meat herds the goats are seen as terminal. However, it occurs in dairy herds as well. It is imperative that goat breeders be aware of, and vigilant to prevent, CL to protect themselves and their herds.

CL cannot be cured or treated. It is a chronic illness that causes abscesses filled with a thick, cheese-like, white, greenish, or yellow pus. The disease causing the swelling and abscession of infected lymph nodes. External abscesses most often show up around the goat's face, upper neck, lower neck above the shoulder, above the udder, and on the upper hind leg. Abscesses may also be internal in the udder, lungs, or around other internal organs. The process is caused by the goat's lymph system attacking the CL bacteria and isolating it within the lymph system. It enters the body through openings in the skin, mucus membranes, or oral ingestion. When internal, it can be passed through contaminated milk or exude in the lungs. Flies may transmit the disease by landing on an open abscess and then landing on another goat.

There is contradicting information about how long CL lasts in the soil. The Washington Animal Disease Diagnostic Laboratory states that it lives up to eight months in the soil, while information from the book *Goat Medicine* by Mary C. Smith and David M.

Sherman states that is may live for weeks or months in the environment. Hearsay will often state that it can live indefinitely in the ground, but I have yet to see any reputable documentation of this. Should land be contaminated, disinfection of the soil includes killing and burning any plant life, treating the ground with a strong trisodium phosphate detergent, solarizing it, and applying a heavy amount of agricultural lime. Alternatively, the top two layers of soil can be removed. CL may also contaminate infrastructure such as barn walls, milk stanchions, fencing, and the like. A herd eradication program in Norway, cited in *Goat Medicine*, successfully eradicated CL from their herd by culling infected animals, disinfecting and then leaving the environment empty of goats for three months, and removing the top ten centimeters of soil in paddocks.

The best prevention is to buy from clean, tested herds. It is important to remember that blood tests for CL are not as accurate as CAE tests, so you must be vigilant and not rely solely on blood tests. The goat's body isolates the bacteria in the lymph system, so false negatives may occur in goats whose bodies have walled off the bacteria. Occasionally false positives may occur as well; goats with no obvious abscesses who have previously tested negative and are held in an otherwise CL-free herd should be retested. The most accurate method of testing is to have a veterinarian collect and test the exude from an abscess; but of course a CL-free herd will not have abscesses to test. The blood test is the next best option, and it can be a useful tool for evaluating the status of the herd. The blood test is valuable for identifying goats with internal abscesses or early infections (no external abscess). Infections cannot be detected for at least days after infection, which is one reason new animals should be tested twice, at induction and again at the end of the quarantine. CL may incubate for weeks or months before an abscess forms as well. Tests are not accurate in goats under six months of age, and goats who have been given an off-label CL vaccination will always test positive (see below). An eradication program in the Netherlands, cited by *Goat Medicine*, found that culling based on serologically positive blood test results was successful in 53 herds (approximately 13,000 adult goats total).

To prevent CL from entering your herd, purchase only from trusted and tested herds, isolate new animals, perform blood tests, and monitor for abscesses. New goats added to the herd should be watched closely for abscesses on at least a monthly basis for at least a year after introduction. When visiting the herd from which you are purchasing goats, keep your eyes open and look for abscesses or abscess scars on the animals in the herd. Ask the breeder about their prevention methods in addition to testing. This should include purchasing animals only from clean herds, quarantining new goats and retesting before introduction to the herd, and basic biosecurity practices that limit the risk of spreading disease.

Not all abscesses are caused by CL. To prevent non-CL abscesses that may mimic the disease, keep your facilities as free of things that can injure goats as possible. Note your vaccine locations as sometimes a lump or abscess may develop at a vaccination site. When vaccinating, be sure to fully break through the outer skin layer—and to not go into the skin on the other side—and administer the vaccine into the space in the "tent." Vaccines given in between skin layers are more likely to cause abscesses. In a herd that has been CL-free, you shouldn't assume any abscess is CL. If a goat in your herd develops an abscess, immediately isolate them from the herd. Have a vet remove the abscess intact or drain it and collect the exude while being sure to treat the abscess and exude as a biohazard. The abscess should be disinfected, and the goat should remain isolated until negative tests are returned. The pus should be tested for the CL bacteria, and positive animals should be culled.

There is a vaccine designed for sheep that some people choose to use off-label on goats. There are a few problems with this vaccine. First, any goat that has been vaccinated will test positive for CL for its lifetime; this prevents potential buyers from knowing the true status of a vaccinated herd. In addition, the vaccine does not cure CL in infected animals and is not completely effective at preventing CL in non-infected animals. In a herd where vaccines are used, there may still be positive animals shedding the bacteria, but testing will have become useless to determine which animals are positive or negative. The vaccine is also reported to cause adverse reactions in adult goats immediately following vaccination, including lack of appetite, lameness, a severe drop in milk production, depression, or fever.

Johne's ("yo-knees") Disease (Paratuberculosis)

Johne's is a devastating disease in ruminant species such as goats and cattle. It can also affect other species as well including wildlife like deer and even some non-ruminant wildlife like rabbits. It causes chronic wasting and eventually death through damage to the digestive system. The method of digestive failure is not completely understood. Essentially the infected goat starves to death over time despite being provided an appropriate diet and sufficient calories. Johne's can be transmitted across livestock species, especially among cows and goats. In cows, diarrhea is a prominent symptom. However, goats do not typically present with diarrhea. The primary symptom in goats is wasting. Johne's is caused by a bacteria known as Mycobacterium avium subspecies paratuberculosis (Map).

There is a potential link between Johne's disease and Crohn's disease in humans, but it has not been definitively established. In 1972 it was suggested the Johne's could be useful in study for understanding Crohn's because of the similarities between the two diseases. Then in 1984 the bacteria, Map, was discovered in the diseased tissue of four Crohn's patients; this suggested that Johne's may be a potentially zoonotic disease. Map bacteria are present in the milk of infected animals and may even survive pasteurization. A study by the National Research Council in 2003 determined that there was insufficient evidence to either prove or disprove that Map causes some or all cases of Crohn's disease in humans and that new research needed to be conducted. There are some in the medical community that believe that there is enough evidence of a potential link to be concerned, while others do not feel that enough evidence has been found to make the connection. Ultimately, we cannot know for certain either way until more research emerges and either confirms or disproves the association.

Johne's is a disease that may remain dormant for years before the goat shows symptoms. Interestingly, infected goats may also not shed the bacteria for this time as well. Goats may be infected and asymptomatic but not shedding, infected and asymptomatic but shedding the disease, or symptomatic and shedding. Symptomatic goats eventually become emaciated and weak before finally dying of what is essentially starvation. Weight loss, loss of appetite, depression, listlessness, dull coat, and chronic heavy parasite loads are common symptoms. Johne's is most often contracted in young kids, often shortly after birth, and typically through fecal-oral transmission. The infected goats typically do not start to shed or show symptoms until later in life. There is no cure for Johne's disease.

Blood and fecal tests are available for Johne's. As with CL, Johne's tests can return false negatives. Because the disease may incubate for such a long period of time before something triggers the goat to start shedding or become symptomatic, infected goats can test negative during the time that they are not shedding. This is one reason why repeat testing is recommended, because young, non-shedding goats may test negative early in life but eventually begin to shed the disease and test positive. Again, buying from clean, tested herds with no signs of chronic wasting is important for preventing the disease, and it is important to continue yearly testing your own herd in case of previously negative goats converting. Other important preventative methods are to raise feeders above poop-height, use rotational grazing to make browse taller, and to practice good sanitation. Goats housed in close, confined quarters or unsanitary, manure-laden quarters are more likely to contract Johne's. Does should give birth in a clean environment as well, kept clean from excessive manure. Due to the nature of Johne's, finding an infected goat in your herd indicates that other goats in the herd are most likely infected as well.

There is much speculation among individuals about how long Johne's may live in the soil. According to both *Goat Medicine* and *The Merck Veterinary Manual*, Johne's may survive in the soil for over one year.

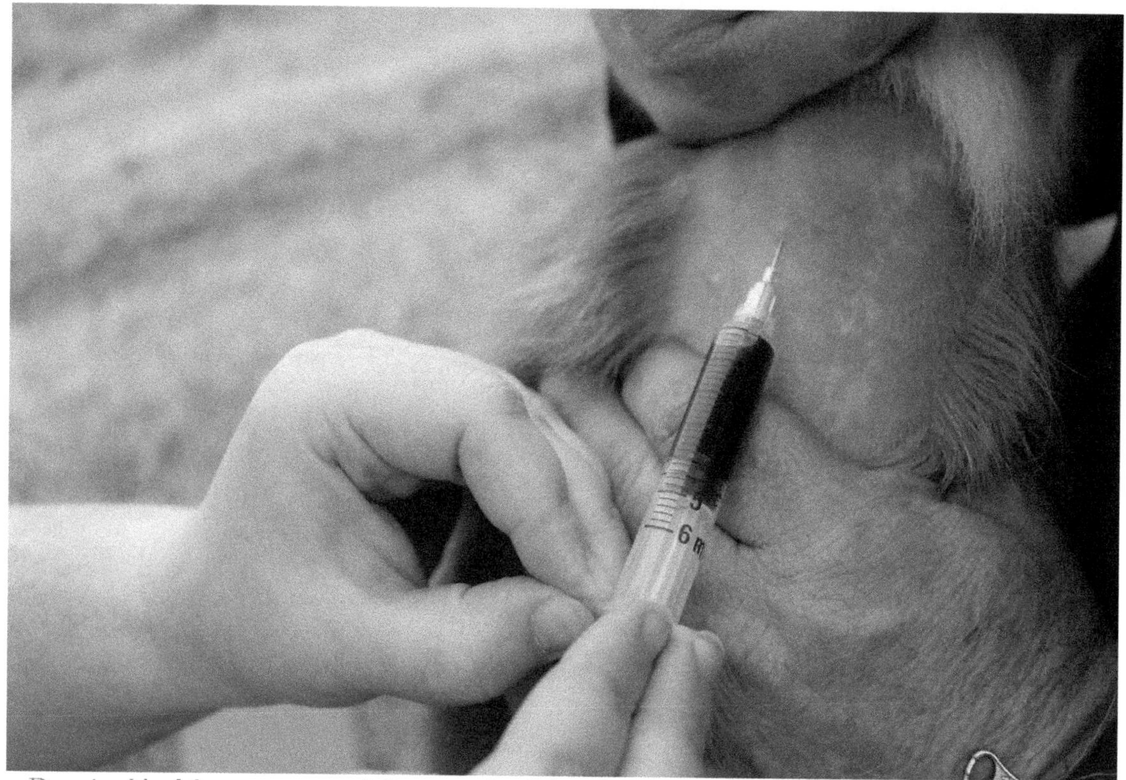

Drawing blood for pregnancy and disease testing. Note that the needle is inserted into the vein at an angle, not perpendicular. You can also see the bulge the vein creates thanks to the pressure applied at the base of the neck. When touched, the vein is soft and squishy, not hard like muscle.

How to Draw Blood

In order to perform disease testing and pregnancy testing, your goats must have their blood drawn. While you may opt to pay a veterinarian to do this, it is a simple procedure you can learn to do yourself as well. Learning to draw blood on your own can save you money and time as well, especially in larger herds. In some cases, your veterinarian may even request a blood sample from you in lieu of bringing a goat in or having the vet come out for testing. Drawing your own blood is an extremely useful skill to have as a goat breeder. If possible, you may also have your veterinarian teach you the process in person as well.

In order to draw blood you will need a few essential supplies. These include 5 ML capacity luer lock syringes, 1" long 18- or 20-gauge needles, 5 ML red top blood collection tubes, rubbing alcohol, cotton balls, a pair of clippers to shave the neck, and gloves. You will also need someone to hold the goat or a secure headcatch that holds the goat in place. The process is no more painful than any injection or needle poke, but goats do not like to be restrained; it will be very difficult or impossible to draw blood without help or the proper restraint. Most supplies can be purchased online through retailers such as Jeffers Livestock or purchased at your local farm supply store. The red top tubes can be ordered from BioTracking online, which also performs pregnancy and CAE testing, or procured from your veterinarian. Depending on the test and the laboratory, you will need to collect three to five milliliters of blood. BioTracking sells double sided needles and special plastic adaptors to allow you to collect blood directly into the tube instead of into a syringe, but I have found these messy and more difficult to use than a simple syringe pull.

I recommend drawing blood on overweight goats last as they will have the least prominent neck veins. For your first attempt, chose the calmest goat with the most prominent veins. When goats jerk around, even while being restrained, it makes it more difficult to draw blood. Also keep in mind that you may not successfully hit the vein perfectly every single time, or you may accidentally blow the vein (by going all the way through) if the goat jerks unexpectedly. This is okay. Even veterinarians and human doctors and nurses sometimes make mistakes and miss or blow a vein. Blowing a vein does not cause any permanent damage to the goat. However, if a vein has blown you will not be able to draw blood from it. Switch to a fresh needle and the opposite side of the neck. I have drawn blood on my goats for many years, but occasionally a particularly difficult goat jerks and makes me miss or blow the vein. It can be frustrating, but it's not the end of the world. The more you practice the better you will be at drawing blood.

Step 1: Prepare

Before ever going to the barn, label your red top tubes and gather your supplies. Be sure to write each goat's name on its tube in permanent marker or another ink that will not rub off. It goes without saying that you will need a fresh syringe and needle for each goat as well to prevent cross contamination. I also like to carry an extra needle with me as well in case I need to make a second stick on a goat. Each use dulls a needle slightly, so even on the same goat I prefer not to use the same needle twice.

Step 2: Shave and Clean the Goat's Neck

The goat's neck needs to be hairless and cleaned prior to drawing blood. Shave the neck down to the skin so that you can clearly see the vein. Use rubbing alcohol and a cotton swab to wipe down the goat's neck and clean the surface. You will be surprised how much dirt may rub off of the skin underneath all that hair.

Step 3: Restrain the Goat

Have your helper securely hold the goat or fasten it into a head catch. A normal milk stanchion will not work for this, because the goat will still have too much freedom to move its neck. I have also found that regular milk stanchions are not useful even with a helper holding the goat's head because the bars get in the way of drawing the blood.

The goats head should be held slightly upward but not too high. The head should be neutral in the center or even turned slightly toward the side from which you will be drawing blood. I've found that holding the head too high or turning it away from you can make the vein difficult to find.

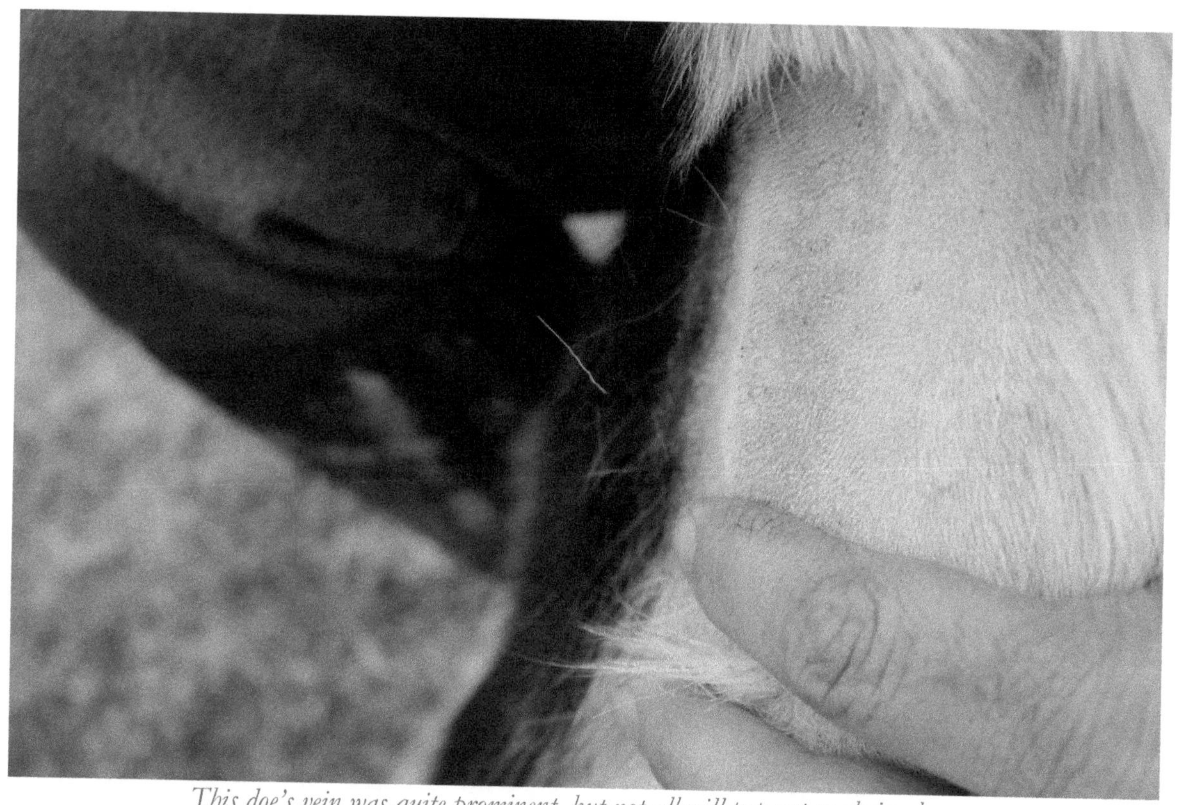

This doe's vein was quite prominent, but not all will pop out so obviously, especially in slightly overweight goats.

Step 4: Draw the Blood

While your goat is restrained, hold your uncapped needle and syringe in your dominant hand and use the other hand to press at the base of the goat's neck. The pressure will cause the vein to bulge slightly under the skin. Some goats will bulge more than others. You can feel the vein as well before sticking it; it will feel softer and more squishy than the surrounding hard muscle.

Insert the needle into the center of the vein at an angle. It should be nearly parallel to the vein. If you try to access the vein from a perpendicular angle the needle will go straight through the other side and blow the vein. You want the needle to pierce one side of the vein and slip inside the center of the vein without going through the other side.

Pull back on the plunger of the syringe. If you have successfully entered the vein you will see blood flowing into the syringe. Keep filling it until you have four or five milliliters of blood, depending on what the laboratory requests. If no blood enters the syringe and the plunger feels difficult to pull back, you have missed or gone straight through the vein and will need to try again.

Remove the needle and apply pressure to the sight where you inserted the needle for a few moments to prevent bleeding. Repeat steps one through four for each goat being tested. Remember to switch needles, syringes, and gloves for each goat to prevent cross contamination.

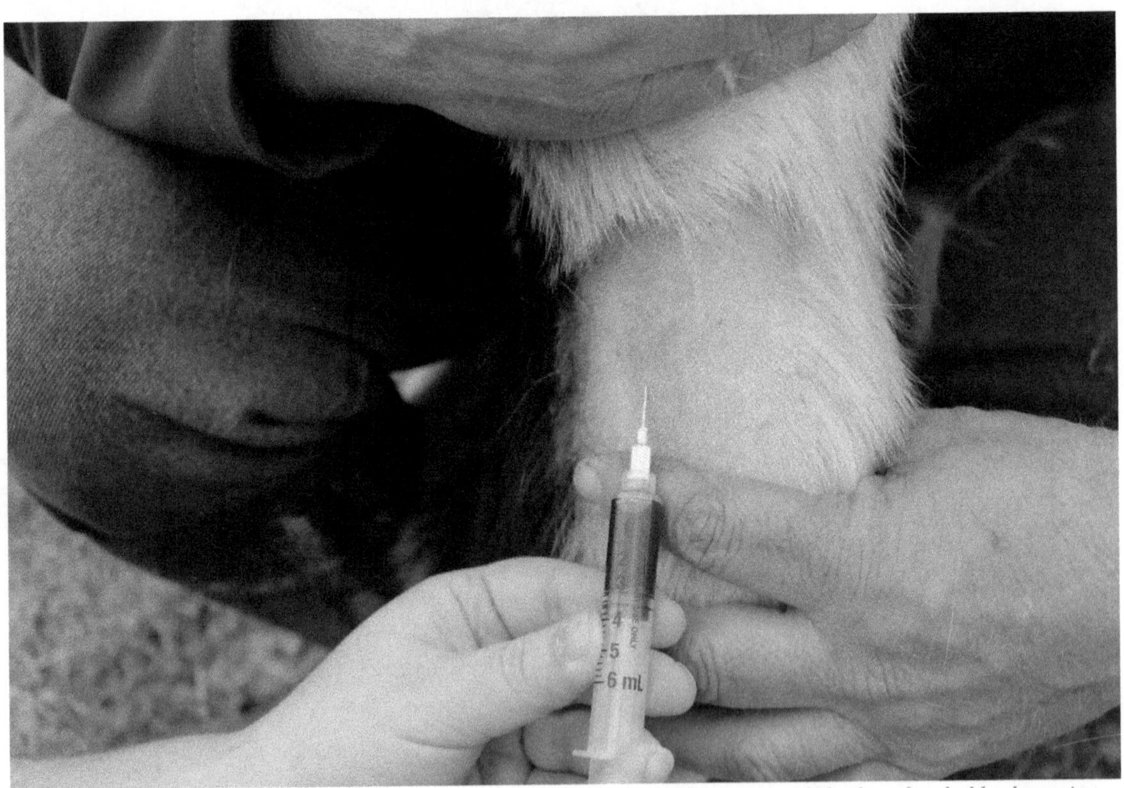

When you have help, one person can apply pressure to the base of the neck while the other holds the syringe with both hands. If you don't have help, you can use one hand to apply pressure and one to hold the syringe. It can be a bit awkward the first time, but you can pull the plunger of the syringe with one hand b using your first two fingers to press against the syringe while your remaining fingers and thumb pull the plunger down.

Step 5: Store the Blood and Send it Off

Depending on what tests and which laboratory you use, you will need to follow their instructions for shipping and storing the blood. Most laboratories want the blood to be refrigerated before shipping and shipped with an ice pack during the hot summer months. Choose expedited shipping to ensure the blood is fresh when it arrives to the laboratory. Always pack plenty of absorbent materials in the box so that if a tube should break it does not leak out of the box. Never ship blood in an envelope, and include plenty of cushioning material in the box to protect from breakage. I like to tape or rubber band my vials together, wrap them in a thick layer of paper towel, put that bundle into a plastic bag, then put that bag into a larger bag with more paper towels. I also stuff the box with paper towels to cushion them. I have not had a vial break using this method.

Trusted guardian Mellow relaxes while her charges play on a wooden platform.

Predators

I don't feel that any book about goats, even one centered on reproduction, can go without mentioning predators. Goats are extremely susceptible to predators, and kidding season is the most vulnerable time. Goat kids are quite small and make easy targets for all manner of predators. Likewise, a doe in labor out in the pasture rather than a secure barn is also an easy target. Wandering dogs, coyotes, bobcats, mountain lions, bears, and more are all capable of easily killing your goats. While secure fencing goes a long way toward protection, predators can and do find ways into fences and even barns. According to the USDA's National Agricultural Statistics Survey (NASS), 60,000 adult goats and 120,000 goat kids were killed by predators nationwide in 2011. Typically, the first predators that come to mind are wildlife such as coyotes, and that line of thinking can lull people with small farms in areas with fewer predators—such as backyard farms in suburban communities—into a false sense of security regarding predators. However, dogs are common predators—even of cows. The 2000 NASS survey found that coyotes killed 95,000 cows and calves, dogs killed 26,000 cows and calves, mountain lions and bobcats kill 11,000, bears killed 2,800, and wolves killed 1,600. Clearly goats do not stand a chance against the same predators without our help.

Thankfully there are several ways to protect our goats. The first line of defense should always be secure fencing and housing both to keep goats in and predators out. High tensile woven wire fencing is the best type to use in my experience. It remains tight for a longer period of time, does not break and bend like welded wire, and travels over hills more easily than welded wire. It's important that it be installed and stretched correctly with the appropriate use of corner bracing posts and appropriate fence post spacing. Holes in or underneath the fence make easy entry and exit for predators and goats. In high predation areas, barns should be able to be closed and secured at night with the goats locked safely inside during the high predation times—kidding, nighttime, dawn, and dusk. Does who are giving birth and kids are the most susceptible to predators, so they should be housed in the most secure area closest to your main house. If you have a lot of land with some pastures farther away than others, use the furthest pastures during lower predation times such as late spring and summer and bring goats in closer during higher predation seasons when natural food may be scarce such as winter and early spring.

Predators can, of course, dig, climb, or even break into secure fences or barns, so housing must not be your only line of defense. Vary the times at which you visit the pastures outside of your normal milking and feeding times so that predators cannot count on you being gone from the pasture at specific times of the day. A strand of electric wire around the outside of fences and barns can also deter predators. Motion detecting flood lights can also be installed around the barn or fences to startle predators. Some people will use a radio to make unnatural, human noises in their barn at night as well. For many reasons including predator prevention, it is always recommended to be present during births as well.

Livestock guardians are also an excellent, invaluable line of defense between your goats and predators. Livestock guardians are my preferred method to protect my livestock, because they not only deter predators, but they are capable of defending against them if necessary. Livestock guardian dogs (LGDs) are the best option for protecting goats and other livestock. Livestock guarding breeds have been bred and used to live with and protect livestock for centuries in places all over the world. These dogs live and bond with their livestock and defend both their livestock and their territory. Guardian dogs are intelligent, independent, and protective. They have also been specifically and intentionally bred to have low prey drives and protective natures. Guardian dogs protect goats in a few different ways. First, their presence deters many predators. Depending on the breed and individual, some guardian dogs bark at night to alert predators to their presence. They also mark their territory with urine and will patrol their pastures periodically to check for threats. They bond with the livestock and consider them part of their pack, and for that reason they will defend the livestock as well. Lastly, they are territorial as well and are naturally protective of the area they consider their home turf. Livestock guardians work best in pairs or more. I have often observed one or more dog go to patrol the perimeter or check a suspicious sight or sound while one or more stay with the herd.

Guardian dogs are prone to roaming due to roaming due to the nature of how they were developed. Traditional guardian dogs would roam over vast acres of land with their flocks. Since most of us do not have such a wide area, secure fencing is necessary. Livestock guarding breeds are incredibly clever and are adept at finding ways out of fences, including digging and climbing. When seeking out a livestock guardian dog, find a reputable farmer who uses the parents as working guardian dogs living with the same type of livestock you intend for your dogs to guard. Never trust any non-guarding breeds—including herding, hunting, or other breeds of dogs—as livestock guardians. Livestock guardians should be living with their working parents from birth, observing the flock and bonding with them. Immature livestock guardian dogs should not be trusted with newborns and birthing goats until they are mature adults, at least two years old, who have proven themselves safe with stock. Livestock guardian breeds are amazing dogs and so wonderful to own, but they are quite different than other breeds of dogs. I recommend researching these breeds to find the one that will work for you, learn about their behaviors, and find a reputable, experienced breeder to procure your livestock guardian pups from. Be sure that the puppies have stayed with their parents a minimum of three months to learn proper guarding behavior. Keep in mind that these dogs did not develop with the intent of guarding poultry and are not always able to successfully protect (and not eat) poultry.

Some people choose to use donkeys or llamas (not alpacas—they are two very different species) to guard their goats. This can work under certain circumstances, but I personally do not recommend either llamas or donkeys as your sole guardian animal. Donkeys and llamas are known to hate coyotes and will attack them. However, when faced with a pack of coyotes or dogs or larger predators, donkeys and llamas can be overwhelmed. Remember that predators frequently kill much larger prey, including cattle; donkeys and llamas will not work in high-predation situation. As a rule, the larger, more aggressive, and more numerous the predators, the larger and more numerous your guardians need to be. If you live in an area where wolves are a problem, for example, you will need several large livestock guardian dogs; anything less will be ineffective. If you choose to incorporate donkeys or llamas, you must never use intact males of either species. Donkey studs are frequently aggressive and may bite or otherwise abuse goats. They have been known to bite the back of goats' necks (a common breeding behavior) and toss them. Llama studs may also try to mate goats, and because llamas mate laying down, this behavior can suffocate or crush goats.

In extreme predator cases it can be useful to set up a perimeter guard in addition to the guardian animal living with the goat herd. This involves setting up a second fenced area containing only guardian animals. This fenced area acts as an additional buffer between predators and your livestock. Creating perimeter guard areas can also be useful for poultry in cases where livestock guardian dogs have not worked out living with the flock. One other thing to note regarding llamas and donkeys is that, while they may be useful for protecting poultry from a coyote or two, they will likely completely ignore smaller predators like foxes or raccoons. I know a farmer who had a llama living with her chickens to protect them but was still experiencing losses. She looked out her window one day to see a fox exiting her coop while the llama chewed its cud nearby. Because llamas and donkeys don't bond to the herd or flock in the same way that dogs do they will typically not defend against anything that they do not view as a threat to themselves.

The more difficult it is for a predator to access your goats, the less likely you are to experience a predator problem. This is ultimately the goal: To be proactive in preventing predator losses rather than reactive in responding to predator losses that have already occurred. If your defenses fail and a predator has become a problem, it will continue to come back to the free buffet until it becomes impossible for it to do so. If a predator becomes a repeat offender, it may need to be physically removed. Live trapping and relocating is not usually recommended because a predator who has learned that livestock are easy prey will likely become a nuisance for another farmer later on. Predators can also have very large ranges and may simply return. Know your local laws regarding legally protecting your livestock from predators using lethal methods to ensure that you are acting legally. Also keep in mind that some species, such as black vultures and eagles, are federally protected. If an endangered or protected predator species is killing your livestock, contact your local wildlife management resources agency for assistance.

Parasites

This section was the last one to be written, because it is arguably the most important, and I wanted to be sure I got it right. Parasites are the biggest health risk for goats and are one of the leading cause of illness and death in goats. Goats are highly susceptible to internal parasites, and parasites are increasingly resistant to deworming medications due in part to incorrect usage over the years. Goats are not designed to thrive in the types of environments often found on our farms and homestead. Goats originated in either desert (hot and dry) or mountainous (cold and scrubby) locations. They are selective browsers who, under proper conditions, eat up into shrubs, weeds, and small trees rather than down into grass. On most farms goats are required to eat pasture like cows and sheep, and the hot and humid summers are ideal conditions for internal parasites to thrive. Selecting goats for your breeding program that display a high natural resistance to internal parasitism is a vital part of breeding management. While parasitism is environmental, there is also a genetic component to natural resistance. In my experience, the goats who frequently become parasitized are repeat offenders throughout their lives, frequently becoming re-infested and further weakening their immunity in addition to breeding and shedding increasingly dewormer resistant parasites.

Parasites are an inevitable fact of life with livestock. They are naturally present in the environment, and they are also naturally present within the livestock themselves. No goat will ever be completely devoid of all internal parasites—that is not the goal. The goal is to keep the number of parasites low enough that the goat can thrive with its natural immunity and low rate of infestation. Parasites are also one of the primary reasons that raising goats completely organically is almost impossible. Deworming medication is also a part of life with goats, and while it should never be used when not needed, it must be used when it is needed. There are certain management practices and naturally antiparasitic substances that can reduce the need for dewormers, which will be discussed further later in this chapter, but they are not treatments and cannot prevent infestation completely. Some goats may almost never require deworming due to management and genetic resistance, but when goats do need to be dewormed, natural remedies are not shown to be effective treatments. Studies have shown that certain herbal deworming blends and other natural "dewormers" like garlic, diatomaceous earth, or papaya seeds are not effective at reducing parasitism. Chemical dewormers are most often necessary to treat an infected goat.

There are several types of internal parasites which goats may contract—including things such as tapeworm, hookworm, and roundworms—but for the sake of this book I will focus only on the most common and dangerous internal parasite, the barber pole worm (haemonchus contortus or HC). I highly recommend additional research into parasites, using reliable sources, to better understand the risks and treatments. The American Consortium for Small Ruminant Parasite Control (www.wormx.info) is an excellent place to start.

Lice and Mites

In addition to internal parasites, goats are also susceptible to external parasites—namely lice and mites. Lice are most commonly present in the winter and early spring while the goat's undercoat is thick. Lice are species specific, meaning that you do not have to worry about contracting lice from your goats. There are two types of lice: biting lice, which feed on skin cells, and sucking lice which feed on blood. Sucking lice are the most common. The symptoms of lice including scratching, biting at the skin, rubbing along fences and other structures, and anemia in the case of sucking lice. Hair loss is not caused directly by lice but may occur as a secondary symptom caused by the goat scratching and biting incessantly in a severe infestation. Lice can be seen by the naked eye, and they look like small brown flecks of rice or dirt. Lice typically go away on their own in the summer after the goat sheds, but before then they can be treated with topical medications applied down the spine of the goat. There are a few over the counter options for lice treatment. Shaving the goat in spring will also eliminate lice.

Mites are microscopic and cannot be seen by the naked eye. Mites are also species-specific, and they are often brought in to your herd via bedding like straw. Mites cause hair loss (sometimes called mange), itching, and dry, uncomfortable skin. Hair loss will often start on the limbs or sometimes the face. Since certain mineral deficiencies can also cause issues with hair, those should be ruled out as well, especially if treatment for mites does not improve the condition. Mites can be treated using a topical sulfur-based cream, purchased over the counter and usually online, applied twice daily until the hair begins to regrow. Wear gloves when applying so that your hands do not smell like sulfur (rotten eggs).

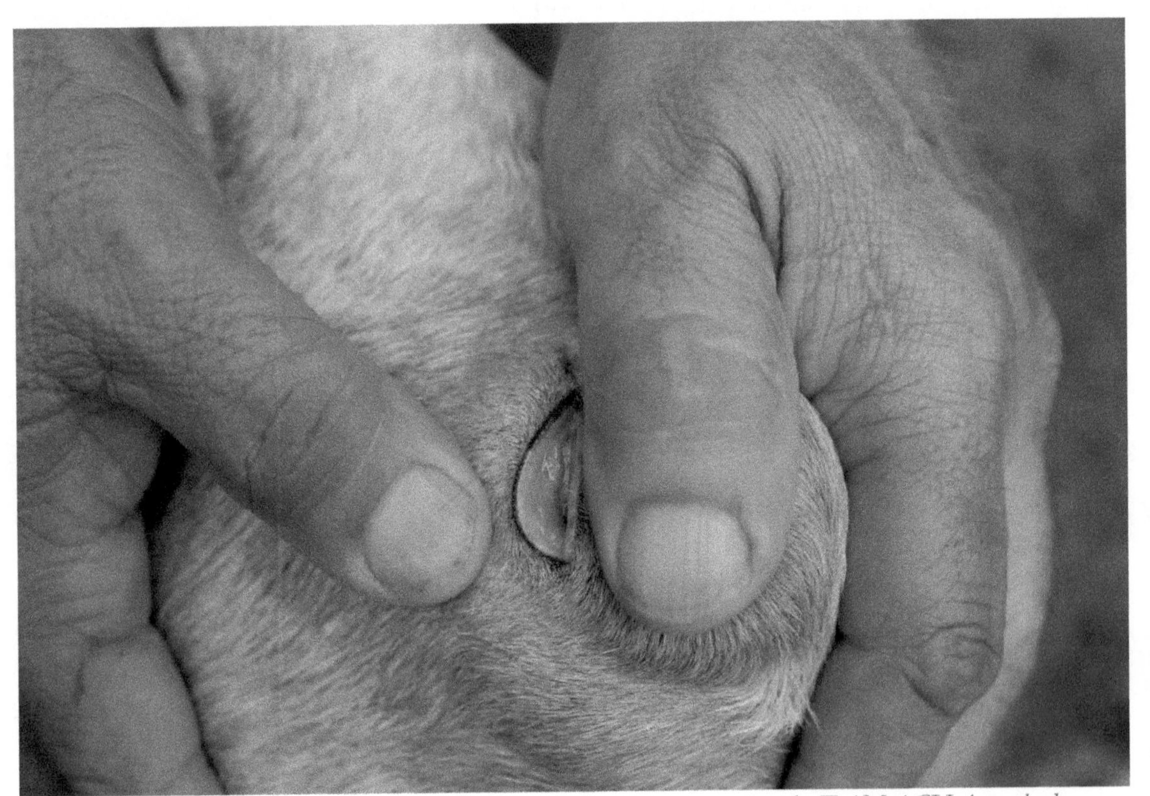

A goat is checked for anemia caused by haemonchus contortus using the FAMACHA method.

Haemonchus Contortus (Barber Pole Worm)

Haemonchus contortus (HC), also called barber pole worm, is the most common and most dangerous internal parasite (gastrointestinal nematode) of goats. Barber pole worms feed on the blood of the goat, causing anemia, weight loss, and eventually death. The first sign of barber pole is anemia; goats typically do not get diarrhea from internal parasites (with the exception of coccidia, discussed later), and weight loss typically begins after anemia, though in some rare cases weight loss may begin before evident anemia. I did have one doe who showed no anemia—not even in her blood tests—but had weight loss and a high fecal egg count of barber pole eggs. That kind of situation is the exception rather than the rule.

Infestation is detected using either fecal testing or by monitoring anemia via the FAMACHA method. Using the FAMACHA method, the mucus membranes of the inner lower eyelid is examined and compared to a FAMACHA card. The card shows five stages of color, varying from pale white to dark red. A pale white membrane indicates severe anemia and a need to deworm immediately. A very dark pink or red membrane is an indication of a healthy goat with no anemia, and therefore a corresponding low level of haemonchus contortus parasites internally and no need to deworm. On the FAMACHA scale, a score of four or five (pale and palest) indicates a need to deworm. A score of one or two (darker pink and red) indicates that there is no need to deworm for barber pole worm. A score of three (in the middle) is considered borderline, and a goat with a score of three may be dewormed if other factors indicate a need—body condition, recent parturition, a large incidence of infection, stress, etc.—but may not be dewormed if the goat is otherwise in good condition and there are no other indicators. In order to properly view the membrane, the upper eyelid is closed over the goat's eye, gentle pressure is applied against the eye to push it back slightly, and the lower eyelid is pulled down to let the membranes pop out. Looking at the outer eyelid only will not give the most accurate score. Both eyes are checked, and the highest score is followed (meaning that if one eye scores a borderline 3 and the other scores a 4 in need of deworming, the goat is considered to score a 4 overall and is dewormed). The University of Rhode Island offers FAMACHA training as well as the purchase of FAMACHA scoring cards online. They can be found online at www.web.uri.edu/sheepngoat/famacha/ Keep in mind that other things such as blood sucking lice or copper deficiency can also cause anemia in some cases. So, while most often the cause of anemia is barber pole worm, chronic anemia with clear fecal test results is an indication of other underlying problems.

Barber pole worm is uniquely adept at self-preservation and procreation which, combined with growing resistance to deworming medication, makes it a dangerous threat to goats. Barber pole worm, or HC for short, thrives in warm, moist conditions. Several days of deep freezing conditions (20 F or below) will eliminate some of the larvae on pasture, as will hot and dry conditions (90 F or above). Six weeks of 90 F days on rested pasture will kill many of the larvae. HC will also stop reproducing itself when conditions are not ideal for its offspring's survival. Because of this, populations are greatest during hot and humid weather. However, that does not mean that there is no risk of infestation during the winter, especially in climates with mild winters, or during hot days in the summer. Another survival instinct of haemonchus allows it to coordinate its release of eggs to coincide with the birth of the doe's own kids. Following cues from the doe's hormones, the barber pole worms will release their own offspring to infect the offspring of the doe. HC enters the goat's system through fecal-oral transmission, and the eggs are released in the goat's feces.

Management is hugely important to prevent parasitization. Although there are no natural alternatives or practices that can completely prevent parasitism, there are many options that can help minimize the impacts of barber pole worm on your herd. All feed and minerals should be kept up off the ground where they are less prone to being stepped on or pooped in. Keep mineral feeders and grain troughs up at mouth level and hay racks either above the head (which is a natural stance for goats to eat in) or fixed in such a way that goats are not able to tromp on it (such as behind a panel wall on pallets or a feed trough). Water should also be kept clean. Pasture should be kept at a minimum of six inches high whenever possible. HC larvae are able to climb up to four inches in the pasture, and are most concentrated around three to four inches, so keeping pastures higher helps prevent reinfection through fecal-oral transmission. Less than four inches of height also stunts the growth of the grass, and grass higher than twelve inches begins to turn woody and go to seed, making it less appetizing to goats.

Pastures should also be rotated when possible. Allowing the pasture to rest for six weeks at a time greatly reduces the larvae on pasture and prevents the larvae from completing their lifecycle by being consumed by a goat. In certain conditions, particularly in warm humid climates on shaded pasture with less sun exposure, larvae may live up to 60 days. If a pasture cannot be rested six weeks—or if the quality of the pasture is decreasing due to the grass growing too high—then following the goats with another species is also recommended. Horses and cows are ideal pasture cleaners to graze a pasture before goats are placed on it again. They will consume the parasite larvae and become dead end hosts, disallowing the larvae to complete their life cycle and re-infect goats. Barns should be kept clean as well, with bedding frequently changed or covered in winter if using deep bedding methods.

Overcrowding pastures and barns increases parasitism, as does over-grazing. Dry conditions and sun exposure help to kill larvae, as lack of moisture prevents them from developing. Likewise, shaded areas and moist areas (around water troughs, ditches, ponds, etc.) are not only often frequently traveled but also provide a perfect incubator for parasites. To expedite the death of barber pole larvae, pasture can be used to make hay while resting, which kills the larvae, or it can be mowed short to allow greater sun exposure. Mowing short will also slow the growth of the pasture, which can be beneficial if the pasture needs to rest an extended period of time and will become overgrown due to the lack of a second species to graze it. Sowing pasture with a browse such as sericea lespedeza, which has a high tannin content shown to reduce fecal egg count of barber pole worm and coccidia, can also benefit parasite management.

It's important to breed your goats with resistance in mind, and to cull goats from the herd who have lower resistance. A mere ten to fifteen percent of the goats in your herd are responsible for about 50% of the eggs shed on your pastures; 20-30% of the goats in your herd are responsible for 80% of the eggs on your pasture. Culling goats for low resistance is vital to the wellbeing of your herd and the species in general. When we must repeatedly deworm goats with chemical dewormers (anthelmintic), we are increasing parasite anthelmintic resistance with each dose. Failure to selectively breed goats for parasite resistance is in turn effectively breeding parasites for drug resistance. With each exposure to anthelmintic medications, some of the parasites are killed but some inevitably survive. These surviving parasites lived through deworming because of their own ability to resist the medication's effects. Then these hardier parasites are now the ones left in the goat to reproduce themselves, thereby passing on their resistant genes. The weaker worms have now died off and are not interbreeding with the stronger parasites, thus strengthening the parasite and weakening your goat herd.

Never deworm goats prophylactically without need. The old school way of thinking was to deworm the entire herd at once if one goat needed to be dewormed, and to deworm the entire herd on a certain schedule. This is no longer advised, because the overuse of dewormers—which were once effective—has led to dewormer resistance, as discussed. Goats should be dewormed only when infested, and goats without infestation should not be dosed. Goats who need frequent deworming should be culled. Appropriate dosage rates should be used to avoid under-dosing the medication, which also increases resistance. Rather than rotating through multiple types of dewormers, stick with one type for as long as it is working effectively. This way the other classes of dewormer will still be available for your herd if and when the original dewormer stops working. Many dewormers are used off-label for goats. Because suggested dosages sometimes change, I will not include dosage rates. However, your small ruminant veterinarian can advise you of appropriate dosages and suggest a specific medication as well. Many vets do not have extensive experience with goats, so seek out one who has experience with or specializes in small ruminants. Many agricultural universities also provide resources through their extensions and on their websites. Giving dosages of medication twelve hours apart can increase the efficacy. To check that your dewormer is working, have fecal tests done a week after the final dose. If the dewormer is working, the fecal egg count should decrease.

When it comes to natural preventative measures, management is the most important factor. Keeping a clean environment as discussed previously is important. Nutrition is also vital, because the goat's natural immune system needs to be supported to function at its highest potential. Proper mineral supplementation, especially of copper, is incredibly important, as is ensuring high quality hay or forage is available. Many natural "dewormers" have been show in studies to lack efficacy: these include commonly mentioned things such as diatomaceous earth, herbal dewormers, garlic, papaya seeds, and more. Natural things that have been shown to reduce rates of barber pole worm include copper bolus and feed sources with high tannin content such as sericea lespedeza (available in both pellets and hay, depending on your region) and pine (not ponderosa pine, which can cause abortions). The American Consortium for Small Rumen Parasite Control recommends a bolus of one to grams of copper oxide wire particles when dosing for deworming purposes only, and the dosage given for copper deficiency is four grams for adults over 50 lbs and two grams for kids under 50 lbs.

Lastly, take caution when introducing new goats to the herd as well. New stock should always be quarantined for disease testing and to prevent the spread of illness, but new goats can also carry with them new strains of haemonchus contortus as well. These strains may be resistant to deworming medications that the parasites on your land currently are not resistant to, and they may also be strains to which your existing herd has not developed immunity due to lack of exposure. Unfortunately, I have experienced the explosion of parasitism that can occur when a new strain of parasite is brought in from an outside goat, and it can be a nightmare to get back under control. New goats should ideally be quarantined a minimum of three months. When first brought in, they should be disease tested and have fecal tests run to assess parasitism. It is recommended by some sources to deworm the new goat upon intake with one class of wormer, and again at the end of quarantine with a second, different class of dewormer. After the deworming, the goat should have another fecal test run to ensure that the medications were effective; if they were not, the goat may carry dewormer resistant strains of barber pole worm. The new goat should also be initially released onto "dirty" pasture, meaning it should be placed in a pasture that your herd has recently occupied. This way, the pasture is already infected with parasite eggs and larvae from your own herd. Any parasites the new goat sheds will mingle and interbreed with the existing strains, hopefully weakening any anthelmintic resistance and making the parasites more similar to the ones already on your land, to which your existing herd has had exposure and is hopefully somewhat immune.

Coccidia

Coccidia is a protozoan parasite that most commonly infects young goats of six months of age or younger, though it may also sometimes infect older goats who are immune compromised or under severe stress. Coccidia are not a worm and do not respond to any types of dewormers; they are treated for using specific medications called coccidiostats. Again, because recommended medications and dosages sometimes change, I will not list specific drug information in this book.

Coccidia are naturally present in the environment and are shed by adult goats. Adults develop an immunity to coccidia that prevents them from becoming infected (called coccidiosis). However, young goats do not yet have the natural immunity. Coccidia can cause slowed or stunted growth—often with no other overt symptoms, making some breeders miss that the infection is present—scours (diarrhea), wasting, or death. Goat kids are particularly at risk of coccidiosis during times of stress such as weaning. This is one reason I choose not to wean retained doelings; kids who are nursing their dam's milk are less likely to become infected.

Preventing coccidiosis is dependent primarily on good nutrition, reduction of stress, and food hygiene. The barn in which kids are born and housed should be kept clean. Soiled bedding should be removed and replaced with fresh bedding. If the bedding is not clean enough for you to sit on it with the goats, it is not clean enough to prevent coccidiosis for kids. (Clean bedding is also important for the prevention of navel ill and mastitis as well.) the barn floor should be cleaned using an ammonia wash or hot steam and allowed to remain dry and unused, exposed to the sun if possible, prior to kidding. Bleach solutions will not kill coccidia in the environment—sterilizing steam or a 10% solution of ammonia is necessary. Coccidia can live for a very long time in the environment, up to several months, especially in dark, damp environments. Sericea lespedeza pellets have been shown to reduce coccidia when fed to kids as well.

Many people recommend treating for coccidia prophylactically by administering medication once weekly to kids starting at two weeks old and until six months. I personally do not recommend giving any medications, particularly those meant to fight parasites or bacteria, prophylactically due to the risks of resistance. There are certain coccidiostats which are losing effectiveness just as certain deworming medications. If we want medications to work when we need them, we must use them judiciously. I prefer to use non-medicative methods to prevent coccidia as discussed and monitor for issues so that I may treat them when they arise rather than give medicine preventatively.

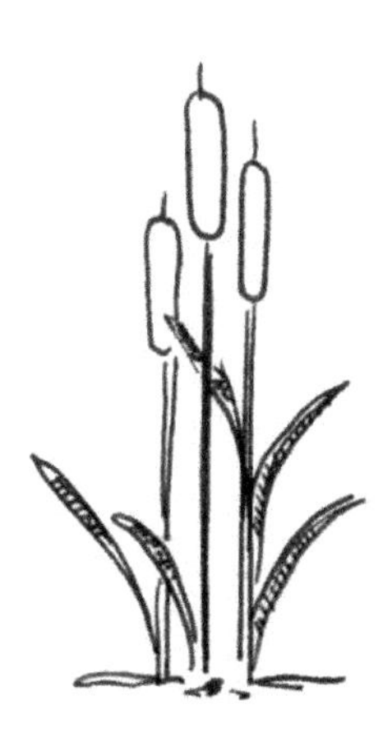

But That's Not Natural!

I so often see people who are wanting to raise their goats naturally push back against anything they perceive as "unnatural." In some cases, this may be something like medicated feed, a sentiment I agree with, but in some cases it's things like deworming, assisting a birth, disbudding, or even giving a copper bolus. Granted, none of those things would happen in the wild—but your barnyard is not nature. We are not raising goats in a natural environment in the wild. Furthermore, nature is cruel. I don't want to be natural with my livestock to the point of cruelty. You may have heard the term "organic by neglect," and unfortunately that is often what happens when people become so focused on doing things all naturally that the wellbeing of the animals plays second fiddle to the desire to be "organic" or "all natural."

There are many things about raising goats that are not natural. Castration is not natural. Feeding them hay or any other supplement is not natural. Putting them in a fence and giving them a nice safe barn to sleep in is not natural. If we really want to push the desire to be natural to its extreme, none of us should be raising goats in captivity in North America. We should be letting them roam mountain ranges or desert plains in the wild in their natural habits, and allowing them to be eaten by predators, die in childbirth, starve or get sick when conditions are poor, and all the rest of the terrible things that sometimes happen to wild animals. Wild animals don't grow old and pass peacefully. They get eaten, they get sick, or they starve. It would be absurd for someone to say, "Oh, I just let the coyotes eat my goats when they feel like it. I like to let nature take its course." So why on earth would it be okay to say, "I don't assist a doe who is having trouble in labor. I let nature take its course?"

Again, this is not nature. These are not wild animals. These are domesticated animals—in fact, goats are one of the first animals to have been domesticated. They bring a richness to our lives in the form of nourishing food, companionship, enjoyment, and more. We in turn owe them the courtesy of providing a decent life for them, treating them when they're injured or ill, and engaging in a few "unnatural" practices to ensure their highest quality of life.

I believe in doing things as naturally as possible and limiting the use of unnecessary medications. I love using herbs and essential oils on myself and my livestock. What I don't believe in is willfully allowing animals to suffer or die because I insist on doing things all naturally. Practices such as supplementing minerals when needed, castration of excess bucklings, disbudding kids, giving medication to sick goats, and treating parasitic infestations when needed increase the quality of life for goats and the humans who work with them.

Goats are also a difficult species in general to raise completely organically, in large part because of their terrible propensity to contract parasite overloads. I talk more about this in the Troubleshooting chapter under "Parasites," but natural dewormers simply don't work consistently for goats with a heavy parasite load. They are beneficial and supportive, and they can be a useful part of your parasite prevention protocol, but they are not usually an effective treatment. I don't like to say that something "never" works, because there are always exceptions, but in my personal experience and the experience of the vast majority of goat owners I know, herbal dewormers won't cut it on their own. Goats are also notorious for becoming sick suddenly and drastically, often taking their owners off guard and requiring emergency treatments, and those often come too late. Many of the illnesses that can strike goats can hit them very hard, very fast. My veterinarian once told me he warned people not to get goats because, "goats just die." And unfortunately, it's true. Sometimes in spite of our best efforts, goats die anyway. They're a hard species to raise, even with modern medicine available.

My personal philosophy for my herd is to never give a medicine that is *not* needed, but also to never withhold a medicine that *is* needed simply because it "isn't natural." We must strike a careful balance as we try to raise livestock naturally in an unnatural environment. Good natural management practices should be the cornerstone of raising healthy animals, but at times medical intervention is required as well. If naturally raising your goats is important to you, keep that in mind as you breed them as well, and choose only the hardiest animals to continue on in your herd and genetics. I always encourage people to "go natural" in as many ways as they can, but to be open minded and willing to do something "unnatural" when it is in the best interest of the goats or their natural methods are not working.

Are the Goats Happy?

Before we move onto the recipe portion of this book, I want to share a few final thoughts. I have gone over many different subjects, and along the way I shared management techniques, tips, and tricks. I want to emphasize now that management is not one size fits all. Each herd is different, and a multitude of factors goes into the care and keeping of goats. Everything from your particular climate, herd size, breed, and the individual characteristics of your goats will affect the type of care that they need. What works for one herd will not always work for another. Although your management may be extremely similar to mine—or someone else's—it will never be exactly the same.

For every opinion I have on goat herd management, there will be someone whose opinion is exactly opposite. While I follow my principles due to personal experience, research, and what I believe are very valid reasons, that doesn't make my word gospel. What works for my goats may not work for yours. Also, what works for my goats sometimes doesn't work for an individual in the herd! Each animal is unique, and some will need slightly different care from others. You will likely find that your own management will adjust from time to time depending on differences between individuals or various outside factors that can influence your goats' needs. Something as simple as moving from one property to another—even within the same area—might have an impact on your herd and their needs. In some cases you may even have an individual goat that just doesn't do as well in your herd as the others; likely that goat might flourish in another herd. I've seen goats' personalities change as well from herd to herd. In one place they may be on the lowest end of the pecking order, and then in another herd they might climb to the top of the hierarchy. Some unfriendly goats might become friendly in a smaller herd or a different setting. We can't forget that these creatures are individuals and their needs, personalities, and quirks will vary.

It's essential to always do your own research, follow your own experiences, and trust your own instincts for your herd. It's not enough to rely on a mentor, a book, or anything else to tell you exactly what to do for your goats. These are wonderful starting places, but you must always be willing to learn, change, grow, and adapt. I still find myself making alterations and trying new techniques with my goats now, nearly a decade after I first started my herd. These goats are your goats after all, and only you can make the final decisions on care. Of course there are certain choices that are always wrong, and certain needs for goats that are universal, but many of the elements that go into daily care for goats are variable and largely impacted by personal choice and preference. Sometimes we even break our rules.

At the end of the day, the most important question to ask yourself is this: Are the goats happy? If your goats are happy and healthy, you're seeing the results you want, and you aren't running into repeated problems, then chances are good that what you're doing is working. If on the other hand you are seeing things that you don't want, then it's time to reevaluate your practices and make changes. Healthy goats, good production, high fertility, easy births, and thriving kids are indications that your management is working well for your herd. Repeat problems, unthrifty goats, low birth rates, and other chronic issues are indications that somewhere along the line there is a management problem. Seeing the results in your own herd is the best way to know if what you're doing is right for your goats. Start out with solid practices such as the ones I've recommended in this book, but never be afraid to make adjustments as needed. I learned early on that following someone else's protocol rigidly with no allowance for flexibility is not a wise choice.

If the goats are happy, I'm happy. That's my ultimate, overarching philosophy.

Mold ripened chèvre.

Recipes

At the end of the day, food is the goal when it comes to our goats! Most of us with dairy goats own them with the primary purpose of producing milk. From the milk comes even more amazing goodness—cheese, yogurt, soap, and more. Raising dairy goats also means inevitably having many buck kids born who do not need to remain intact for breeding, and those wethers make delicious, lean meat that is similar to both beef and venison (with no gamey flavor). I've included recipes here for both dairy goodness and delicious chevon. My recipes are all small-batch, appropriate for the home kitchen, but can be increased for larger families or to share. There is truly nothing quite like producing your own food from start to finish. It's an amazing thing. Enjoy!

A foggy morning on our terroir.

Terroir

When I think of cheese—and delicious food in general—I often think of European countries such as France or Italy. One thing I admire about the European food culture is their attitude toward good food. Food is something to be enjoyed, appreciated, and made with love and care. In our fast paced, workaholic society, we often overlook the simple joys of food in favor of boxed quick meals. There is something to be said for slowing down, savoring the flavors, and taking the time craft high quality foods from premier ingredients. Dairy is no exception—and it's worth noting that raw milk and raw milk products are enjoyed freely in much of Europe. Most people consume at least two meals a day; shouldn't a bit of attention be paid to what is on our plates? One such food concept I find particularly fascinating and beautiful is the French notion of *terroir* regarding food and wine.

While I do not speak French, I can understand what this concept implies. I've heard it described as "specificity of place." In short, it is the belief that food or wine produced in a specific place or region is unlike that of food produced anywhere else. Indeed, some foods carry regulations that require it to be produced in a certain locale to carry a specific name. The literal translation of terroir is soil, but of course the word means much more than that.

Everything that is unique to a particular place—the climate, the soil, the culture, the people, and even the tiny microscopic bacteria that are unique to each local all impact the final product. The cheese, yogurt, kefir, and any other food product you make on your own farm cannot be exactly replicated, reproduced, or cloned by anyone else. I could hand you the most detailed recipe in the world, and you could follow it step by step to the tee, and your cheese would be slightly different than mine. This is terroir.

Another description I have heard is that terroir creates the *character* of the food, while other elements create the *quality* and the *mood*. Anyone can take the time and effort to craft a high-quality cheese, yet the same type of cheese made by two different people in two different places can be so different. Likewise, things like the weather or even the mood of the creator while making the food can impact the "mood" of the food. An especially rainy season might create watery strawberries, while a particularly lush growing season will increase the vitamin quantities of milk. Indeed, the milk of a cow or goat who recently grazed on wild green onions reflects the flavor of its own meal in its milk—not to its advantage, in my opinion. Goodness knows that a bad mood in the kitchen can lead to mistakes and mishaps. But the lasting things that carry on year after year, not influenced by weather or time of year or whims of human emotion, create the character of the food. Terroir once more.

Terroir cannot be scientifically scrutinized or objectively proven, yet we know by our senses that it is true. The many nuances in the flavors of real food—as unprocessed and unadulterated as it can be—are derived from innumerable sources. This seems particularly true of the traditional foods such as cheese, wine, sourdough, and ferments. There are so many unique aspects of each region, and even each farm, that come into play. The forage your goats eat, the bacteria floating through the air in your home, the slightly different way you handle the curds, and on and on, all make your food unique. Imagine this: the grass on your land absorbs its nutrients from your soil and the sun and the rain, your goats eat the grass and put that grass in your milk, you save the milk and turn it into something new, and in the end are you not consuming your own soil and sunshine and rain? I think this is one of the most incredible and beautiful truths about food, that it is inherently unique to both its locale and its creator.

As you follow along with my recipes, don't be afraid to embrace your *terroir*. As you practice and learn, put a bit of your own touch on your creations. Make it as personal as you can. Grow the herbs you mix into your chèvre on your own property. Let the milk be raw so that it captures the complexity of flavor it can offer. Work with your hands. Use all five of your senses to immerse yourself in your craft. Make a fresh loaf of sourdough, spread homemade chèvre over it, and drizzle it with local honey. Embrace the full and wonderful complexity, individuality, and flavor of real food. Then share with your loved ones the truly special food that only your farm could have created.

Milk Magic

Although many delicious dishes are made using dairy and dairy products, I personally hail cheese as the King of Flavor and cultured dairy as the Queen of Health. The recipes I have included here are for some of my favorite dairy products to make and to consume, but I also put an emphasis on choosing simple, easy to make recipes that don't require gobs of milk. When I first began experimenting with home dairy products, I often found myself overwhelmed by complex recipes and recipes that called for gallons of milk. Many recipes I found overcomplicated the process, or didn't explain the process well enough. That resulted in confusion and failure. Yogurt that was way too sour, mozzarella that never stretched, and bland, flavorless cheese. I wanted the recipes in this book to be simple and easy to follow, and good for beginners. I also made these recipes relatively small batches so that they are appropriate for smaller families—and so that not as much is wasted if they fail. They can certainly be increased for larger batches if desired.

I have already discussed the pros and cons of raw milk and pasteurized milk, but I do want to touch on those once more specifically as they pertain to cheesemaking and cultured dairy products. When it comes to making cheese, you want to have the freshest milk possible. Milk should preferably not be homogenized, and if you choose to use pasteurized it should ideally be low temperature pasteurized, but must not be ultrapasteurized. Heating milk denatures the proteins, and ultrapasteurized milk is pasteurized at very high temperatures that badly denature the milk proteins and make it incompatible with cheesemaking and other cultured products. If you are producing your own milk from your goats, you can be sure that it is incredibly fresh and of the highest quality. However, it goes without saying that sometimes we may experience a dry spell in our herds while does are waiting to kid, or we may simply want to make more dairy products than we have the milk to make! So if you are searching your store shelves for milk to substitute, I recommend going to specialty or health food stores and looking for local, unhomogenized, low temperature pasteurized milk with a sell by date that indicates freshness. Remember that the higher quality the milk, the higher quality the result. Goat, cow, sheep, or even more exotic milk types can be used with these recipes. Flavor profiles for different milks will vary, but all can be substituted.

Now, if you are a raw milk enthusiast such as myself, you may still want to low-heat pasteurize your milk prior to making certain fermented and cultured fresh dairy products like yogurt or kefir. Raw milk contains additional bacteria, much of which are beneficial bacteria, though some are inevitably bad bacteria as one would find on any food. While this is not inherently a bad thing, the bacteria in raw milk do compete with the bacteria in yogurt or kefir cultures. Gently pasteurizing your raw milk before making yogurt or kefir will result in a thicker end product and allow the special bacteria in your culture to grow more rapidly with less competition and a smaller chance of failure. Of course, you may use raw milk as well if a runnier texture does not bother you. To help ensure that your cultures succeed, you may want to condition your cultures to being used in raw milk, especially when making kefir. I address this further in the kefir recipe.

There are few terms you should know to be comfortable reading the recipes for cultured dairy and cheese. When I refer to starter cultures, I'm referring to the beneficial bacteria that we inoculate milk with in order to achieve a desired effect such as yogurt, kefir, or cheese. Thermophilic cultures are cultures that require heat to be activated, while mesophilic cultures can be used at room temperature. Room temperature refers to a temperature of approximately 72 degrees. Curds are the resulting milk solids that knit together and separate from the whey, which is the milk liquid, during the cheesemaking process. Cheesecloth is a finely woven fabric that is used to drain whey from cheese curds. A cheese press is a device that applies pressure to cheese to press out excess whey and further knit the curds. A cheese mold is a form that curds are placed in to give cheese a particular shape. Rennet is an enzyme called chymosin which is used to curdle the milk when making cheese. Most rennet is derived from the stomachs of ruminant animals, but there are vegetable sources of rennet as well. Calcium chloride is used to firm the cheese curds, particularly for cheese made from pasteurized milk, which will often not set as firm a curd as raw milk. Most cheese making supplies will need to be purchased online or from specialty shops, as the tools and ingredients are not often found on supermarket shelves. Salt must always be non-iodized (sea salt, cheese salt, etc.) and water should be non-chlorinated. Measurement Conversions: **Dash** = ⅛ tsp, **Pinch** = 1/16 tsp, and **Smidgen** = 1/32 tsp.

All supplies for making cheese or cultured dairy products must be clean and nonreactive (wooden, silicone, stainless steel, enamel). Likewise, your hands should always be kept clean as well. Introducing the wrong kinds of bacteria or mold spores can ruin your cultured products or spoil them prematurely. Avoid culturing dairy in an environment where other products are culturing or growing mold: yeast, bacteria, and spores from other ferments (including sauerkraut, kombucha, etc.) can cross contaminate each other. If you have multiple ferments or cultures going at one time, keep them separated by several feet. Always make your cultured dairy and cheeses with the freshest milk possible for the best results.

Note: Many of these recipes are cultured with specific bacteria. These bacteria may be *thermophilic* or *mesophilic*. Thermophilic cultures require warmth to activate, whereas mesophilic cultures will develop at room temperature.

Supplies:

- Butter muslin
- Thermometer
- Glass jars
- Slotted spoon
- Long curd knife

- Thick-bottomed six-quart stockpot
- Funnel
- Cheese press
- Yogurt maker
- Mixing bowls
- Measuring cups
- Measuring spoons
- Specialty measuring spoons that measure tiny measurements specifically for cheesemaking: pinch, dash, and smidge.
- Clean kitchen towels
- Cheese molds
- Clean refrigerator free from moldy leftovers
- Cheese salt (non-iodized, fine ground)
- Cultures and starters needed for each specific recipe. Sources for purchasing these can be found in the back of this book.

Fresh yogurt made with an electric yogurt machine.

Yogurt

Yogurt is one of the easiest recipes to try first, and it's incredibly versatile. It can be strained to make a thicker Greek-style yogurt, mixed with fruits or honey, made into savory dip, or even used in place of sour cream. You'll notice in this recipe I heat the milk to a high temperature. This isn't strictly necessary, but it will help your yogurt develop a thicker texture. Raw milk yogurt tends to be runny and less reliable. There are many different cultures for yogurt. I like Bulgarian, a nice mild variety. This recipe assumes you are using a thermophilic culture.

1 quart fresh milk
1 packet powdered culture starter OR 2-3 tbsp yogurt from a prior batch*
Toppings such as honey, jam, or fresh fruit, optional

Heat the milk slowly, stirring constantly, to at least 160 F and up to 180 F to ensure a thick-set yogurt. 180 F will ensure the thickest set.

Allow the milk to cool back to 110 F. Sprinkle your starter culture on top and allow to hydrate for a minute if using powdered culture. Then stir in your starter culture (or yogurt from an earlier batch) making sure that it is mixed well.

Pour the milk into glass containers and allow it to culture at 110 F for 4-8 hours until it reaches your desired consistency. This can be done in a yogurt maker that holds the temperature and humidity steady for you, which is the method I prefer for best reliability, but it can also be done in an insulted container or by setting them in an oven set on the lowest temperature with the door cracked. Keep in mind that the longer the yogurt sets, the sourer it becomes.

Check the yogurt at the 4 hour mark to see if it has thickened. If it is still too runny, continue to culture. Remember that raw milk yogurt may never reach a thick consistency. The yogurt should smell fresh and slightly tangy, and you can use taste as well to test doneness.

Allow yogurt to cool at room temperature for two hours, then refrigerate for at least 6 hours or overnight to chill.

If the yogurt does not thicken to your desired consistency, you can strain it to remove excess whey. Alternatively you can also enjoy it as a yogurt drink or in smoothies.

Serve with your desired toppings or blends!

**Store-bought yogurt can be used as a starter culture, but it must be a high-quality brand with live and active cultures.*

Buttermilk

I used to think that I did not like buttermilk. That was before I tried the real homemade stuff. It's tenfold better than any of the typical store shelf options. Of course, traditional buttermilk was the liquid leftover from making butter, which was then cultured (often by simply letting it sit at room temperature for 24 hours). You can make it that way if desired, but most people choose to culture whole milk instead these days.

1 quart fresh milk
1 dash mesophilic culture like flora Danica OR 2-3 tbsp buttermilk from a previous batch*

Allow the milk to come to room temperature. Add in the culture or buttermilk and gently stir, making sure to mix well. You can also gently blend by rotating the jar back and forth if making it in a quart jar.

Place a lid over the milk and allow it to culture at room temperature for twelve hours. After twelve hours it should have a fresh, slightly tangy odor and be visibly a bit thicker.

Store in the refrigerator.

This buttermilk is a starter culture of its own as well, and can be used in place of other cultures for many recipes using mesophilic cultures.

**As with yogurt, you can use a store-bought buttermilk to culture your initial batch. It must be a high quality cultured buttermilk with live cultures in order to work.*

Sour Cream

Sour cream does not lend itself readily to being made with goat milk, but I had to include it because it is a favorite of mine. Even before my birth, I gave my mother sour cream cravings! As the name implies, sour cream requires whole cream. Because goat milk does not separate itself naturally, you will need a cream separator to make sour cream with it. Alternatively, you can drain your yogurt and use it as a sour cream replacement, or you can use whole cream skimmed off cow milk. Homemade sour cream is not as thick as store-bought, but it is delicious! You can also drain out some of the whey through a finely woven butter muslin to thicken.

1 pint whole cream
1-2 tbsp cultured buttermilk

Allow your cream to come to room temperature.

Add in the cultured buttermilk and stir, making sure to fully combine. You can also gently shake the jar back and forth to blend as well.

Cover the jar with a lid and allow to culture at room temperature for twelve hours. After twelve hours you should have a thickened, fresh-but-tangy smelling sour cream.

Store in the refrigerator. (Sour cream will naturally separate, so give a good stir before serving!)

Butter

Butter is an interesting facet of owning dairy goats. Butter is traditionally made from whole cream, which leaves the dairy goat owner in the same predicament as the sour cream—a cream separator is necessary to make butter the traditional way using goat milk. With goat milk, however, there is a bit of a work around. You can make butter from goat milk simply by shaking the milk in a jar until it forms butter. The yield is not extensive, but it's butter nonetheless. Whether you are using a jar, a stand mixer, or a butter churn, the results will be the same. Also, if you do happen to own a cream separator, you can make butter using the same method below, but substituting cream for the milk—doing so will result in higher butter yields.

1 quart fresh milk
Salt (optional)

Pour fresh, cold milk into the bowl of a stand mixer and beat on medium speed until butter forms. The milk will first thicken, and then it will start to break into butter and buttermilk. (If using cream, you will make whipped cream first, and then it will separate into butter.) You will see the chunks of butter coming together when it's ready.

Strain the butter out of the buttermilk, and stick the buttermilk in the refrigerator. It will be similar to a skim milk, or you can use it to create a cultured buttermilk using the recipe on page 243.

Work the butter either with clean hands or using a wooden butter paddle to remove all the liquid from it. To do this, massage or work the butter between the paddles, frequently dipping it in cold water. Change out the water as it becomes cloudy. When the water runs clear and no more liquid is escaping the butter, it's ready to be salted, if desired. Sprinkle salt to taste and mix in or leave unsalted.

Press the butter into a prepared butter mold or spoon it into a container and refrigerate to harden.*

**To prepare a traditional wooden butter mold, soak it in water for thirty minutes beforehand. Allow to air dry just so that water is not collected within it, then press the butter firmly into the mold. Refrigerate at least four hours. When butter is firm, carefully turn the mold upside down. The butter should release easily. If it doesn't, refrigerate longer or place in the freezer for up to fifteen minutes.*

Fresh chèvre logs rolled in Italian seasonings and topped with a bay leaf (front) and rolled in red pepper flakes (back).

Fresh Chèvre

Fresh chèvre is a delicious, mild, and slightly tangy cheese. It is soft and can be left smooth and spreadable or can be drained further until it is dry and crumbly. It takes on the flavors of whatever spices and herbs are blended into it—it can be made sweet with cinnamon and honey or dried fruit, or savory with herbs and spices. It's a wonderful replacement for traditional cream cheese or other soft cheeses in recipes. It's also the easiest possible cheese to make! Although the rest of these recipes can be made with milk from any species, it's not truly chèvre if it's not made from goat milk.

½ gallon fresh goat milk
1 dash mesophilic culture such as flora danica
1 drop rennet
1 drop calcium chloride
Salt

Allow the milk to come to room temperature.

Stir or gently rotate in the flora danica. Repeat with the calcium chloride and then again with the rennet, gently mixing each time.

Allow the milk to culture for 12 hours or overnight. When you check the milk, it should have a clean, fresh scent and be separated into solid (curds) and liquid (whey).

Drain the cheese into a finely woven butter muslin or a bag made from muslin cloth. Hang the cheese from a wooden spoon set over a tall pot for four to eight hours. The longer the cheese drains, the drier and crumblier it will become.

After it has drained, salt the cheese to taste and form into logs or desired shape. Enjoy plain or flavor with herbs, spices, or dried fruits. A beautiful presentation is to roll the cheese in herbs or spices, but they can also be blended in. Keep in the refrigerator or wrap tightly and freeze to keep for longer periods of time.

Mold Ripened Chèvre

This recipe is quite literally the exact same as fresh chèvre, with one exception: the addition of mold. In this case, the mold we are using is geotrichum candidum, the same mold used to make camembert and brie. This cheese ages for a handful of weeks, depending on how quickly the mold grows, and develops into a mold-covered masterpiece. While many recipes for mold-ripened cheese are complex, this one is quite simple and takes less ripening time due to the small cheese molds.

½ gallon fresh goat milk
1 dash mesophilic culture such as flora danica
1 drop rennet
1 drop calcium chloride
1 pinch geotrichum candidum
Activated charcoal
Salt

Allow the milk to come to room temperature.

Stir or gently rotate in the flora danica. Repeat with the calcium chloride and then again with the rennet, gently mixing each time. Lastly, add in the geotrichum candidum and mix once more.

Allow the milk to culture for 12 hours or overnight. When you check the milk, it should have a clean, fresh scent and be separated into solid (curds) and liquid (whey).

Place the curds into small plastic cheese molds. Place molds on a drainage mat or on a cookie rack above a pan to collect the whey and allow to drain for four to eight hours. The longer it drains, the drier and crumblier the cheese will become. I suggest not draining more than six hours, because crumbly cheese will be more prone to breaking during the slipping process.

Place the cheese molds into the refrigerator in a covered container, preferably with a drainage mat in the bottom to prevent them sitting in their own whey if more drains out, as it likely will.

With clean hands, open the container and gently flip the cheese in its mold once daily. Turn the cheese out into your palm and replace it into the mold with the opposite side down. This prevents the cheese from growing into the mold and getting stuck. Continue flipping in the mold for up to one week, until the cheese is firm enough to hold its shape and be flipped outside of the mold.

Once the cheese is holding its shape, sprinkle salt to taste and activated charcoal on the outside of the cheese. The activated charcoal helps encourage mold growth and also makes for a decorative cheese.

Continue turning the cheese over once daily for two to four weeks. How long it takes the mold to grow on the cheese will vary based on humidity and temperature. Slightly warmer storage, such as in a wine cooler, will result in faster mold development.

The cheese is ready when the exterior has completely molded over. The texture of the surface will change as well, into something wavy. You will never be more excited to find mold growing in your refrigerator than when you've grown it purposefully on cheese!

Mozzarella

Many people tout mozzarella as the easiest cheese recipe to make, but I didn't find it so easy to learn. My first few tries didn't turn out well at all, and I wondered if maybe I wasn't meant to make mozzarella. The truth is that anyone can learn to make cheese, but certain things do come easier to certain people than others. For whatever reason, mozzarella in particular challenged me. Part of the problem was also trying recipes that over-complicated the process, so I'm sharing a very simple, straightforward method with you in hopes that your first attempts succeed where mine did not. Also, just a fun fact—mozzarella is traditionally made with milk from the Italian water buffalo!

1 gallon fresh goat milk

1 ½ tsp citric acid
¼ cup water
¼ tsp rennet
2-3 tbsp salt

Add citric acid to water and stir until completely dissolved. Add the water to milk and heat over medium-low heat to 90 F.

In a separate pot, heat water to 165-185 F. This water will be used to stretch your cheese. (You can also heat the whey to do this instead of water as well.)

Add rennet to the milk when it reaches temperature. Stir in quickly, then stop the movement of the milk by holding your spoon still in the milk.

Allow the milk to set for 5 minutes and check the curd for a clean break. If a clean finger inserted into the cheese and then gently lifted creates a clean fracture in the milk with little curd sticking to your finger, your curds are ready. If not, allow them to sit a few minutes more. Another sign the curds are formed is that they will have separate from the whey and coagulated.

Once you have reached a clean break, cut the curd into 1" columns by using a curd knife or long cake decorating spatula to cut line horizontally and vertically through the curd, 1" apart. Allow the curds to heal for 1 minute.

Cut the curds diagonally into 1" cubes by taking the same knife and cutting into the curds at a 45 degree angle from all four directions. Allow the curds to heal once more for 1-2 minutes.

Begin to gently stir the curd while bringing the temperature up to 95 F over a time span of 10 minutes. Do not rush the heating process.

Drain the curd into a colander lined with a piece of finely woven butter muslin. Allow the curd to drain and knit together for 10 minutes, flipping over once halfway through draining.

While curd is draining, fill a bowl with ice water.

Turn the curd out onto a cutting board with towels underneath it. Cut the curd into strips about 1-2" in width. Allow the curd to rest once more for about 1 minute. More whey will drain off during this period.

Place the strips of curd into a bowl, add salt, and then cover with hot water (or whey). Allow to heat 30 seconds to one minute and check for stretching.

Once the cheese is stretchy, go through the cheese and stretch each portion slightly. If the water cools, add more hot water to continue the stretching.

When all cheese has been stretched, remove from hot water and immediately shape into balls. To shape, fold the cheese into itself so that a shiny skin forms on the outside. Then squeeze the cheese through the hole created by pinching together your forefinger and thumb. As the ball squeezes through and is the size you want, pinch off the end by closing your forefinger and thumb. Immediately plunk the cheese balls into the bowl of ice water so that they hold their shape.

This is delicious on pizza, pasta, lasagna, or even on its own drizzled with olive oil and sprinkled with fresh cracked black pepper.

Ricotta

Ricotta is an excellent way to make use of all the excess whey that comes from making cheese and other dairy products. I once heard cheesemaking referred to as "removing the water from milk," which is both a cool way to think of it and truthful. However, the "water" leftover in the form of whey still holds onto some protein, fat, and other nutrients after the cheese has been extracted. The word ricotta literally means "recooked" or "cooked twice" in Italian, and that is exactly what we do to whey to squeeze out the last bit of solids. When this whey is recooked, it becomes ricotta cheese—a fine cheese for use in dishes like lasagna or cannoli.

1 gallon whey
¼ cup milk
1 ½ tbsp salt
¼ cup water
1 dash citric acid

Dissolve citric acid into water and set aside.

Heat the whey over medium-high to high heat. Unlike most cheeses, we want to heat the whey rapidly.

When the whey reaches a 160 F, add milk and salt. Continue to heat.

When the milk is between 190-195 F, add citric acid and stir in quickly. Stop the movement by placing your spoon in and holding it still. The whey will break into small curds.

Remove spoon and allow whey to continue heating. The curds will form a cover over the whey. Allow the whey to heat until it creates a bubble that erupts through the cover of curds.

When the cover of curds erupts, turn off the heat and allow the curd to rest for 10 minutes.

Drain curds in a specially made ricotta basket or a finely woven butter muslin. Drain until it reaches your desired consistency. Typically, about 20-30 minutes is good for a moist ricotta. Drain longer for a dry, firm ricotta.

Transfer ricotta to a jar and store in the refrigerator. Ricotta has a shorter shelf life, so use quickly.

Farmer's Cheese

I've seen many different types of cheeses referred to as farmer's cheese, from soft cheese similar to chèvre to loose cheese similar to cottage cheese to hard pressed cheese similar to mild cheddar. To me, farmer's cheese refers to a mild, semi-hard cheese that is lightly pressed and eaten fresh rather than aged. In my personal opinion, this farmer's cheese is the easiest cheese to make outside of fresh chèvre.

1 gallon fresh goat milk
1 dash flora danica
¼ tsp rennet
¼ cup water
¼ tsp calcium chloride
1-2 tsp salt

Pour milk into a large stockpot and slowly heat to 80 F.

Sprinkle flora danica over the top and allow it to rehydrate for 5 minutes, keeping milk around 80-85 F.

Gently stir culture into the milk in an up-and down fashion for 2-3 minutes.

Stop stirring and allow milk to rest for thirty minutes, keeping the temperature around 80-85 F.

Dissolve calcium chloride in water. Stir gently into milk and allow to rest for 5 more minutes, still holding temperature.

Slowly increase temperature of milk to 95 F.

Add rennet to milk and stir in quickly. Stop motion of milk by inserting the spoon into milk and holding it in place.

Remove milk from heat, cover, and allow to rest for 30 minutes. After 30 minutes, check for a clean break. If a clean finger inserted into the cheese and then gently lifted creates a clean fracture in the milk with little curd sticking to your finger, your curds are ready. If not, allow them to sit a few minutes more—up to a total time of 1 hour. Another sign the curds are formed is that they will have separate from the whey and coagulated.

Once you have reached a clean break, cut the curds into 1" each pieces with a curd knife or long cake decoration spatula. Cut lines horizontally and vertically through the curd, 1" apart, then cut the curds diagonally into 1" cubes by taking the same knife and cutting into the curds at a 45-degree angle from all four directions. Allow the curds to heal for 1-2 minutes.

Heat the curds over low heat to 120 F. Do not rush the heating process; it should take about 20 minutes to reach temperature. Stir gently for the first few minutes, then stir once every few minutes after that.

Pour the curds into a colander lined with a finely woven butter muslin. Cover the curds with muslin and allow to drain for 1 hour.

Transfer the cheese to a bowl and salt to taste.

Line a cheese mold with butter muslin and fill with curds. Cover the top of the curds with muslin as well, apply the top of the mold, and press with about two pounds of weight. You can do this with a specially made cheese press or by simply using something you have on hand to apply weight, such as canned goods. (Be sure to set your cheese mold over something to catch the dripping whey.) Press for two hours.

Serve with crackers or fresh fruit.

What to Do with Whey: *Whey has many uses, and you will have quite a bit of whey leftover after making cheese. I once heard someone describe cheesemaking as "taking the water out of milk." The whey is all that leftover water from the cheesemaking process. It's not just water, though—it contains bits of protein and nutrients leftover from the cheese. The whey can be used to make ricotta, as you read earlier, but it can also be used in several other ways. Whey makes a great treat for pigs or chickens. It can be added to juice or smoothies for a probiotic protein boost. It can be cooked down over several hours to a thick, caramel colored cheese called gjetost, and you can add a tablespoon to your vegetable ferments such as sauerkraut or kimchi.*

Goat Milk Soap

Soap was the very first thing I learned to make with goat milk—in fact, I learned to make soap before I had goats and learned to make it with milk. My mom, my late Aunt Pat, and I gathered at my grandmother's house and dove into both an old recipe of my grandmother's and a new recipe I'd found. My aunt brought copious amounts of bacon grease for my grandmother's soap, and PVC pipe to create homemade molds. We dove in with ingenuity and enthusiasm, and I have been crafting soaps ever since.

This soap recipe is for cold process soap. That means that the soap is not "cooked" while making it, and it must cure at least 21 days before it is ready to be used. Uncured cold process soap will not be sufficiently hard and can still contain traces of unsaponified sodium hydroxide. Speaking of sodium hydroxide, all handmade soap must be made with sodium hydroxide, more commonly known as lye. All soap is made using sodium hydroxide. Soap itself results from a chemical reaction between lye and fat called saponification. When the saponification process is complete after curing, there is no more sodium hydroxide present in the soap. Instead the fats and the lye have created something new, and that something new is soap. All soap is also superfatted by at least 4% or more (I prefer a 6% superfat), which means that slightly more fat is used in the recipe than can be turned into soap by the sodium hydroxide. This excess fat becomes moisturizing. If you are concerned about using sodium hydroxide, you may buy soap bases—plain, premade soap—which can be melted down, altered in whatever way you choose, and remolded.

Sodium hydroxide is sold as a powder, and it can be difficult to find in stores. The best option for soap makers is to purchase their lye online (see the Resources section). Sodium hydroxide is a caustic chemical, and it must be used with caution. However, you should not fear soapmaking! It's a fun, safe hobby so long as you follow proper safety protocol. First, wear protective gloves and protective eye glasses or goggles. This will prevent accidently burning your skin by touching raw soap or damaging your eyes via splashes. Even during clean up, always wear gloves—that semi-solid soap is still going through its chemical reaction and will burn your hands. Always allow soap to cure a minimum of 21 days to ensure all sodium hydroxide has become soap. Always check your recipes using a lye calculator (see Resources section) to ensure the fat:lye ratios are correct and the soap is superfatted by at least 4%. That prevents any unsaponified lye from remaining in the finished soap. Make soap in a well-ventilated space, outdoors or with windows open, to avoid fumes. (The fumes are greatly reduced when using frozen milk versus using water.) Always add the lye to the liquid and never add liquid to lye: lye gets sprinkled onto the frozen milk, then the milk is added to the melted oils. Keep small children and pets safe and out from underfoot while making soap.

Any cold process soap recipe can be made with goat milk. Simply replace the liquid (usually water) with frozen goat milk. Because sodium hydroxide reacts with water and creates heat, milk should be frozen when used to make soap. Otherwise the sodium hydroxide will burn the milk and turn it into a dark orange color. While this is only an aesthetic issue, freezing also has the benefit of speeding up the soapmaking process. Lye creates a lot of heat as it interacts with liquid, but the frozen milk slows this process down. Lye that cools faster is able to be blended into the fats faster as well. I recommend either freezing your milk into ice cube trays so that it can be easily measured or premeasuring your milk and labeling the weight on the container. I do not recommend using freezer jars to freeze it because it is very difficult to get the milk back out without completely thawing it first, defeating the purpose.

There is a huge variety of fats and oils that can be made into soap. This ranges from soaps made with nothing but olive oil, called castile soaps, to soaps made with several different oils and fats. The recipe I am sharing in this book is made using a very common trio of fats: palm oil, coconut oil, and olive oil. These are very popular fats and will make a nice bar of soap that is moisturizing yet firm and with a good lather. Each type of fat reacts differently to the saponification process. Some create softer bars, some hard, some make large bubbles, some create little foam, and so on. Some are also more moisturizing whereas others are more cleansing. What type of fats you use is personal choice, but it's important to know what the fat is going to do when it saponifies so that your bar of soap matches what you want it to. If you want a cleansing bar with a heavy lather, for instance, you do not want to make a castile soap, which is very mild and does not lather much. Softer bars will require longer curing times, not due to saponification but to harden the bar. I age my castile soaps six months. The best all-purpose bars are made by blending oils that have complementary properties. Moisturizing oils tend to make softer bars with lower lather, while fats that make hard bars with a heavy lather are often more cleansing. Combining a mixture of these oils, such as we do in a palm:coconut:olive oil blend makes a nice bar that is both moisturizing, mildly cleansing, not too soft, and with a nice lather.

After learning the basic process of soapmaking, you can have a lot of fun experimenting with various add-ins and extras. These range from essential oils to exfoliants to coloring micas and more. Popular additions include essential oils for fragrance, clays, colloidal oatmeal, honey, herbs, activated charcoal, coffee grounds, and even things like egg yolks. These types of additions are added at a stage called "trace." Adding them too soon in the process can damage them due to too much loose sodium hydroxide that has not saponified yet. You will know that the soap has reached trace by the consistency. At trace, the soap should be homogenized, meaning that you should not see loose oils shining on the surface, and you will see a line remain on the top of the soap when you dribble some off of a spoon onto the surface. Before trace, any soap dripped across the surface will immediately sink into it, whereas at trace you will see the line where the soap was dribbled. Some additives, particularly synthetic fragrance oils, can accelerate saponification. Be prepared to immediately pour the soap into molds after adding your extras in case it starts to rapidly harden. There are many resources available in books and online that provide information about various additives

The process of soapmaking remains the same no matter which fats or extras you are using. You will always follow the same principals from start to finish each time with little change. Whenever trying a new recipe, I recommend running the recipe through a lye calculator (sometimes called a soap calculator) to check the superfat percentage and sodium hydroxide amounts. These calculators can also be used to resize soap recipes to make them larger or smaller—without overloading your brain with mathematic equations and conversions. Most soap failures result from bad recipes rather than mistakes in the process. You will need a kitchen scale that weighs in ounces, as soap recipes are done by weight and not volume for greater accuracy. All supplies must be nonreactive (glass, wood, stainless steel, heat-resistant plastic and silicone), and you will need a mold for your soap as well. Wooden loaf molds can be purchased or handmade; these make long logs that need to be cut into bars after 24 hours while the soap is still somewhat soft. You can also purchase various sizes and shapes of silicone molds, wooden bar molds, and more. You can also wear gloves and shape soap into balls after 24 hours while still soft.

If your protective gear fails and raw soap touches your skin, rinse immediately and then wash with soap and water. This may result in mild discomfort; if exposure or chemical burns are severe, seek medical attention immediately. Likewise, if raw soap or lye enters your eye, flush immediately with lukewarm water for 20 minutes, remove contact lenses with clean hands, and seek medical attention. Do not rub your eye, and do not put anything other than water or saline in your eye unless directed by a medical professional.

Homemade Goat Milk Soap (1lb Oils and 6% Superfat)

2.3 oz sodium hydroxide (lye)
5.3 oz frozen goat milk
4.8 oz coconut oil
4.8 oz olive oil
6.4 oz palm oil

Don your protective gear (gloves, goggles) and ensure the room is well ventilated (open a window or work outside).

Gently melt oils over low heat until the solid oils are completely dissolved. Remove from heat.

Sprinkle sodium hydroxide over frozen milk. Stir constantly as the milk begins to melt. The lye mixture will heat up during this process.

Use a thermometer to check the temperatures of the oils and the lye mixture. These two must be close to the same temperature before mixing, ideally around 90-100 degrees F. The cooler the materials are when mixed, the faster they will saponify, but the most important thing is that they be near the same temperature. I heat my oils first so that they are cooling while the lye reacts with the frozen goat milk. It is easier to heat the oils back to 90 F if they drop too cool than it is to cool them if the lye reaches temperature before the oils. If your lye has reached 90 F and your oils are still too hot, submerge their container in an ice bath to cool them down quickly. The lye cools more quickly using frozen milk than if you use water instead.

Once both the oils and the lye mixture are between 90-100 F, gently stir the lye mixture into the oils. Stir constantly until the soap starts to homogenize and thicken. A stainless-steel immersion blender will make this process much faster than stirring by hand the entire time, but be careful not to lift the blender and sling raw soap around your kitchen.

When the soap begins to thicken, check for trace by dribbling soap over the top of the bowl. If the line remains on the surface of the soap, it is ready for additives or to be poured into the mold.

Carefully pour the soap into your desired mold. Cover the top with freezer paper to prevent air exposure and the development of soda ash, if desired. Soda ash is a harmless white film that can develop on the surface of the soap due to air exposure; it is aesthetic only and does not affect quality. Do not wrap goat milk soap in towels; some recipes call for wrapping soaps in towels to insulate them and keep them warm, but this is only appropriate for water-based soaps. Wrapping can cause goat milk soaps to overheat.

After 24 hours, the soap should be firm enough to remove from the mold and cut or shaped as desired.

After unmolding, allow the soap to cure in open air for at least 21 days. Softer soaps will require a longer cure. The curing process allows the soap to complete the saponification process, making it safe for use, and also hardens the soap so that it will last longer.

Always store soap in a dry environment. Keep it in well-drained soap dishes (I prefer metal dishes with slatted bottoms) that allow all water to drain off the soap in between uses. Soap kept in a moist environment will melt away much faster.

Savory Suppers

In addition to the dairy products and the recipes that can be made with them, goats provide healthy and delicious meat, too. I know that many people start out with goats thinking there's no way they could ever eat their precious caprines. That's how I started, too. However, I highly encourage you to consider trying goat meat. The fact is that dairy goats always have more male kids than are needed, and only the best of the best should be kept as intact bucks. That leaves many wethers, and in my experience wethers are difficult to place and unfortunately often do not get proper care in their new homes. Pet goats are seldom valued and cared for appropriately, in part because people don't know any better and in part because "it's just a goat."

Goat meat is a healthy, lean, and delicious food. Raising your wethers up for processing ensures that the meat on your table comes from an animal that was cared for properly, only fed what you believe is healthy, and processed humanely. After having more than one negative experience selling wethers, I knew I didn't want to do it anymore. I would rather see them on my plate nourishing my family than wonder what kind of treatment they're having at their new home. That said, goat meat is very similar to beef or venison, so you can easily sub in your meat of choice for these recipes.

Mushroom Cream Sauce

½ pint mushrooms of choice (I like baby portabellas or shitake)
1-3 cloves garlic
16 oz goat milk or cream
¼ cup white wine (or substitute chicken broth)
3 tbsp butter
Salt
Pepper
¼ cup finely grated parmesan cheese, optional

Thinly slice mushrooms and garlic.

Melted butter in a deep-sided skillet and toss in the mushrooms. Be sure to use a large enough pan so that the mushrooms are not crowded; mushrooms release quite a bit of moisture. Sauté over medium heat.

When the mushrooms are softened but not yet fully browned, add in the garlic and continue to sauté until mushrooms are browned and garlic is golden. (Overcooked garlic becomes bitter, so don't add it too early.)

Add the wine or broth to deglaze the pan, scraping the bottom with your spoon to release the browned bits that are clinging to it.

Add the milk or cream and salt and pepper to taste. Reduce heat to medium-low and continue to simmer, stirring frequently to prevent scorching.

Continue simmering until the sauce reaches your desired consistency. The sauce will thicken as it simmers, but how quickly it thickens will depend on the fat content of your milk. Straight cream will thicken the quickest, whereas milk will take a bit longer. If adding parmesan, add it while the sauce is a bit thinner than you want, because it will thicken it further as well. Keep in mind the sauce will continue to thicken as it cools also.

Serve warm over baked chicken, steak, or pasta.

Macaroni and Goat Cheese

Macaroni and cheese has been my favorite dish for as long as I can remember. It's the ultimate comfort food, and honestly, how can you go wrong when cheese and pasta is involved? I grew up eating homemade mac n' cheese on Christmas, Thanksgiving, and pot luck days, but it was almost always made with fakey American "cheese." Since moving my diet to focus on real foods, I've also changed my mac n' cheese. The blend of cheeses in this four-cheese mac is wonderful. The cheddar adds sharpness, the chèvre is creamy and slightly tart, the mozzarella adds a nice stretch, and the gruyere has a wonderfully rich, almost nutty flavor. I didn't include a recipe for gruyere in this book because it is a more complex, aged cheese that I haven't yet mastered, but it's worth including and can usually be found at the grocery store.

32 oz noodles of choice
8 oz cheddar cheese
4 oz soft chèvre
4 oz gruyere
4 oz mozzarella
3 cups goat milk

2 tbsp butter or ghee
2 tbsp all purpose flour
1 tsp paprika
Salt
Pepper

Preheat oven to 350 degrees F. Shred hard cheeses and cut chèvre into cubes. Bring a 6 quart pot of salted water to a boil.

While water is heating, melt butter in a skillet over medium heat and add flour to make a roux. Stir until smooth and golden to remove raw flour taste. Add milk and allow to come to a simmer, stirring constantly to prevent scorching. When the milk becomes bubbly and starts to foam, reduce heat to medium-low and add cheese. Add paprika and salt and pepper to taste. Stir until cheese is melted. Optional: Reserve some of the mozzarella to sprinkle on top before baking, if desired.

Meanwhile, add pasta to water when it reaches a boil and cook until al dente. Drain.

Combine pasta and cheese sauce and pour into a 9 x 9 baking dish. Bake until bubbly and top is lightly browned, approximately 35 minutes.

Variation: You can use this same sauce for a delicious dish of scalloped potatoes with a few adjustments. Start a pot of water boiling for your potatoes, then make the cheese sauce as above, omitting the mozzarella. Boil 5-6 medium potatoes in their jackets until they are tender enough to poke with a fork, but still firm. Submerge in ice water. Once the potatoes are cool enough to handle, peel them by scraping with a knife and cut into thin slices about ¼" thick. Layer potatoes in the bottom of an 11 x 7 pan, slightly overlapping each disk. Salt, pepper, and paprika the first layer to taste. Cover the first layer with cheese sauce, then sprinkle mozzarella cheese. Then repeat with additional layers until the pan is full and top with more mozzarella. Bake at 400 degrees F until potatoes are fully done and top is lightly browned, about 35 minutes.

Hidden Veggie Chevon Chili

I like to make this chili in the crockpot. Dishes like chilis and sauces benefit from a slow cooking to really meld all their flavors together, and the crockpot is the perfect (and easiest) solution—but it's also easy and delicious to simmer it on the stovetop! This is a small batch recipe sufficient for about four people, but it can easily be doubled if needed. This is a mild, savory chili with just a hint of heat. To make it spicier, increase the red pepper or add additional heat from cayenne pepper, red pepper flakes, and/or jalapenos. This recipe is also the perfect way to sneak in some extra veggies for picky eaters—they'll never know the difference! Serve with shredded cheese, sour cream, fresh chopped green onions, or a slice of cornbread.

1.5 pounds ground goat
16 oz plain tomato sauce
2 large carrots
1 medium onion
2-3 cloves garlic, minced
1 poblano pepper (substitute bell pepper if poblano is unavailable)
3 tbsp chili powder
2 tbsp cumin

2 tsp garlic powder
2 tsp onion powder
1/2 tsp red pepper (adjust to increase or decrease heat)
1 tbsp honey
1 tbsp coconut oil
Salt
Pepper

Roast the poblano with the broil setting on your oven until skin is wrinkled and charred.

Finely chop or shred the carrot. A food processor makes quick work of this. Evenly dice onions and roasted poblano into ½" pieces, or smaller or larger depending on personal preference.

Heat coconut oil in a 6 quart stockpot over medium heat. Add carrot, poblano, and onion and sauté until soft. Add chevon, garlic, onion powder, garlic powder, and salt and pepper to taste. Brown meat until no longer pink.

Add remaining ingredients to the stock pot and bring to a boil. Reduce to a simmer and cook on low for thirty minutes or more. Cooking longer will further meld the flavors. If the chili starts to get a bit too dry, add bone broth to thin.

This may also be cooked in a crockpot by following the steps up until browning the meat, then transferring all ingredients into a crockpot to cook on low for four to six hours.

Serve with shredded cheese, fresh sour cream, or whatever toppings you prefer.

Chevon a la Crockpot

This is one of the first impressions I had of goat meat, and I was blown away by how tender and delicious it tasted. If you're hesitant to try goat meat, I would recommend this as a starter meal. It's very similar to beef roast and nearly foolproof. If you don't want to use a crockpot you can cook the roast in a covered dish in the oven at 325 degrees F for one to two hours until it's tender and falling apart. Cooking time will vary depending on the size of the roast.

1 leg of goat or goat shoulder roast
1-2 large yellow onions
3-4 large carrots
4 cloves garlic
1 cup broth

1 cup mushroom cream sauce
1 tsp garlic powder
1 tsp onion powder
2 tbsp coconut oil
Salt
Pepper

Peel the onion and cut in into quarters. Place onion in the bottom of the crockpot.

Heat a cast iron skillet over medium-high heat and add coconut oil to melt. Salt and pepper all sides of the roast. When the skillet is hot, sear each side of the roast until browned. Be patient; don't try to move the roast before the meat has browned or it will stick.

Place the roast on top of the onions. Pour the broth into the hot skillet to deglaze it, and use a wooden spoon to get any stuck on bits up into the broth. Pour the broth into the crockpot along with the mushroom cream sauce. Sprinkle the garlic powder and onion powder over the roast. Place peeled garlic cloves on top of roast.

Cover and set crockpot to low. Peel carrots and cut into three large chunks and set aside in refrigerator.

Cook for a total of six to eight hours until roast is tender and falling apart, adding the carrots in the last two hours of cooking. (I prefer a firmer carrot; if you want very soft carrots, add them earlier.) Cooking time varies slightly based on the size of the roast.

Optional Gravy: If desired, save drippings from roast to make gravy. Gravy can be made by adding 1 tbsp tapioca starch dissolved in ¼ cup water to the broth and simmering until thick or by making a roux of 1 tbsp butter and 1 tbsp flour, cooking in skillet until smooth and golden, and adding broth to simmer until done.

Chevon Taco Meat

Taco night is one of my favorite nights. Tacos are easy to make, fun to eat, and able to convert even the pickiest eaters. Combine this recipe with homemade tortillas for amazing tacos, pile on top of chips for taco salad, or use it to stuff burritos, enchiladas, or Mexican casseroles. This is also a good recipe to make in bulk and reheat through the week in different preparations. This is a mild recipe, but you can turn up the heat by increasing the red pepper flakes or adding cayenne powder.

1 pound ground goat meat
1 medium onion
1-2 cloves garlic
2 tbsp tomato paste
1 tbsp chili powder
2 tsp ground cumin
½ tsp onion powder
½ tsp garlic powder
½ tsp paprika
¼ tsp dried oregano
½ tsp red pepper flakes, optional (adds heat)
1 tbsp coconut oil
Salt

Pepper

Preheat a skillet over medium heat. Finely chop onions by hand or in a food processor and mince or finely chop the garlic.

Add coconut oil, meat, and onions to the skillet. Cook until onions are translucent and meat is browned. Goat meat is lean, so you most likely will not need to drain any grease off.

Add spices, garlic, and tomato paste. Continue cooking for about five more minutes to allow flavors to meld.

Serve warm with desired accompaniments.

Swedish Chevon Meatballs

Swedish meatballs are one of my favorites. They are delicious and creamy, and they pair perfectly with mashed potatoes, rice, or egg noodles. These can also be finished in a crockpot instead of the oven if you want to make them for a potluck. The recipe can easily be doubled if needed.

½ pound ground goat meat
½ pound ground pork
1 tbsp dried parsley
1 tsp garlic powder
1 tsp onion powder
Salt
Pepper
1 large onion
½ cup mushrooms, thinly sliced
1 ½ cups broth
½ cup goat milk
2-3 tbsp butter or ghee
Salt
Pepper
1 tbsp tapioca starch or 1 tbsp flour
¼ cup water

Preheat oven to 350 F.

Thinly slice the onion and mushrooms. Add butter, onion, and mushrooms to an oven safe skillet to sauté over medium heat until caramelized. Salt and pepper to taste.

While onions cook, mix together the goat meat, pork, parsley, and salt and pepper to taste until well combined. Form into even sized balls about an inch thick. I like to use a cookie dough scoop to portion the meat into even sizes. This makes about 17 meatballs.

When onions are caramelized, move to sides of pan and add meatballs. Sear meatballs on all sides until browned and lift out of skillet.

Add broth to deglaze skillet. Once deglazed, lower heat to medium-low and add goat milk. Dissolve tapioca starch in water (or additional broth) and add to sauce. Salt and pepper to taste. Return meatballs and simmer until sauce just begins to thicken. Transfer skillet to oven and cook until meatballs are done, approximately 30 minutes.

***Variation:** To use flour as a thickener instead of tapioca starch, add flour to skillet immediately after removing the seared meatballs. Stir well into onions and cook for several second to remove raw flour taste. Then add broth and continue with recipe as normal. Omit water.

Serve warm with mashed potatoes or over noodles or on their own as an appetizer.

Basil Chèvre Alfredo Sauce

There are two things I love: basil pesto and alfredo sauce. This recipe marries the two flavors in a delicious, creamy, and mildly tangy alfredo sauce. It is delicious on any kind of pasta, as a white pizza sauce, or over chicken. If you want to make it even more rich and creamy, substitute half of the milk for cream. You may leave out the pesto if you want a plain alfredo sauce. Keep in mind that parmesan, chèvre, and pesto all have salt in them, so taste before salting. You may also add 1 tbsp flour to the butter to form a roux and make the sauce thicken more quickly if desired, but it will thicken on its own over the course of about 10 minutes.

16 oz milk (or ½ milk, ½ cream)
8 oz grated parmesan
4 oz fresh chèvre, plain
1 tbsp butter
2 tbsp basil pesto
1 garlic clove, minced
Salt
Pepper

Melt butter in a saucepan or deep skillet and add in garlic.

Once butter is fully melted, add chèvre, milk, and pesto. Stir continuously while slowly bringing the milk to a simmer. Don't heat too quickly or the milk will scorch.

Once the chèvre is melted and incorporated, add the parmesan. Continue to simmer, stirring constantly, until the parmesan is completely melted and the sauce has thickened to your desired consistency. Keep in mind that it will thicken further as it begins to cool. Salt and pepper to taste.

Serve over pasta or in any other way you'd enjoy alfredo sauce.

Sweets and Treats

Everyone secretly has a bit of a sweet tooth. I proclaim myself to prefer salty over sweet most of the time, but even so, the allure of a rich dessert is too much to resist sometimes. Dessert gets even sweeter when it's made by hand with love. I think of the many ways we celebrate special occasions with loved ones, from holidays to birthdays to potlucks, and inevitably a homemade dessert almost always makes an appearance. Something about sharing sweets touches the heart—and the taste buds—in a special way.

The next time you have a person or event to celebrate, try one of these desserts. It's doubly sweet to make a dessert that isn't just handmade but homegrown as well. Every step of the way, from milking the goat to plating the treats, these desserts are a true labor of love perfect for sharing with loved ones—or just treating yourself!

Riz au Lait de Chèvre (Rice with Goat Milk)

Once upon a time, I thought I didn't like rice pudding. I had only tried the American version of rice pudding, which usually involves cooked minute rice and an egg-based custard with the occasional addition of raisins. Then I tried the French version of rice pudding—riz au lait. This version is thick and creamy, mildly sweet, and so delicious and filling. While no one will stop you from adding raisins if you wish, I encourage you to try this recipe as-is first. It's perfectly rich and luscious on its own.

½ cup short grain rice, uncooked
3 cups whole milk, divided
⅛ cup cane sugar
1 vanilla bean or 1 tsp vanilla extract
1 cinnamon stick
Pinch of salt
Butter or milk to serve, optional

Combine rice, two cups milk, sugar, scrapings of the vanilla bean or extract, cinnamon stick, and salt in a small saucepan. Bring to a boil over medium-low heat, stirring frequently to prevent scorching.

Reduce heat to low and allow to simmer, covered, for 15 minutes. Keep an eye on it so as not to let it boil too fast and boil over.

After 15 minutes, add the remaining cup of milk. Increase heat slightly to bring milk back to a simmer and continue cooking, stirring constantly, until the rice is tender and thickened, approximately 25 minutes. The rice should simmer but not boil during this time.

Once rice is tender and thickened, remove from heat. This can be served warm or chilled. I like to eat a warm bowl with a pat of butter on top. Some people like to drizzle a bit of milk over chilled rice pudding similar to a breakfast cereal.

The pudding can also be topped with fruit, a sprinkle of additional cinnamon, a drizzle of honey, or anything your heart desires!

Chèvre Cheesecake

Cheesecake is one of my favorite desserts. There are many substitutions, from no bake to frozen store-bought, but nothing beats a classic homemade cheesecake. I adapted this recipe from the one my Granny uses, which she procured from a friend named Sue D'Agostino many years ago. A few tweaks later and this chèvre cheesecake was born.

Cheesecake

24 ounces fresh, plain chèvre at room temperature
4 eggs
1 cup cane sugar
1 tsp vanilla extract
1 cup sour cream
2 tbsp cane sugar

Crust

1 ½ cups graham cracker crumbs
1 tbsp honey
1/3 cup butter, melted
½ tsp cinnamon

Preheat oven to 350 F. Line the bottom of a springform pan with parchment paper.

Mix together the ingredients for the crust and press into the bottom of the pan.

Mix together the chèvre, eggs, 1 cup sugar, and vanilla and beat well with a mixer or by hand until smooth.

Pour cheesecake batter into pan and bake for 55 minutes.

Mix together 1 cup sour cream and 1 tbsp sugar. Smooth evenly over top of the cheesecake and bake for 5 more minutes.

Remove cheesecake from oven and allow to cool until almost room temperature. Continue cooling the cheesecake in the refrigerator overnight.

Run a knife around the outside of the cheesecake and release springform pan. Serve with fresh fruit, chocolate, cajeta, or plain! There's no wrong way to eat a cheesecake.

Cajeta (Goat Milk Caramel Sauce)

1 quart fresh goat milk
1 cup cane sugar
½ tsp baking soda
2 tsp vanilla extract
Dash of salt
1 cinnamon stick, optional

Stir together milk and sugar in a 4 or 6 quart sauce pan. Add vanilla, salt, and cinnamon sticks.

Heat over medium heat, stirring constantly to avoid scorching. When the milk reaches a boil, remove from heat and stir in baking soda. The mixture will foam. Return to heat and bring it back to a simmer.

Cajeta takes a good bit of time and patience. As the milk simmers, keep stirring every few minutes to prevent scorching. Scrape the sides and bottom of the pan well. It will take an hour or two to progress to the next stage.

When the mixture begins to darken, remove the cinnamon stick. Watch the cajeta closely now. It will begin to foam again as it gets near its final stage. The cajeta will begin to cook down much more quickly at this stage.

The cajeta is ready when it's a rich caramel color and at least thick enough to coat the back of a spoon. Continue cooking down until it reaches the thickness you want. To test consistency, drop a bit onto a chilled plate.

Use a funnel to pour the cajeta into a jar and allow to cool. Store in the refrigerator and serve over ice cream or cake or use as a dip for fruit.

Homemade Ice Cream (Frozen Custard)

Growing up, homemade ice cream was a staple at any summer get-together. It wasn't the Fourth of July without my mom's homemade ice cream and fresh watermelon. Homemade ice cream was made to celebrate family reunions, birthday parties, and sometimes "just because." This recipe is a frozen custard variety that first creates a cooked custard mixture before freezing. Start this recipe a day in advance so it's ready for your celebration. For a faster, slightly less rich version, see the next recipe for raw ice cream.

1 quart fresh goat milk
½ cup cane sugar*
4 egg yolks
1 tsp vanilla
1 vanilla bean

Whisk together milk, sugar, vanilla, and the scrapings of one vanilla bean in a saucepan. Heat the mixture over medium-low, stirring constantly to prevent scorching, and allow to scald. The milk should be heated to just prior to reaching a simmer.

Whisk the yolks in a bowl. Add a small amount of the hot milk mixture to the yolks and whisk them to temper. This prevents the yolk from scrambling when added to the milk.

Slowly whisk the yolks into the milk. Bring the milk to gradually to a boil, continuing to stir frequently. When the milk reaches a boil, remove from heat.

Pour the milk through a fine mesh strainer to catch any bits of egg that may have scrambled. Store in the refrigerator for several hours or overnight until cold.

Pour the chilled milk into a prepared ice cream machine and process according to the machine's instructions until it reaches your desired thickness. Ice cream machines make a soft-serve texture, so stick it in the freezer for a bit if you want to really firm it up. The higher the butterfat content in the milk, the thicker the final ice cream will be.

Serve with cajeta, chocolate syrup, or plain.

**You can substitute the sugar with natural sweeteners. Maple syrup will give the ice cream a maple flavor, honey will also give it a mild honey flavor. You may need to increase the amounts as certain natural sweeteners are less sweet than sugar.*

Homemade Ice Cream (Raw)

This is the ice cream recipe my mom made every single summer. The recipe originally came from my dad's mother, Mamoo. This recipe is slightly less rich and less thick than the frozen custard variety, but it's fast and easy to put together. There's no cooking involved, just mixing and freezing, so if you enjoy your milk raw this one will keep it that way. The butterfat content of your milk will change the thickness, too; the first time we made this recipe with full-cream raw milk, we were all surprised at how much thicker it became than when it was made with 4% milk from the store.

6 eggs

1-2 tbsp vanilla extract*
2 cups sugar
14 oz sweetened condensed milk**
Fresh goat milk

Beat the eggs with a mixer or by hand. Add sugar, vanilla, and sweetened condensed milk. Put a small amount of milk in the mixture and warm it on the stove to dissolve the sugar.

Put the egg mixture into the canister of a 4-quart ice cream maker and fill the remaining space up to your machine's fill line with milk.
Process according to your ice cream machine's instructions until thickened. This recipe makes a looser consistency, so if you would like it to be thicker, stick it in the freezer for a few minutes to thicken further.

Best eaten outside on a hot day with friends and family!

**Do not use homemade vanilla extracts made with alcohol. The alcohol content will be too high and prevent the ice cream from freezing. We learned that the hard way!*

***You can make your own sweetened condensed milk by following the cajeta recipe but stopping the process early, because it becomes fully caramelized. It should be light tan and slightly thickened. You can also substitute cajeta for the sweetened condensed milk for a different flavor.*

A Last Word of Encouragement

A Facebook friend of mine once wrote, "sometimes farming feels like a series of unfortunate events." She shared this in a post about why she farmed and the joy she found in her goats. Her post struck a chord with me, as I imagine it did many fellow farmers, because her words were so true. Yes, sometimes farming feels like a series of unfortunate events. Yet for those of us who love this life, the rewards are enough to outweigh the unfortunate events that sometimes make farm life hard.

You will make mistakes. We all do. I have made plenty and will surely make more, as will you. There will be days when you think, "Why didn't I do this? What if I had done that?" There will be hard days on the farm. There will be days when you feel responsible for something that has gone very wrong. There will be days when your livestock inevitably becomes deadstock. There will be days when you feel like quitting, and there may be times when you need to take a step back from it all. There will be days when you are reminded by your farm just how little control you actually have, and there will be moments that make you wonder why you ever thought this was a good idea. This is part of farming.

But there will also be incredible days. Days filled with joy and sunshine. There will be moments when you reap the fruits of your labor and find that nothing has ever tasted so sweet. There will be bouncing baby goats and delicious creamy milk and laughter. There will be days when you question why it took you so long to do this, and moments when you are certain the farm is where you belong, and a farmer is what you were created to be. You will experience he peace and beauty and love of the farm.

Be willing to accept and, most importantly, learn from the bad days. Keep going forward. The past is in the past; you don't live there anymore. Each day is a new chance to get it right, and in the grand scheme of things the good days will outnumber the bad. So, when you make those mistakes and have those bad days, remember the sunshine. Don't forget why you started, and don't give up in moments of pain or heartbreak. There is a lesson in every hardship, and you can only reap the benefits of your hard work if you continue to preserve. If farming is truly meant for you—and you are truly meant to be a farmer—it will be worth it in the end.

Always remember that even after the darkest nights, the sun still rises.

Cheers,

Rachel

Name	Date of Birth	Sex	Retained Kids in Herd	Sold Date	Deceased Date	Notes

Date Bred	Doe	Buck	Due Date	Date Kidded	Bucks	Does	Sold	Retained	Notes/Reservations

Recommended Reading

Raising Goats Naturally by Deborah Niemann

Small-Scale Livestock Farming: A Grass-Based Approach for Health, Sustainability, and Profit by Carol Ekarius

The Natural Soap Book: Making Herbal and Vegetable-Based Soaps by Susan Miller Cavitch

Nourishing Traditions: The Cookbook that Challenges Politically Correct Nutrition and Diet Dictocrats by Sally Fallon

Goat Medicine, 2nd edition by Mary C. Smith

Butchering: Poultry, Rabbit, Lamb, Goat, Pork by Adam Danforth

The Home Creamery by Kathy Ferrell-Kingsley

Soap Book by Sandy Maine

Home Cheese Making by Ricki Carrol

Resources

Caprine Supply
General goat supplies.
www.caprinesupply.com

Hoegger Supply Co.
General goat supplies.
www.hoeggerfarmyard.com

Jeffers Livestock
General livestock supplies.
www.jefferspet.com

Valley Vet Supply
General livestock supplies.
www.valleyvet.com

Hamby Dairy Supply
Dairy supplies.
www.hambydairysupply.com

Cultures for Health
Cultures and supplies for cheese and cultured dairy.
www.culturesforhealth.com

New England Cheese Making Supply Co.
Cheesemaking supplies and cultures.
www.cheesemaking.com

Bulk Herb Store
Dried herbs.
www.bulkherbstore.com

Simple Pulse Professional Home Milking Systems
Economical home milking machines.
www.simplepulse.com

Brambleberry
Soapmaking supplies and lye calculator.
www.brambleberry.com

Soaper's Choice
Oils and butters for soapmaking.
www.soaperschoice.com

Land of Havilah
Herbal supplements.
www.landofhavilahfarm.com/loh/

Bulk Apothecary
Soapmaking supplies.
www.bulkapothecary.com

American Dairy Goat Association
www.adga.org

The Livestock Conservancy
www.livestockconservancy.org

The Weston A. Price Foundation
www.westonaprice.org

The Farm To Consumer Legal Defense Fund
www.farmtoconsumer.org

Bibliography

ADGA (American Dairy Goat Association). Accessed December 2017. www.adga.org.

ADGA, "DHIR Breed Averages - 2016 Lactations." Accessed January 2018. http://adga.org/knowledgebase/breed-averages/

Alello, Susan and Michael Moses, *The Merck Veterinary Manual, 11th Edition,* Merck, 2016.

Ball, Don, Jorge Mosjidis, "Sericea Lespideza: A Pasture, Hay, and Conservation Plant," Alabama Cooperative Extension System. Last modified 2007. http://www.aces.edu/pubs/docs/A/ANR-1318/ANR-1318.pdf

Bathgate, R., "Birth of Kids after Artificial Insemination with Sex-Sorted, Frozen-Thawed Goat Spermatozoa," *Reproduction in Domestic Animals* vol. 48, no. 6. (2013). doi:10.1111

Bernard, Gregory, Mulumebet Worku, and Mohamed Ahmedna. "The Effects of Diatomaceous Earth on Parasite Infected Goats." *Bulletin of the Georgian Academy of Science* Vol 3, no 1. (2009). http://science.org.ge/old/3-1/Bernard.pdf

BioTracking, "BioPRYN for Goats." Accessed December 2017. www.biotracking.com/goats

Bowen, R., "Placentation in Ruminants," Colorado State University. Last modified August 2000. http://www.vivo.colostate.edu/hbooks/pathphys/reprod/placenta/ruminants.html

Boyles, Stephen, Ladon Johnson, "Oats as Feed for Beef Cattle," North Dakota State University. Accessed March 2018. https://agnr.osu.edu/sites/agnr/files/imce/pdfs/Beef/OatsAsFeedForBeefCattle.pdf

Burke, J.M., A. Wells, P. Casey, R.M. Kaplan, "Herbal dewormer fails to control gastrointestinal nematodes in goats," *Veterinary Parasitology* 160, Pages 168–170. (2009). https://pdfs.semanticscholar.org/432c/a008b3b515f6a7f9255ae2a512668501b

Burke, J.M., J.E. Miller, "Control of Haemonchus contortus in goats with a sustained-release multi-trace element/vitamin ruminal bolus containing copper," *Veterinary Parasitology* Volume 141, Issues 1–2, Pages 132-137. (2006).

https://doi.org/10.1016/j.vetpar.2006.04.014

Burke, J.M., J.E. Miller, D.K. Brauer, "The effectiveness of copper oxide wire particles as an anthelmintic in pregnant ewes and safety to offspring," *Veterinary Parasitology* Volume 131, Issues 3–4, Pages 291-297. (2005). https://doi.org/10.1016/j.vetpar.2005.05.009

Burke, Joan "Management of Barber Pole Worm in Sheep and Goats in the Southern US," Small Farms Research Update. Last modified February 2005. https://docs.wixstatic.com/ugd/aded98_a07518be5cb94816a3ed729e0220cc31.pdf

Campaign for Real Milk, "Health," Weston A. Price Foundation. Last modified October 2015. https://www.realmilk.com/health/

Centers for Disease Control and Prevention, "Antibiotic Resistance Threats in the United States," Last modified 2013. https://www.cdc.gov/drugresistance/threat-report-2013/index.html

Christensen, Karen, "Reproduction in the Goat," Biology of the Goat. Last modified 2015. http://www.goatbiology.com/animations/reproduction.htm

Coffey, Linda, "Copper Oxide Wire Particles," American Consortium for Small Ruminant Parasite Control. Accessed February 2018. https://docs.wixstatic.com/ugd/6ef604_10cb6517fbab453b8ac787c538ed92f0.pdf

Concha, Andres de la and Juste, Ramtin, "Floppy Kid Syndrome," Texas A&M University Agricultural Experiment Station. Accessed March 2018. http://goatdocs.ansci.cornell.edu/Resources/GoatArticles/GoatHealth/KidCare/Floppykid1.pdf

Cornell University, "Glucosinolates (Goitrogenic Glycosides)," Department of Animal Science, Plants Poisonous to Livestock. Last modified 2015. http://poisonousplants.ansci.cornell.edu/toxicagents/glucosin.html

Correa, Julio E., "Digestive System of Goats," Alabama A&M and Auburn Universities. Last modified February 2016. http://www.aces.edu/pubs/docs/U/UNP-0060/UNP-0060.pdf

Cultures for Health, "The Differences Between Cow and Goat Milk." Accessed January 2018. https://www.culturesforhealth.com/learn/general/differences-cow-milk-goat-milk/

Darby, Tracy, "Figure Eight Disbudding Tutorial," Zanzabeez Nigerians. https://Goatcaretips.weebly.com

Dairy One, "Pregnancy and Disease Testing." Accessed December 2017. www.dairyone.com/analytical-services/pregnancy-testing/

Eaton, Orson N., "The Relation Between Polled and Hermaphroditic Characters in Dairy Goats," Bureau of Animal Industry, U. S. Department of Agriculture. (1944). https://www.ncbi.nlm.nih.gov/pmc/articles/PMC1209274/pdf/51.pdf

Ekarius, Carol, *Small-Scale Livestock Farming: A Grass Based Approach for Health, Sustainability and Profit.* Storey Publishing, 1999. Emlab Genetics, "P-Test." Accessed December 2017. www.emlabgenetics.com/Pages/PTEST.aspx.

Evans, F. D., A. T. Critchley, "Seaweeds for animal production use," *Journal of Applied Phycology*. Volume 26, Issue 2, pp 891–899. (2014). https://link.springer.com/article/10.1007/s10811-013-0162-9

Farke, Andrew A., "Frontal sinuses and head-butting in goats: a finite element analysis," *Journal of Experimental Biology* 211: 3085-3094. (2008). doi: 10.1242/jeb.019042

Fehr, P. "*Goat Nutrition*," Food and Agriculture Organization of the United States. Accessed March 2018. http://edepot.wur.nl/317383#page=113

Flores, J.A., F.G. Véliz, J.A. Pérez-Villanueva, G. Martínez de la Escalera, P. Chemineau, P. Poindron, B. Malpaux, J.A. Delgadillo, "Male Reproductive Condition Is the Limiting Factor of Efficiency in the Male Effect During Seasonal Anestrus in Female Goats." *Biology of Reproduction* Volume 62, Issue 5, Pages 1409–1414. (2000). https://doi.org/10.1095/biolreprod62.5.1409

Glennon, Heather, "Best Management Practices for Internal Parasite Control in Small Ruminants," American Consortium for Small Ruminant Parasite Control. Accessed March 2018. https://docs.wixstatic.com/ugd/6ef604_71bcda722c8949b688ad05e3cb828615.pdf

Hart, Steve, "Alternative dewormers: do they work?" American Consortium for Small Ruminant Parasite Control. Last modified 2017. https://www.wormx.info/part5

Hart, Steve, "How to Grow Worms (or Not)," American Consortium for Small Ruminant Parasite Control. Last modified March 2017. https://www.wormx.info/growworms

Hart, Steve, "Parasite Control with Multispecies and Rotational Grazing." Last modified

2014. http://kerrcenter.com/wp-content/uploads/2014/04/hart_multispp_presentation.pdf

Hartnack, Amanda K., Molly Jordan, Allen J. Roussel, "Complications associated with surgical dehorning in goats: A retrospective study of 239 cases," *Veterinary Surgery* Vol 47 Issue 2. (14 December 2017). DOI: 10.1111/vsu.12743

Heath, A.M., David Gartrell Pugh, and M.S. Edens, "Urogenital Surgery in Goats," *Current Therapy in Large Animal Theriogenology,* Pages 524-528. (2007). https://doi.org/10.1016/B978-072169323-1.50070-2.

Heidrich, Clara, "Introduction to Dairy Goats," American Institute for Goat Research, Langston University, Dairy Goat Certification. Accessed March 2018. http://certification.goats.langston.edu/

Hines, Murray E. II, "Enterotoxemia in Sheep and Goats," University of Georgia College of Veterinary Medicine. Accessed March 2018. http://vet.uga.edu/news/view/enterotoxemia_in_sheep_and_goats

Hi-Pro Feed, "Black Oil Sunflower Seeds Nutrition." Accessed March 2018. https://www.hiprofeeds.com/products/black-oil-sunflower-seeds

Hogberg, Madelein, "Milk yield and composition in Swedish landrace goats (Capra hircus) kept together with their kids in two different systems," Swedish University of Agriculture Sciences. Accessed January 2018. https://stud.epsilon.slu.se/2551/1/hogberg_m_110511.pdf

Holmes, Andrew, Dr. Carly Rosewarne, "Gut bacteria: the inside story," Australian Academy of Science. Accessed March 2018. https://www.science.org.au/curious/people-medicine/gut-bacteria

Hutchens, Terry K., "Urinary Calculi in Goats," University of Kentucky. Accessed March 2018. http://www.ansc.purdue.edu/SP/MG/Documents/SLIDES/Urinary%20calculi.pdf

Johnson, Eugene H., Khalid Al-Habsi, Evelyn Kaplan, Anandarajah Srikandakumar, Isam T. Kadim, Kanthi Annamalai, Rashid Al-Busaidy, Osman Mahgoub, "Caprine hepatic lipidosis induced through the intake of low levels of dietary cobalt," *The Veterinary Journal* Volume 168, Issue 2, Pages 174-179. (2004). https://doi.org/10.1016/j.tvjl.2003.10.012

Kadim, Isam T., Eugene H. Johnson, Osman Mahgoub, Anandarajah Srikandakumar,

Dawood Al-Ajmi, Andrew Ritchie, Kanthi Annamalai, Abdulla S. Al-Halhali, "Effect of low levels of dietary cobalt on apparent nutrient digestibility in Omani goats," *Animal Feed Science and Technology* Volume 109, Issues 1–4, Pages 209-216. (2003). https://doi.org/10.1016/S0377-8401(03)00174-3

Kaiser-Klinger, Sharon, "Small Ruminant Anesthesia," Premier Equine Veterinary Services. https://www.acvs.org/files/proceedings/2012/data/papers/170.pdf

Kentucky Equine Research Staff, "Lespedeza Hay for Horses," Kentucky Equine Research. Accessed March 2018. http://www.equinews.com/article/lespedeza-hay-horses

Kerr, Susan, "Tube Feeding Neonatal Small Ruminants," Oregon State University Small Farms Vol. III No. 3 (Summer 2008). http://smallfarms.oregonstate.edu/sfn/su08ruminants

Leite-Browning, Maria Lenira, "Biology of Reproduction of Goats," Alabama A&M and Auburn Universities. Accessed March 2018. http://www.aces.edu/pubs/docs/U/UNP-0107/UNP-0107.pdf

Merck Veterinary Manual, "Nutritional Requirements of Goats." Accessed December 2017. www.merckvetmanual.com/management-and-nutrition/nutrition-goats/nutritional-requirements-of-goats.

Metzger, Mike, "Colostrum is the Key to Raising Healthy Goat Kids and Lamb," Michigan State University Extension. Last modified 2013. www.msue.anr.msu.edu/news/colostrum_is_the_key_to_raising_healthy_goat_kids_and_lambs

Mgongo, F. O. K., S. Gombe, J. S. Ogaa, "The influence of cobalt/vitamin B12 deficiency as a stressor affecting adrenal cortex and ovarian activities in goats." Reproductive Nutritional Development 234 (6), 845-854. (1984). https://rnd.edpsciences.org/articles/rnd/pdf/1984/07/RND_0181-1916_1984_24_6_ART0003.pdf

Miller, Dan, "Late Horn Removal," Pygmy Goat WORLD. Last modified 1996. http://kinne.net/latehrn1.htm

Miller, James E, "Major Internal Parasites Affecting Small Ruminant Production," Oral presentation, Small Ruminant Production Workshop, Mississippi State University. 17 March 2018.

National Sunflower Association, "Sunflower as a Feed." Accessed March 2018. https://www.sunflowernsa.com/wholeseed/sunflower-as-a-feed/

Niemann, Deborah, "Do Goats Need Grain During Pregnancy?" Thrifty Homesteader. Last modified 2014. thriftyhomesteader.com/do-goats-need-grain-during-pregnancy/

Niemann, Deborah, "Goat birthing: Patience is a virtue," Thrifty Homesteader. Last modified April 2015. https://thriftyhomesteader.com/goat-birthing-patience-is-virtue/

Neimann, Deborah, "Is copper oxide really safe for goats?" Thrifty Homesteader. Last modified September 2016. https://thriftyhomesteader.com/is-copper-oxide-really-safe-for-goats/

Niemann, Deborah, *Raising Goats Naturally,* New Society, 2013.

Ott, R. S., D. R. Nelson, J. E. Hixon, "Effect of presence of the male on initiation of estrous cycle activity of goats." *Theriogenology* Volume 13, Issue 2, Pages 183-190. (1980). https://doi.org/10.1016/0093-691X(80)90127-2

Petersson, Katherine "Why and How To Do FAMACHA© Scoring," USDA Sustainable Agriculture Research and Education Program. Last modified April 2016. https://web.uri.edu/sheepngoat/files/FAMACHA-Scoring_Final2.pdf

Predator Friendly, "Predator Friendly Practices." Accessed January 2018. http://www.predatorfriendly.org/how-to/index.html

Premier 1 Supplies, "Using a stomach tuber—a safe, easy method for feeding weak lambs." Accessed March 2018. https://www.premier1supplies.com/sheep-guide/2012/10/using-a-stomach-tuber%E2%80%94a-safe-easy-method-for-feeding-weak-lambs/

Rey-Crespo, F., M. López-Alonso, M. Miranda, "The use of seaweed from the Galician coast as a mineral supplement in organic dairy cattle," *Animal* 8(4):580-6. (2014). doi: 10.1017/S1751731113002474

Rood, Kerry A., "Reproduction and Immune Impacts from Vitamin or Mineral Deficiencies: Determining If Your Herd Is Deficient," *AG/Animal Health* vol. 2011, no. 01. (2011). www.extension.usu.edu/rangelands/ou-files/Mineral_repro_and_immune.pdf

Rushing, Brett, "Toxic Plants for Small Ruminants," Oral presentation, Small Ruminant Production Workshop, Mississippi State University. 17 March 2018.

Ryel, Byeng, "Sustainable Methods for Managing Internal Parasites in Small Ruminants: Natural Dewormers," Min. Sustainable Agriculture Research and Education Accessed March 2018. https://www.umes.edu/cms300uploadedFiles/1-AcademicAffairs/Agriculture_and_Natural_Sciences/_Research/ARD/Impact_Statements/Tuskegee%20Small%20Ruminants.pdf

Shaik, S.A., T.H. Terrill, J.E. Miller, B. Kouakou, G. Kannan, R.M. Kaplan, et al, "Sericea lespedeza hay as a natural deworming agent against gastrointestinal nematode infection in goat," *Veterinary Parasitology* Volume 139, Issues 1–3, 30, Pages 150-157. (2006). https://doi.org/10.1016/j.vetpar.2006.02.020

Shoenian, Susan, "Diatomaceous earth (DE): Is it an effective dewormer for sheep and goats? A review of the scientific literature." Maryland Small Ruminant Page. Last modified 2013. https://www.sheepandgoat.com/de

Smith, Mary C., *Goat Medicine,* Wiley-Blackwell, 2009.

Soller, M., Huguette Angel, "Polledness and Abnormal Sex Ratios in Saanen Goats," *Journal of Heredity* Volume 55, Issue 3, Pages 139–142. (1964). https://doi.org/10.1093/oxfordjournals.jhered.a107313

Sponenberg, D. P., "Goat Color Explained," Virginia-Maryland Regional College of Veterinary Medicine. Last modified 2016. http://abga.org/wp-content/uploads/2016/01/Goat-Color-Explained.pdf

Standlee Premium Western Forage, "Nutritional Analysis of Premium Western Alfalfa." Accessed March 2018. https://standleeforage.com/nutrition

Suavet, Florence, Jean-Luc Champion, Luc Bartolini, Maryline Bernou, Jean-Pierre Alzieu, Roland Brugidou, Séverine Darnatigues, et al, "First Description of Infection of Caprine Herpesvirus 1 (CpHV-1) in Goats in Mainland France," *Pathogens* 5(1): 17. (2016). doi: 10.3390/pathogens5010017

Swarup, D., R.C. Patra, Ram Naresh, Puneet Kumar, Pallav Shekhar, M. Balagangatharathilagar, "Lowered blood copper and cobalt contents in goats reared around lead–zinc smelter," *Small Ruminant Research* Volume 63, Issue 3, Pages 309-313. (2006). https://www.sciencedirect.com/science/article/pii/S0921448805000994

Thorvin Kelp, "Thorvin for Animals Product Information." Last modified 2014. http://www.thorvin.com/downloads/THORVIN_AG_SS_032514.pdfUS Patent, "Seaweed supplement diet for enhancing immune response in mammals and poultry." Accessed March 2018. https://www.google.com/patents/US6312709

United States Department of Agriculture Animal and Plant Health Inspection Service, "Livestock Losses to Predators." Accessed March 2018. https://www.aphis.usda.gov/aphis/ourfocus/wildlifedamage/operational-activities/sa_livestock/ct_livestock_losses

United States Department of Agriculture Animal and Plant Health Inspection Service, "Status of Current Eradication Programs." Last modified February 2018. https://www.aphis.usda.gov/aphis/ourfocus/animalhealth/animal-disease-information/ct_status_of_eradication_programs

Van Saun, Robert J., "Feeding the Pregnant Doe: Understanding the Need for Supplements, Minerals, and Vitamins," Department of Veterinary Science Penn State University. Accessed March 2018. goatdocs.ansci.cornell.edu/Resources/GoatArticles/GoatFeeding/FeedingPregnantDoes1.pdf

Villalba, J.J., F. D. Provenza, and J. O. Hall, "Learned Appetites for Calcium, Phosphorus, and Sodium in Sheep." *J Anim Sci* 86:738-747. (2008).

Villalba, J.J., F. D. Provenza, J. O. Hall, and L.D. Lisbonlee, "Selection of Tannins by Sheep in Response to Gastrointestinal Nematode Infection," *J Anim Sci.* 88(6):2189-98. (2010). doi: 10.2527/jas.2009-2272.

Villaquiran, M., T. A. Gipson, R. C. Merkel, A. L. Goetsch, and T. Sahlu, "Body Condition Scores in Goats," American Institute for Goat Research. Accessed March 2018. http://www2.luresext.edu/goats/research/BCS_factsheet.pdf

Vogt, Dale, Helen A. Swartz, and John Massey, "Inbreeding: Its Meaning, Uses, and Effects on Farm Animals," University of Missouri Extension. Accessed December 2017. www.extension.missouri.edu/p/G2911

Washington State University, "Washington Animal Disease Diagnostic Laboratory." Accessed December 2017. www.waddl.vetmed.wsu.edu/

Wildeus, Stephan, "Goat Reproduction," Langston University. Accessed March 2018.

http://www2.luresext.edu/goats/training/reproduction.html

Young, Lawrence S., "Distinct Distal Gut Microbiome Diversity and Composition in Healthy Children from Bangladesh and the United States," *PLOS One.* (January 22, 2013). https://doi.org/10.1371/journal.pone.0053838

Index

ABOUT THE AUTHOR

Rachel Payne writes and farms from a small homestead in rural Tennessee. She is a third-generation goatherd on her mother's side and a fourth-generation farmer on her father's. She bought her first dairy goats, two Nigerian Dwarf does named Brownie and Sandy, in December 2008 and never looked back. She now raises Nigerian Dwarf, LaMancha, and MiniMancha dairy goats. In addition to her goat herd, Rachel also cares for a couple of milk cows, a few pigs, and a flock of chickens with her family. She graduated from the University of Memphis with a BA in English Literature. Rachel is passionate about farm life, good food, writing, reading, and sharing with others. She can be found online at www.tiramarhomestead.com.

CPSIA information can be obtained
at www.ICGtesting.com
Printed in the USA
LVHW060420220422
716753LV00005B/324

9 780692 039540